The Essentials

Real

LOVE

BIBLE
WORKBOOK

GREG BAER, M.D.

For use with *The Essentials of Real Love*
DVDs, CDs, and online video

BLUE RIDGE PRESS

The Essentials of Real Love® Bible Workbook for DVDs or CDs
Copyright © 2005 by Greg Baer, M.D.

First Edition

Baer, Greg
    The Essentials of Real Love® Bible Workbook
    ISBN 1-892319-22-5
    1. Relationships 2. Self-help 3. Psychology
Published by Blue Ridge Press PO Box 3075 Rome, GA 30164
    877-633-3568

Also by Greg Baer, M.D.—

Published by Gotham Books, a division of Penguin USA Group:
Real Love® — The Truth About Finding Unconditional Love and
    Fulfilling Relationships
Real Love® in Marriage — The Truth About Finding Genuine Happiness
    Now and Forever

Published by Blue Ridge Press:
Real Love® — The Truth About Finding Unconditional Love and Fulfilling
    Relationships, Unabridged Audio Book — Seven 60 minute CDs
The Real Love® Companion — Taking Steps Toward a Loving and Happy
    Life
Real Love® for Wise Men and Women — The Truth About Sharing Real Love
Real Love® in Dating — The Truth About Finding the Perfect Partner
    — Book and Unabridged Audio Book
Real Love® in Marriage — Unabridged Audio Book, Blue Ridge Press
Real Love® in Parenting — The Truth About Raising Happy and
    Responsible Children — Book and Unabridged Audio Book
Real Love® and Freedom for the Soul— Breaking the Chains of
    Victimhood
Real Love® in the Workplace - Eight Principles for Consistently Effective
    Leadership in Business
The Truth About Love and Lies — Three 60 minute CDs
The Essentials of Real Love® — Six DVDs, or Six CDs
The Essentials of Real Love® Workbook for DVDs or CDs

Printed in the United States
10 9 8 7 6 5 4 3 2 1

Table of Contents

The Essentials of Real Love Bible Workbook

INTRODUCTION

In *The Essentials of Real Love* video, you'll see, hear, and *feel* the power of Real Love as the core principles are presented to a live audience. This engaging and humorous presentation has enabled hundreds of thousands of people around the world to greatly enhance their personal happiness and find much deeper levels of fulfillment in their relationships. You will discover the real power of these principles, however, only as you actually apply them to your own life and *feel* unconditionally loved—loved by other men and women and by God.

You will accelerate this process of feeling loved as you use the tools found in two workbooks:

1. *The Essentials of Real Love Workbook.* Throughout this workbook I:

   - discuss the principles of Real Love in greater detail.
   - make suggestions about how you might apply a principle from the video to situations and relationships in your own life.
   - ask you to tell the truth about yourself.
   - provide exercises for you to complete.
   - ask you to discuss incidents that illustrate principles from the video.

This workbook was written for a secular audience, although most people find that as they complete it they have a heightened sense of connection to God.

2. *The Essentials of Real Love Bible Workbook*

For the remainder of this Introduction we'll discuss the purpose and structure of *The Essentials of Real Love Bible Workbook.*

The Essentials of Real Love Bible Workbook

The principles found in the book *Real Love* and in the DVD set *The Essentials of Real Love* have made a profound impact on the lives of people all over the world. Despite the power of this message, however, on many occasions I have been asked why there are so few references to God in the Real Love books and other materials.

An explanation is warranted. In my experience the very mention of the word *God* will often instantly divide any group of people who hear it. The old adage that in polite conversation politics and religion should be avoided is not without a strong foundation in experience. Many people are rather attached to their particular notion of God, so they are both quick to defend their beliefs and eager to convert others to their way of thinking. After all, they reason unconsciously, the more people who believe as I do, the more correct—and therefore more worthwhile—I must be.

Real Love is a power capable of healing the emptiness, fear, and conflict of this world, a power that has largely been ignored in our attempts to resolve the unhappiness we see almost everywhere. It is my primary intent to make that healing power more available to everyone, and in most of my books I have intentionally avoided discussion of *any subject*—politics, religions, God, or anything else—that could become a distraction from that primary aim.

To illustrate this point further, imagine that you're preparing to discuss the possibility of a tax hike with a local group of businessmen. During the discussion of taxes, would you be wise to also to throw in a brief summary of the pros and cons of using nuclear power to replace coal-burning power plants? No, you wouldn't, because bringing up the subject of nuclear power—or any number of other subjects—would hopelessly distract most audiences from a meaningful discussion of the primary topic. That doesn't mean that nuclear power isn't worth discussing, only that it would be a distraction from your primary goal of talking about taxes.

Similarly, there is nothing in the world I enjoy discussing more than our relationship with God. And there are no two subjects more closely related than those of Real Love and God. God *is* love. I have learned from considerable experience, however, that at least in the beginning of the process of learning about Real Love, most people are distracted by discussions about God. They tend to become occupied by defending their own beliefs, or they react negatively in the present to past experiences where other people pushed their personal beliefs about God on them.

In truth, a complete understanding of Real Love—and a grasp of its power—is quite impossible without an understanding of God. Although I do speak in the Real Love books and other materials about our need to find unconditional love from one another, the love of other human beings is but an introduction to the infinite and divine source of love available to all of us.

My ultimate purpose in creating all the Real Love materials is to facilitate our relationship with God. Let's consider a couple of the enormous obstacles that most of us encounter on our path to a knowledge of God. God is known by many names and associated with many descriptive words, but perhaps the two words with which God is most commonly associated are *love* and *Father*. Let's examine the effects of just those two words on our relationship with God.

- *Love.* All our lives most of us have been consistently taught by experience that love is conditional, traded, shallow, fleeting, and often painful. And the people who taught us this view of love—our parents, teachers, and others—occupied god-like positions of authority and respect in our lives, so we naturally accepted what they taught us. Now when someone tries to teach us about God, therefore, specifically using the phrase "God is *love*," it's little wonder that we tend to avoid that relationship. Why would we want even more of the love that has caused us so much pain—the love we've had to earn with so much manipulation and by giving up who we are.

- *Father*. Most of us have received from our flesh-and-blood fathers the conditional love we've known from everyone else: When the name *Father* is applied to God, therefore, it's virtually unavoidable that we would picture God as a larger version of our mortal fathers—conditionally loving, angry, and so on.

Now, to illustrate the importance of our finding Real Love from one another as human beings, allow me to paraphrase a passage found in the book *Real Love*: Imagine that you're communicating by e-mail with a creature who lives on a planet with no water. Describing an ocean would be very difficult, but if you brought that alien to Earth and dipped his hand in a single bucket of water, he could begin to understand an ocean. You'd only need to say, "An ocean is a billion times *that*."

Similarly, most of us have never seen consistent unconditional love, and that is why we have a confusing or non-existent relationship with God: because His most important characteristic is perfect love, a quality we have no experience with. When we begin to feel the unconditional love of other men and women, their love is like encountering our first bucket of water. Knowing that water exists, we can begin to imagine a God who offers us an ocean of love, or as Jesus describes it, "living waters."

Jesus once came to a well and was approached by a woman whose nationality was despised by the Jews. When He asked her for a drink she said, The Jews normally have nothing to do with us, so why do you ask me for a drink? Jesus said, if you knew the gift of God and who I am, you would have asked me to give you living water. And the woman said, but the well is deep, and you have nothing to draw water with, so how can you give me living water? Jesus said, whoever drinks the water of this well will be thirsty again, but whoever drinks the water I will give him will never thirst, because the water I give him will become a well of water springing up into everlasting life. (John 4:7-14)

Most people who learn to tell the truth about themselves and find the unconditional love of other people eventually develop an ability to tap into the power of the living waters offered by Christ. I have been impressed with the consistency of this process.

Our ability as mortals to love each other is often severely affected by our emptiness and fear. God, however, isn't affected by those feelings and can therefore love us perfectly. When we exercise faith, we can learn to feel the abundance of God's perfect love and never feel afraid or alone. In the absence of emptiness and fear, seeing and loving other people become natural and effortless. A loving relationship with God, therefore, is the greatest gift in this life, and it is equally available to all of us.

It is my experience that as people begin to see how truly loving God is, they invariably feel closer to Him. People feel distant from Him only because their understanding of Him is wrong. They have been taught about—and come to believe in—a God who doesn't exist: a God who is distant, punitive, angry, and conditionally loving. It is my hope that in this Workbook we'll take a few steps closer to a true understanding of God and the love He offers.

WHAT WILL NOT BE DISCUSSED

Every religion teaches doctrines that distinguish it from others, and it is about these differences that people often argue. Some of these doctrines include:

- The nature of God (the Trinity, physical nature of God, and so on)
- Baptism (necessity, effect, method of performance)
- Grace
- Sin
- Damnation
- Heaven

In this book, I do not intend to address these subjects, which belong to the study of religion. Almost everyone already has his or her own religious beliefs already. There is no reason for me to either re-state or refute them. Instead I will discuss what the Bible says about Real Love and the subjects associated with it. I have taught the principles of Real Love to people from all the world's major religions—and to people from a cross-section of most Christian religions—and I am impressed with how these principles form the foundation of all of them. Again and again, after presenting a Real Love seminar, people have said to me, "I am so impressed with your understanding of (Hinduism, Islam, Catholicism, Lutheranism, the Baptists, and so on)." It's Real Love that brings us all together.

As we discuss the biblical underpinnings of Real Love, we'll be talking about what brings us all together, rather than what divides us.

THE ATONEMENT

There is considerable variation among Christian religions in their beliefs on the subject of the atonement:

- Whether it's necessary
- Why it's necessary
- How it works (grace vs. works, for example)
- To whom it applies
- And so on

I will not be addressing these details. I will be discussing the God of the Bible, however, and the vast majority of religions that use the Bible as an integral part of their foundations do agree on the following:

- Jesus is the Son of God and is therefore divine.
- Through His life and death He accomplished what is known as the atonement, whereby it becomes possible for men to overcome the consequences of their sins and be reconciled to God.

- This atonement is *available* to all men, although there are religious differences about how and whether all men actually benefit from it.
- Because Jesus is the Son of God, and because He accomplished the atonement, He is also known as Christ, Jesus Christ, the Savior, the Redeemer, the Messiah, and other similar names.

In this book, I will make the assumption that the reader agrees with these major points—or at least understands them—although I will not dwell on them at length.

GOD OF THE NEW TESTAMENT

Because this is a book about the Bible, I will refer to the God described therein, and I will mostly talk about God as described in the New Testament. For that reason I will refer to God as He or Him or Father, as a divine personage, rather than as a disembodied Higher Power.

QUOTATIONS FROM THE BIBLE

My goal is to make the wisdom and beauty of God's teachings on the subject of love available to the greatest number of people. One stumbling block that many people experience in their search for God's wisdom and love is the language in which the Bible is written.

The Bible was originally written in ancient languages that are themselves difficult enough to translate, but it was also written in the context of ancient cultures, about which we can make only barely-educated guesses in many cases. Let me illustrate the potential difficulties of translation from a language alone, without an adequate cultural context.

In modern-day Samoa—a relatively small island nation in the south Pacific—a guest might come into your thatched hut, sit on a mat of woven palm leaves, and say:

"E le falala fua le niu, 'ae falala 'ona o le matagi."

With access to a Samoan-English dictionary, you could translate the *language* to its English version:

"The palm tree doesn't bend for no reason but bends because of the wind."

So now you have the strict translation of the language, but do you understand the *meaning* of the phrase? No, not without a cultural context. I've lived in Samoa, however, and I'm somewhat familiar with their culture. In those islands, there are no doors or windows on the traditional open-air huts, so when a guest comes to your home, he can't knock on the door. He simply walks in and sits down on a mat in a strictly-prescribed cross-legged fashion.

Although that behavior would be quite rude in Western society, it's acceptable and even expected in Samoa. It is nonetheless considered ill-mannered for a guest in Samoa to simply launch into some matter of business immediately after sitting down. Some social or cultural pleasantries must be exchanged, to set the stage for any acceptable conversation. The real meaning of the phrase above is this:

"Just as the palm tree bends because of the wind, so is my coming to your home the result of a purpose. I have matters to discuss, if you will permit it."

Similarly, the Bible was written within the context of ancient cultures, and this has contributed to difficulties—sometimes extreme difficulties—in understanding some biblical passages. These problems of translation are proven by the dozens of translations available. Considering the difficulties of translation of any language—multiplied greatly with *ancient* languages—it is remarkable that the translations of the Bible agree in so many respects. Nonetheless, in a great number of verses there are significant differences among the available translations.

Rather than use a single translation, as I quote from the New Testament I have chosen what I believe to be the clearest phrases from twenty-six translations of that book. I acknowledge my own weaknesses in making my choices but hope I have taken the best from many scholars. In the process, I will attempt to accomplish a number of goals, as listed below:

- Omit words or phrases that don't contribute to the meaning of the passage
- Provide historical context or clarity within verse, where needed
- Change archaic words to modern usage
- Change archaic phrases and metaphors to modern usage
- Join separated verses
- Clarify who is speaking
- Combine two or more verses

I will refer often to the King James Version of the Bible (KJV), the translation used more throughout the world than any other. In most cases where I have made changes in a verse I will be indicating changes made from the KJV.

Omit Words or Phrases That Don't Contribute to the Meaning of the Passage

The Bible contains many words and phrases that were in common usage when it was originally written but contribute little or no meaning to our understanding today. Biblical authors also had a tendency to repeat themselves for emphasis. In many cases, I will simplify the verse for the sake of brevity and clarity. For example:

- The phrase, "And it came to pass" will be omitted or replaced with, "And then . . ."
- Repetition of concepts will be eliminated. "When they saw the star, they rejoiced with exceeding great joy" (Matthew 2:10, KJV) will be rendered "When they saw the star, they rejoiced."
- "But He answered and said, It is written," (Matthew 4:4, KJV) will be rendered, "Jesus said, It is written . . ."

Provide Historical Context or Clarity Within Verse, Where Needed

In many verses the Bible refers to the names of people and places that make sense only to Bible scholars. In these cases, rather than include names that would be meaningless to most people, I will replace the exact words found in the King James Version with what the verse *means* in our day.

For example, the KJV of Luke 13:1-2 reads:

There were present at that season some that told him of the Galilæans, whose blood Pilate had mingled with their sacrifices. And Jesus answering said unto them, Suppose ye that these Galilæans were sinners above all the Galilæans, because they suffered such things?

Without an understanding of the historical and cultural context, this passage could be quite confusing: Who were the Galileans? Who was Pilate? What is the significance of Pilate killing these people? What does it mean to mingle blood with sacrifices?

Rather than provide a history and culture lesson at every turn— which could become quite cumbersome—I have chosen to render these verses, and others like it, in such a way that they communicate the intended *meaning*. Luke 13:1-2 will be rendered as follows:

Some people told Jesus about some Jews who had been killed in a humiliating way by soldiers of the Roman occupation army, implying that those people must have sinned in some way. And Jesus said, do you suppose that those men were sinners because they suffered?

Change Archaic Words to Modern Usage

Word like *hath*, *shouldst*, *ye*, and *wrought* will be replaced by their more modern versions *has*, *should*, *you*, and *worked*.

Change Archaic Phrases and Metaphors to Modern Usage

Ancient metaphors or phrases will be presented in a form that is
more understandable but which still retains—according to my own
judgment and that of as many other scholars as I could consult—the
intended meaning of the original authors. I do not claim that the way
I have rendered any verse or passage is the best way, only the best
I could do. If any quote in this book seems doubtful or confusing
to you, you are encouraged to read that passage from whatever
translation of the Bible you are most comfortable with.

For example, in Matthew 3:7-8 (KJV):

O generation of vipers, who hath warned you to flee from the
wrath to come? Bring therefore fruits meet for repentance.

The terms "generation of vipers," "flee," "wrath," and "fruits
meet for repentance" are not generally heard in everyday speech.
Taking the best from other translations, I have rendered this passage
as follows:

You're like poisonous snakes. Who has warned you to run from
the punishment that is waiting for you? Go and do something to
show that your hearts are really changed.

Another relatively difficult passage is found in James 3:2-6
(KJV):

For in many things we offend all. If any man offend not in
word, the same *is* a perfect man, *and* able also to bridle the
whole body. Behold, we put bits in the horses' mouths, that
they may obey us; and we turn about their whole body. Behold
also the ships, which though *they be* so great, and *are* driven of
fierce winds, yet are they turned about with a very small helm,
whithersoever the governor listeth. Even so the tongue is a little
member, and boasteth great things. Behold, how great a matter
a little fire kindleth! And the tongue *is* a fire, a world of iniquity:
so is the tongue among our members, that it defileth the whole
body, and setteth on fire the course of nature; and it is set on fire
of hell.

A more modern and simpler rendition:

We all stumble in many things, but if a man isn't offensive with his words, he is perfect and able to control himself entirely. We turn the whole body of a horse with a small bit, and with a small rudder we control ships, even though they are large and driven by fierce winds. In a similar way, the tongue is small, but it has great power, just as a little spark can set an entire forest ablaze. The tongue is a fire, and with a flame from hell causes a world of wickedness and sets fire to the course of nature.

Join Separated Verses

I will take minor liberties with some passages, putting some sentences together that are separated by several verses. In those cases, I will not disrupt the flow with the use of ellipses (. . .). Again, the goal is to make every passage easier for the reader.

Clarify Who Is Speaking

Sometimes when a single verse is quoted, it's difficult to know who is speaking without reading the many verses that precede it. In these cases, I will make plain who is speaking.

For example, the passage, "Then said He also to him that bade him" (Luke 14:12) will be rendered, "Then Jesus said . . ."

Combine Two or More Verses

On many occasions, two or more of the authors of the first four books of the New Testament (Matthew, Mark, Luke, and John) describe the same event with small variations. I will sometimes combine their versions of the same event or passage. For example, I have combined the KJV of

Matthew 23:23 Woe unto you, scribes and Pharisees, hypocrites! For ye pay tithe of mint and anise and cumin, and have omitted the weightier matters of the law, judgment, mercy, and faith: these ought ye to have done, and not to leave the other undone.

AND

Luke 11:42 But woe unto you, Pharisees! For ye tithe mint and rue and all manner of herbs, and pass over judgment and the love of God: these ought ye to have done, and not to leave the other undone.

to make a more complete verse containing elements of both authors' accounts:

Jesus said, a curse on you, because you pay tithes on the herbs you grow in your gardens, but you ignore the more important matters of the law: justice, mercy, faith, and the love of God. You should have done these without neglecting the others. (Matthew 23:23; Luke 11:42)

THE MULTI-MEDIA USE OF THE ESSENTIALS OF REAL LOVE BIBLE WORKBOOK

The *Bible Workbook* can be used with these media:

- *The Essentials of Real Love* DVDs, a 6-DVD video recording.
- *The Essentials of Real Love* CDs, a 6-CD audio recording.

HOW TO USE THE *WORKBOOK* WITH *THE ESSENTIALS OF REAL LOVE* ON VIDEO

As you watch the *video*, you can see your exact location in the video in the following ways:

- DVD Player: On the display of your DVD player, your location is continuously displayed by chapter and by a time code written in hours, minutes, and seconds.
- On Television Screen: You can hit the "Display" button on your DVD remote, after which the chapter and time code written in hours, minutes, and seconds will be displayed on your television screen.

Each section of the *Workbook* is then also labeled with a time code that directly corresponds to a timed segment of the video.

For example, on page 165 of the *Workbook* you'll first notice that the header in the upper left hand corner of the page reads, "Module Two," meaning that you're in the section of the *Workbook* that corresponds to Module Two of the video. Further down on the page you'll find the following notation at the left hand margin:

NINE, 36:51 - 44:40   Emptiness and Fear are Like . . .
CD Track Nine, 0:00 - 7:48

The first line of this notation (NINE, 36:51 - 44:40) is for the *video* recording. This time code—along with the header (Module Two)—has the following meaning:

1. Watch the segment in Module Two, Chapter Nine of *The Essentials of Real Love* video that begins at 36 minutes 51 seconds and ends at 44 minutes 40 seconds.

2. Then read the section of the *Workbook* that follows the heading NINE, 36:51 - 44:40 (pages 165-78), in which you will find a discussion of the video segment that begins at 36 minutes 51 seconds and ends at 44 minutes 40 seconds.

HOW TO USE THE *WORKBOOK* WITH
THE *ESSENTIALS OF REAL LOVE* ON AUDIO

The second line of the above time notation (CD Track Nine, 0:00-7:48) is for the *audio* recording on CD. With each track of a CD, the time notation begins again at zero, so the time code for the CDs is different from the time code for the video. The second line of the time notation, therefore, has the following meaning—along with the header (Module Two):

1. Listen to the segment in Module Two of *The Essentials of Real Love* CDs that begins at Track Nine, 0:00 and ends at 7:48.

2. Then read the section of the *Workbook* with the following heading:

**NINE, 36:51 - 44:40   Emptiness and Fear are Like . . .
   CD Track Nine, 0:00 - 7:48**

in which you will find a discussion of the audio segment that begins at Track Nine, 0:00 and ends at 7:48 (pages 165-78).

DIFFERENT WAYS TO USE THE *WORKBOOK*

Throughout the *Bible Workbook*, I will:

- discuss the principles of Real Love in greater detail than is found in the video.
- make suggestions about how you might apply a principle from the video to yourself.
- ask you to tell the truth about yourself.
- provide an exercise for you to complete.
- ask you to discuss an incident that illustrates a principle from the video.
- ask you to compare yourself to someone who appears in the video or is described in the video.

As you read the *Workbook*, you can answer the questions and complete the exercises in one or more of the following ways:

- By yourself
- With a friend
- In a Real Love Group
- In a facilitated class

By Yourself

You can answer all the questions or complete the exercises by yourself. Although one important reason for telling the truth about ourselves is to feel the unconditional acceptance of *others* as they see us clearly, we can still accomplish a great deal by simply examining our behavior by ourselves. As we do:

- we can begin to understand the true meaning and causes of our behavior.
- when we examine our behavior in the light of true principles, we can let go of the anger that has poisoned our lives.
- we can let go of guilt.
- we can begin to abandon old, unproductive patterns of thinking and behavior and make far more effective choices.

You'll find that you can examine your behavior more closely as you actually *write* your thoughts and feelings. In the process of writing, we tend to be more reflective and thorough. You'll learn even more about yourself as you come back and read your answers at a later time.

With a Friend

You can read the *Workbook* with a friend. As you answer the questions, you will create the life-giving opportunities to feel accepted and loved by another person. I cannot over-emphasize how valuable it can be to complete the *Workbook* with a friend.

How would that look? How would you enlist a friend in this activity? I suggest some answers to this question because many of us are paralyzed by fear of the first step. Once we know how to take it, we can keep going in the process that will bring so much into our lives.

People all over the world are sharing Real Love with friends, so let me share with you some of their successful approaches in using the video and *Workbook* with their friends:

- Simply hand your copy of the *Essentials in Real Love* video to a friend and say something like, "I saw this the other day, and it was great. Really made me think about some things in my life, and already it's made a difference in how I interact with my (husband, wife, children, and so on). We fight less. I'm more peaceful, and I thought you might enjoy it." Then when your friend returns the video, you could say, "I have a workbook that goes with the video, which really helps me apply the principles to my own life. One suggestion Greg makes is that people do the workbook with a friend. Is that something that might interest you?"

- Say to a friend, "I just got a DVD set called *The Essentials of Real Love*. It suggests a new way to understand what love is, which changes the way we relate to everybody around us. It's six DVDs, and I'm going to watch them gradually, one at a time. I wonder if you'd be interested in seeing a couple of them with me." After you've seen the first DVD or two, you can then suggest doing the workbook together.

- Give a copy of the book, *Real Love*, to a friend. When he or she has read it, you might say, "There's a video now that makes these principles even clearer. Would you be interested in seeing it with me?"

- Book clubs are quite common. Set up a night where you invite several friends to see the video. Then invite those who are interested to participate in completing the workbook with you.

As you share the principles of Real Love with people—and as you share *yourself* with them—you *will* find people capable of accepting and loving you for who you really are. I call such people wise men and women, terms that come from a story we'll discuss in Module Three, Chapter Two and on pages 222-7. I'll be referring to the term *wise man* on several occasions.

In a Real Love Group

If you have a sincere interest in finding Real Love and learning how to share that love with others, your efforts will be far more successful if you intentionally associate as often as possible with people who have the same interest. When two or more people are consciously making an effort to tell the truth about themselves and be wise men for each other, I call them a group of wise men, or a group of wise men and women, or a loving group, or—more often—simply a *group*. A group is just a loose association of people with the common interest I've described. A group is not a place.

You don't have to *join* a group; if you're deliberately involved in the process of giving and receiving Real Love, you're already in a group, whatever your numbers or location.

How do groups form? Let me describe a pattern common to most. One person sees the video, *The Essentials of Real Love*, or reads *Real Love—The Truth About Finding Unconditional Love and Fulfilling Relationships*, and then he or she shares the truth about himself with several friends and discovers that one or more of them are interested in seeing and accepting him. They also want to share the truth about themselves. As these friends continue to talk about themselves and the principles of Real Love, they naturally become a group. A group is not therapy. It's not a cult. It doesn't make arrogant claims to fix people. It's not exclusive, does not require loyalty or money from its members, and is not characterized by a formal organization.

Groups exist only to increase the opportunities of its members to be seen and loved. I personally need all the wise men I can get, and I love the time I spend in groups of loving men and women. For most people, a group becomes a loving family, healing the wounds of the past and changing their lives forever.

When I talk about groups of *wise men*, I'm not implying that everyone in the group is loving—or *anyone* in the group, for that matter—only that these men and women are *consciously trying* to see and love others.

Once you find people interested in telling the truth and experiencing Real Love, you could allow loving experiences with them to just *happen*. Or you could actually *create* and accelerate these experiences by arranging regular times and places to meet with these developing wise men. These planned gatherings are *group meetings*.

Although you can have loving experiences anywhere, in group meetings you can share who you are with more people in less time, and you learn more as you listen to the many experiences of others and watch the effect of Real Love in their lives. You also have more opportunities to accept and love other people. The effect of association with one wise man can be life-changing. Group meetings simply make it possible to multiply that effect.

One way to greatly facilitate the process of learning about Real Love is to use this *Workbook*. As group meetings first begin, people often have difficulty knowing how to begin telling the truth about themselves. As you view the video as a group, and as you use the *Workbook*, you'll find it much easier for members of the group to share who they are with others.

For much more information and guidance about group meetings, see *Real Love for Wise Men and Women—The Truth About Sharing Real Love*, available on the website at www.RealLove.com.

In a Facilitated Class

You may find it possible to attend a class facilitated by an experienced Real Love Professional. In such classes, the facilitator will often use *The Essentials of Real Love* video and this *Workbook* as a framework for conducting the class.

MODULE ONE

CHAPTER ONE
Introduction

ONE, 0:00 - 1:27 The Power of Real Love
  CD Track One, 0:00 - 1:27

Laura describes a condition quite common in relationships: We keep having the same unproductive arguments with people, over and over. As we're headed into one of these unpleasant interactions, we even know that it's about to go downhill—"there we go again," in her words—but we just don't know what to do about it, so we keep repeating the same old patterns.

Laura shares her experience that since learning about Real Love, she knows "what to do to change that," and she adds that "it's transformed my life." It's the purpose of *The Essentials of Real Love* video and audio recordings, along with this *Workbook*, to give you the tools to "change that" in your life too. As we learn how to eliminate—not just manage or control—the fear, anger, and conflict in our lives, the natural result is a blooming of the joy that a loving Father in heaven has always intended for us. Jesus said, "I am come that they might have life, and that they might have it more abundantly." (John 10:10) It is with Real Love that we find a simple, clear, practical path to that abundant life.

This abundant, joyful life has a price, and the price must be paid in full. Too often we attempt to make significant changes in our lives without a willingness to go all the way, without a commitment to make the sacrifices necessary to effect such change. Half-measures will not succeed in bringing us the joy we seek in this life and the next. Jesus spoke of this when He said to Nicodemus, "Unless a man is born again, he cannot see the kingdom of God." (John 3:3)

In order to find the kingdom of God on earth or in heaven we must actually be born again. We must put to death our old ways and be born of the Spirit unto life. That is not a half-measure. God spoke of this to the house of Israel when He said, "Throw away all your sins and make yourself a new heart and a new spirit; for why would you want to die?" (Ezekiel 18:31)

In the space on the next page describe an unpleasant situation or pattern in your life that has repeated far longer than you would like. To help you understand the intent of this exercise, you might find it useful to read first some answers that other people have given in response to this exercise. Some examples of their answers:

- My husband and I keep having essentially the same argument about money. I try to re-state my position in different ways, but it ends up the same every time: We're angry at each other and frustrated, and then we avoid the subject for another long period.
- I keep going through one relationship after another. Every time I think I've found a guy who is different from the others, he turns out to be like all the rest.
- No matter how I bring up the subject of sex with my wife, it's the same. We argue about it, she tells me I'm a sex maniac, I prove to her how seldom we have sex, and I still don't get sex.
- My boss irritates me more than I can tell you. He doesn't appreciate a thing I do, and he doesn't listen to anybody. I've tried talking to him, but it's like talking to a wall. I'm tired of it.
- I'm at my wits' end with my son. If I don't talk to him, he does what he wants. If I do talk to him, he does what he wants

but hates me. The more I talk to him, the more angry and rebellious he becomes.

- I pray, I read the Bible, and I give to my church. But still I don't feel the closeness to God that I would like. I don't know what to do to change that.
- My mother butts into my affairs at every possible turn. She has an opinion on my job, my house, my children, my ex-wife, everything. If I don't listen to her, she talks louder and longer. If I do listen to her, I want to choke her.
- My brother and I haven't had a decent conversation in years. We try to talk about subjects that aren't threatening, but he still gets offended every time. I don't think it's possible to talk to him.
- I feel like nobody in my family appreciates me, no matter what I do for them. They take me for granted, and if I bring it up, they just get offended.
- I don't like being around my wife's family, but she's always bugging me to do stuff with them. If I go with her to see them, I hate it. If I stay home, she nags me to death. It's a no-win deal.
- Putting my children to bed is enough to make me pull my hair out. Every single night, it turns into hours of complaining, whining, getting out of bed, and yelling.

Now, your own situation(s) or pattern(s):

These repetitive, unproductive interactions cause so much anger and frustration in our lives that happiness often becomes impossible. What a tragedy.

What would you give to be able to change these patterns? Are you weary yet of fear, anger, and contention? What would you be willing to do to eliminate the tension and frustration you now experience and instead make choices that consistently lead to peace and happiness?

For most of us, life is riddled with fear, anger, and contention, and it need not be that way. Jesus said that the day will come when "the King will say to those on his right hand, Come, you who are blessed by my Father, inherit the kingdom prepared for you from the foundation of the world." (Matthew 25:34) Can you feel the peace and power in these words? Can you sense that with this simple invitation all the worries of this world just fade away into nothingness? We don't have to wait for some distant timelessness— for the next life—to experience this kind of peace and power. We can have it *now*. In fact, we must. Those who inherit the kingdom of God in the end will be those who have already experienced it here in mortality. How can we hope to inherit a place of peace and joy when we have lived lives of fear, anger, and contention here on earth?

This transformation—from anger and confusion to peace and confidence—begins with a sincere desire to change and an acknowledgment of our weaknesses. "Blessed are those," Jesus said, "who see their spiritual poverty, for theirs is the kingdom of heaven." (Matthew 5:3) As you describe here the situations and relationships in your life that need to be changed, you will be taking the first steps on the path to the kingdom of heaven.

ONE, 1:27 - 1:44 The Promise of Real Love
CD Track One, 1:27 - 1:44

It is the mission of the Real Love Institute to teach the true meaning of love, which gives people everywhere the ability to choose peace and confidence instead of anger and confusion in their individual lives and in their relationships.

The power of this promise is beyond expression. Hundreds of thousands of people around the world have experienced this power. The results are consistent: If people will diligently apply themselves to the application of Real Love principles, they *will* see fulfillment of the promise I make here on the video and audio recordings.

The Savior made a similar promise when He said, "Come unto me, all you who labor and are overworked, and I will give you rest. Take my service upon you, and learn of me; for I am gentle and humble, and you will find rest for your souls. For serving me is easy, and my burden is light." (Matthew 11:28-30)

ONE, 1:44 - 4:41 Our Confusion about Real Love
CD Track One, 1:44 - 4:41

Most of us in this world really don't know the difference between "love" and "Czechoslovakia." We've lost our understanding of love and turned our hearts to other things. Jesus made it plain that the people in his day were in a similar position, that they had replaced love with other values. He said, "A curse on you, because you pay tithes on the herbs you grow in your gardens, but you ignore the more important matters of the law: justice, mercy, faith, and the love of God." (Matthew 23:23; Luke 11:42) Jesus wasn't talking to people who had overtly turned to wickedness. He was talking to people who were so meticulous in their following of the letter of the law that they even paid tithes of the herbs they grew in their gardens. But they had lost their understanding of love and its importance, and Jesus said that without attending to this "weightier matter" they were cursed, despite their precise obedience to the law in other matters.

Following this section is an abundance of evidence to prove the assertion that we—as was the case with the people in Jesus' time—have lost our way.

CHAPTER TWO

The Need for Real Love

TWO, 4:41 - 9:05   One Sign That We're Not Happy:
The Condition of Our Marriages
CD Track Two, 0:00 - 4:25

The apostle Paul said to the Ephesians,

> Men should love their wives as they love their own bodies,
> just as the Lord nourishes and cherishes the church. For this
> purpose shall a man leave his father and mother and be joined
> with his wife, and the two shall be one flesh. So let every one of
> you love his wife as himself; and the wife respect her husband.
> (Ephesians 5:28-33)

It should be obvious that as a society we're not doing well
in keeping this commandment. 60% of marriages end in divorce,
and only 1-2% are genuinely successful. Could there be a stronger
indication that we're not genuinely happy? The condition of our
marriages screams that we really don't know what love is, and yet
we keep entering into this most sacred relationship where love is
absolutely required. There's a real insanity in that.

In the space on the next page, describe some of your own
experiences with marriage—or with the marriages of other people—
including, among other observations you might make:

- How wonderfully romantic and blissful it can all seem in the
  beginning
- How thoroughly committed we are in the beginning to follow
  the counsel of Paul to the Ephesians, only to discover that we
  were ill-equipped to do so
- The creeping dissatisfaction that seems to steadily grow in so
  many of our relationships, without obvious cause
- The anger and blaming that so often replace the kisses and
  roses that originally brought us together

Marriages begin with such promise and hope. Bells are ringing, angels singing, and violins playing. The fact that so many of our marriages fail is indisputable proof that we simply don't understand what is required for healthy relationships. As we understand the principles of Real Love—and as we apply them—we can begin to follow the path the Lord has described and dramatically improve the experiences we have in our marriages and in other relationships.

TWO, 9:06 - 11:14 Other Signs That We're Not Happy
CD Track Two, 4:25 - 6:33

On the whole, we human beings are not happy. In the space on the next page describe the evidences you see to support that statement. You might include some of the following:

- The condition of our marriages
- Our use of alcohol and drugs
- The incidence of indiscriminate sex among our youth and adults
- The level of anxiety demonstrated in our children
- The way we scream at each other on the highways
- The incidence of crime and the condition of our prisons
- The violence in our school

- Racial tension
- Our courts' being filled with lawsuits against one another
- Wars, within and between nations

These circumstances have long been prophesied. In a letter to his friend Timothy, the apostle Paul spoke of the conditions we see in our day. He said:

Understand that in the last days dangerous times will come. For men will be self centered, lovers of money, proud, abusive in their speech, disobedient to parents, ungrateful, unholy, unloving, truce breakers, false accusers, lacking self control, hot-headed, looking down on good things, traitors, arrogant, lovers of pleasures more than lovers of God; having an outward form of godliness but denying the power thereof.
(2 Timothy 3:1-5)

And all these problems are either persisting or getting worse, despite all our efforts, programs, legislation, money, worry, and tears.

In the space on the next page discuss the evidences in your own life that you are not as happy as you'd like to be. Examples might include:

- I argue frequently with my husband about all kinds of little things.
- I often raise my voice at my children.
- I feel unappreciated.
- I get angry when people don't cooperate with what I need done.
- I fantasize about women and often look at pornography.
- I often complain about my job.
- I feel like I'm always having to push my children to do what they're supposed to do.
- I feel like I have to beg for sex or manipulate for it.
- I drink more than I should.
- My boss just doesn't understand all I do around here.
- I just can't seem to be able to quit smoking.
- I really get irritated when I'm driving in heavy traffic.
- I shop a lot, probably more than I should.
- I talk about my co-workers and boss behind their backs.
- The people around me fear my temper.
- I find myself impatient about the smallest things: waiting in line, people who are late, and so on.

TWO, 11:14 - 12:38 Bandaging Wounds vs. Addressing the Real Problem
CD Track Two, 6:33 - 7:57

As in the story of the two mountain climbers, we tend to become quite involved in:

- bandaging wounds instead of learning the cause of the disease.
- putting out fires instead of learning why they begin and preventing them.
- living from crisis to crisis instead of understanding how to be genuinely happy and prevent them.
- running after the cows who have escaped the barn rather than building a strong barn to begin with.
- cleaning up after floods rather than building dams to control them.

Jesus described the people of his day in a similar way when He said:

Woe unto you, hypocrites, because you are like white-washed tombs, which appear beautiful on the outside but inside are full of dead men's bones and filthiness. In the same way, you appear good to men on the outside, but on the inside you are full of hypocrisy and wickedness. (Matthew 23:27-28)

Jesus chastised the Jewish leaders for focusing their efforts on outward appearances and solutions, while ignoring the real problems—leaving them in a condition of spiritual decay, even death. We're doing the same today.

In the space on the next page describe a behavior or inconvenience that you often try to control without understanding the real problem. This exercise requires unusually rigorous honesty and courageous self-examination. Following are some examples that might help you get started:

- I keep nagging my husband to spend more time with me, but I don't try to learn *why* he doesn't want to spend time with me.
- I tell my children to be quiet, but I don't stop to ask why they're so demanding and difficult.
- I stay irritated with my boss, but I've never wondered why he behaves as he does, nor do I consider what I could do to actually help him.
- I push my wife to have sex with me instead of asking what there is about *me* that is obviously pushing her away.
- I drink to get a "buzz" or a sense of relaxation instead of addressing the tension I'm trying to escape.
- I keep getting angry at people—spouse, children, friends, co-workers—rather than asking the important question: What's missing in *my* life that is causing me to be angry?

Rushing in and fixing problems in the short-term is seductive. As we scurry about—putting out fires and solving crises—we are tempted to believe that we're actually doing something worthwhile. Certainly we create that appearance for others. We even get a rush of adrenalin from fixing things and rescuing people, but in the long term we don't accomplish much that matters. We must learn to divert our focus from the bandaging of wounds and take the longer view. If we really want to be happy, we must find out where the boulders are coming from and do something about them.

TWO, 12:38 - 13:37   What Happiness is Not
CD Track Two, 7:57 - 8:56

We demonstrate what we believe will make us happy not with our words but with what we do—with how we spend our time, energy and thoughts.

Jesus talked about this principle in a parable when He said,

A man had two sons; and he said to the first, go work today in my vineyard. The son said, I will not, but later he thought better of it and went. The man said the same to his second son, who said, I will go, but he did not. Which of the two did his father's will? And they said to Jesus, the first son. And Jesus agreed with them. (Matthew 21:28-31)

Jesus taught that it doesn't much matter what we say with our lips. We demonstrate our desires with what we do. This counsel applies to us today as well as it did to those in His day.

Imagine, then, what it would be like for an alien race to come and observe us from orbit. What would they conclude about what matters most to us? If they observed the commercials we watch on television, for example, as an indication of who we really are—not unreasonable, since commercials are professionally attuned to the activities we enjoy the most—they could conclude only that our top two priorities are the two B's: beer and breasts.

Using our behavior as the sole criteria, discuss in the space below what we believe will make us happy. You might discuss some of the following:

- Sex
- Money
- Power
- Money
- Alcohol
- Entertainment
- Excitement
- Control
- Shopping
- The conditional approval of others
- Praise
- Popularity

Then in the space on the next page discuss how effective these activities are in producing genuine, long-term happiness. You might ask the following questions, among others:

- How many people do you know who have great quantities of one or more of these things, and yet they're still miserable? How many people are wealthy, popular, powerful, and so on but still have unhappy relationships, marriages, and children?

- How many examples from history have we seen of people who have achieved great success in acquiring these "things" and yet are never satisfied?
- How many examples do we see on television and in magazines of people who have "everything" (from the list above) but are still unhappy and desperate for more?
- How often have you achieved some of these things yourself, only to discover that the satisfaction is fleeting and superficial?

In the space below and on the next page discuss some examples from your life where you acquired some of the things above that the world believes will lead to happiness—sex, money, power. Talk about how exciting and *real* the satisfaction seemed at the time. Then talk about what happened to that sense of fulfillment over time.

Read Luke 15:11-32 for the story of the prodigal son, who spent all his fortune on riotous living, only to discover that happiness was not to be found in that way of living.

With our behavior, we demonstrate that we simply do not know what happiness is, much less how to achieve it. So what is real happiness?

TWO, 13:37 - 15:51 My Own Story
CD Track Two, 8:56 - 11:10

All my life I listened to what people told me would make me happy, and it included many of the things listed on page 33. In the video and audio recordings, I shared a brief summary of the successes I achieved.

People commonly say to themselves and to one another, "If only I had more _____, I'd be happy." But I had all the _____s, and I still wasn't even close to happy. I had achieved everything the world promised would make me happy, and yet I still felt alone and miserable, and I couldn't understand why. I became a drug addict for years and was even suicidal.

Jesus once told the story of a "rich man, who wore the finest clothing and enjoyed rich feasts daily. And there was a beggar named Lazarus, who was laid at the rich man's outer door, full of sores and begging to be fed with the crumbs that fell from the rich man's table. The beggar died and was carried by angels into Abraham's arms. The rich man also died and was buried, and in hell he lifted up his eyes in anguish and saw Abraham in the distance, with Lazarus at his side. And he cried out and said, Father Abraham, have mercy on me, and send Lazarus, that he may dip the tip of his finger in water, and cool my tongue; for I am tormented in this flame." (Luke 16:19-24)

I had come to the point in my life where I felt like I was living in that hell described by Jesus. Many of us have. Despite our best efforts, we experience great pain and pray for a drop of water to "cool our tongues." Fortunately, there is a way out of this hell, and the water available to us comes not in mere drops but in a "fountain of living waters." (Jeremiah 17:13)

TWO, 15:51 - 18:00 What We Need In Order to Be Happy
CD Track Two, 11:10 - 13:19

Thousands of orphans died after the first World War simply from a lack of physical affection. To this day, millions of people all over the world are still dying—physically, emotionally, and spiritually— from a lack of love. So far, we're not learning much from our experiences.

Love is inseparable from our happiness in every respect. Not only is it the primary contributor to our emotional happiness, but medical studies have increasingly demonstrated that people who feel loved suffer less—often far less—from physical and psychiatric ailments, including:

- Heart disease
- High blood pressure
- Cancer
- Digestive abnormalities
- Depression
- Chronic pain syndromes
- Chronic fatigue
- ADD/ADHD
- Infectious diseases
- Asthma
- Ulcers
- Autoimmune diseases (lupus, arthritis, fibromyalgia)

Even without the medical studies, the connection is obvious to most of us. Almost all of us have experienced episodes when we've become physically ill during or shortly after a period where we've been upset emotionally. Emotional upset is well known to bring on chest pain (angina) and high blood pressure. The connection of body and spirit is powerful indeed.

Describe below an occasion (or pattern of occasions) when your feeling depressed, discouraged, angry, upset, or otherwise unloved has led to physical illness in your life.

CHAPTER THREE
Real Love

THREE, 18:00 - 18:43   The Love We Have Received
CD Track Three, 0:00 - 0:43

What we all long for—what we need more than anything in order to be happy—is to feel loved. Our yearning for that feeling is the motivation for more books, movies, and human behaviors than anything else.

Some people might suggest that I have placed too great an importance on love as I have discussed its importance here in the video and audio recordings of the seminar, but Jesus Himself didn't hesitate to put love in that position of pre-eminence. When a lawyer among the Jews asked Him, "Which is the greatest commandment in the law?" the Master's answer could be distilled into a single word: Love.

He did further specify that within that single-word answer were two commandments: "You shall love the Lord your God with all your heart and with all your soul and with all your mind. This is the first and greatest commandment. And the second is like it, You shall love your neighbor as yourself." Jesus went on to add, "On these two commandments hang all the law and the prophets." (Matthew 22:35-40) By this He meant that all the commandments and everything written by the prophets descend directly from the commission to be loving.

It should also be obvious that not just any kind of love will make us happy, because our overall level of unhappiness has persisted despite the many, many occasions when we've received:

- bedtime kisses when we were children.
- other expressions of affection from our parents.
- praise for doing the right things.
- fiercely romantic and tender *I love you*s from boyfriends, girlfriends, and spouses.

- enthusiastic commendations for being "good boys" or "good girls."
- birthday and Christmas gifts, all wrapped up with beautiful paper and bows.

Clearly, something is missing from these expressions of "love," or we'd all be much happier than we are.

In the space on the next page describe some occasions or relationships in your life where:

1. you received communications of affection that convinced you that you were loved,

   BUT

2. subsequent events made you wonder about the nature or sincerity of that love or relationship.

Some examples of this might include—but would not be limited to—the following:

- On many occasions my mother told me she loved me, but then she often yelled at me and said unkind things to me.
- When my husband and I were dating, he told me he loved me every day—told me that he'd love me forever, in fact—but now he's usually distant and cold, sometimes even critical and angry.
- Two relationships ago, I was engaged to a women who told me she loved me, but not long after that she ran off with one of my best friends.
- My father told me that I could always count on his love, but even though some days he is kind and generous, on other days he's very angry and harsh toward me.
- My boss has said that his primary concern is for the welfare of his employees, but he rarely listens to what we really want.
- My sister says she loves me, but she picks at me and finds fault with almost everything I do or say.

Our Confusion around the Words, "I Love You"

Talk is cheap. It's very easy to *say* the words *I love you*, but just because they are spoken doesn't mean they're true, any more than my saying "I can fly" will make it so.

Jesus also recognized and taught that we often demonstrate a glaring difference between our words and our deeds when He said, "You will recognize good people by what they *do*. Not everyone who just says to me, Lord, Lord, will enter into the kingdom of heaven, only those who actually do the will of my Father in heaven. In that day many will say, Lord, in your name have we not prophesied and cast out devils and done many wonderful things? And then I will tell them, I don't recognize you. Leave me, you who do wickedly." (Matthew 7:20-23)

Many of us make claims to be loving—often with fervent sincerity—that are not sufficiently supported by our behavior. Jesus reserved harsh words, in fact, for those who make such claims, and He put His condemnation in the form of a metaphor. One day He "was hungry, and when He went over to a fig tree He discovered that it had only leaves but no fruit. So He said to it, You will be without fruit forever, and immediately the tree withered up." (Matthew 21:18-19) When we use loving words but fail to demonstrate true compassion, we are like a fruit tree that appears—with its abundance of leaves—to be healthy but bears no fruit.

In great part we are deeply confused about the real nature of love precisely *because* the words *I love you* are spoken so easily. We tend to say *I love you* for several reasons:

- We know we *should* be loving. We know that being loving is a higher quality than being selfish and hateful, so at least we want to create the *appearance* of being loving.
- Other people like to hear it. When we claim to be loving toward people, they're grateful to us, and we enjoy that feeling of importance.
- If we say, "I love you," we've learned that we can often get other people to do what we want. Everyone in a relationship has learned the magic of saying those words: Hearts melt, offenses are forgiven, minds are persuaded, and hands reach out to serve.
- It's expected. There are few moments more uncomfortable than the pause between one partner in a relationship saying "I love you" and the other partner responding with a similar expression. On some occasions, we're just *expected* to say those words.
- To our credit, we really do *want* to be loving. No matter how selfish our reasons often are for expressing affection—as listed above—we really do have an innate desire to be genuinely loving toward other people.

In the space on the next page discuss some occasions when you have said, "I love you" for some of the reasons above. Possible examples might include or be similar to the following:

- Sometimes I say, "I love you" to my wife only because I know that if I *don't*, she'll be irritated at me.
- Often I say, "I love you" to my children at bedtime just because I know I should, even though I may actually be irritated and not be feeling loving at all.
- When my girlfriend is mad at me, there's nothing that gets her to forgive me faster than my saying, "I love you."
- I say, "I love you" to my mother on the phone even when sometimes I want to choke her, because if I *don't* say it, she'll sulk about it for days.

- Sometimes I say, "I love you" to my wife only because then I know I'm more likely to get sex from her.
- If my girlfriend says, "I love you," what else can I do but say the same thing back to her? It would be pretty uncomfortable if I didn't.
- If I tell my husband I love him—with words and by doing things for him—I can often get him to give in and let me have my way about something that he's been resisting me about.

So look at the situation we have here. All our lives people have used the word *love* when it wasn't necessarily love at all. On many occasions that "love" was used for manipulation or out of a sense of duty or obligation. How confusing this has been for us—especially when we were children.

In their defense, when we were children and the people around us used the word love in inappropriate and confusing ways, almost never was their deception intentional. They simply passed on to us the meanings of love that they themselves were taught from childhood.

And when all these people used the word "love," we naturally tended to *believe* them. We believed that what they were giving us *was* love. Why? Why did we believe people, even when their messages were mixed and contradictory?

- Because the people who taught us the meaning of "love"—however inaccurately—were very powerful figures in our lives. When we're small children, our parents don't just *influence* our understanding of the world around us. They virtually *define* the world for us. When a parent says to a four-year-old, "I love you," no four-year-old has the insight or courage to say, "Now, Dad, in what sense do you use the word *love*? Do you mean that you love *me*—that you unconditionally care about *my* happiness—or are you saying you love me out of a sense of duty or to make yourself feel better?"

- Because we very much *wanted* to believe that we were loved. We wanted it so much that we were willing to believe that people loved us even when they didn't. Our desire to be loved is still that great. Witness, for example, how quickly many young girls are willing to have sex with teenage boys who are obviously using them. These girls are blind to what the boys are doing because they *want* to believe they're being loved. Even when the lie becomes exposed with time, they fall for the same deception in the next relationship.

Sorting out the Love in our Lives

Now here's a hard part for most people, but I promise you that if you'll engage in this next piece of self-examination, you will create an opportunity to be freed from a great deal of confusion. Think about the examples you discussed on pages 39-40. No doubt you've had a number of people in your life who have expressed affection to you, but now you recognize that:

- on many occasions these people have also behaved in ways that have been far less than loving—quite incompatible with their words.
- people often say "I love you" for selfish—not genuinely loving—reasons.

Now go one step further with me. After counseling with thousands of people, I have discovered that one of the most baffling frustrations of our lives is the contradiction that occurs when the people *closest to us* say they love us, but then they behave in strikingly unloving ways. On countless occasions people have said to me variations on the following:

- "I'm sure my husband loves me, BUT (he behaves in all these seemingly unloving ways)."
- "I know my mother loves me, BUT (she keeps treating me badly and controlling me)."

It absolutely makes us crazy when we try to make sense of the contradiction that exists when we hear the verbal expression "I love you" from people who then behave in ways that are angry, critical, harsh, controlling, manipulative, and otherwise selfish. It's puzzling, even painful.

In the space below discuss in greater detail the feelings you've experienced as people have claimed to "love" you but have treated you in unloving ways. You might use some of the examples you already provided on page 40.

- Did you feel loved on those occasions?
- Were you confused?
- Were you frustrated?
- Were you angry?
- Were you hurt?

When people claim to love us, but we don't *feel* loved as a result of their behavior, how can we make sense of it? Actually, it's easy. Everything begins to make sense when we begin with a foundation of the truth, instead of building on a foundation of what we'd *like*. We established earlier that we more reliably express the truth about ourselves with our behavior than with our words. So let's apply this realization to the situations in our lives where words and behavior are in conflict.

We've been trying to reconcile angry and selfish behavior with our *belief* that the person demonstrating these behaviors actually loves us. Instead of attempting that impossible task, let's just work with the truth: When people behave in unloving ways, they are *not* loving us—at least in that moment. We'll discuss this a great deal more—to the point where this concept is undeniable and unforgettable—in the following two sections.

Now, instead of saying, "I'm sure my husband loves me, *but* (he behaves in all these seemingly unloving ways)," we can say, "My husband behaves in unloving ways *because*—at least in those moments—he is *not* loving me." When we see behavior for what it *is*, instead of what we *want* it to be, it makes much more sense.

We tend to avoid the truths that are unpleasant to us, but until we face them, we can never make sense of our lives and usually remain stuck in patterns of feelings and behaviors that cause us great confusion and pain. We are strongly attached to the hope—an expectation, really—that certain people in our lives love us. To let go of that dream could be a huge potential loss. To admit that we're actually not loved much of the time—perhaps most of the time—is frightening. If our own parents—not to mention spouses, children, and others—don't love us, what does that say about *us*? In the face of that possibility, we can feel quite alone and worthless.

Let me hasten here to emphasize that when I say that someone in your life demonstrates with his or her behavior that he or she doesn't love you, I'm not making an accusation, nor am I insulting anyone. When people don't love you—as proven by their behavior—you need to understand the following:

- They fail to love you not because they *won't* but because they *can't*. In the moment they are being unloving, they simply don't have any love to give. More about this in Module Two.
- This failure to love you doesn't make them *bad*. Again, they're simply *unable* to love you. Most of us never learned *how* to love unconditionally, and there's no crime in not knowing how to do something we were never *taught*. Most of us don't know how to play the violin, for example, and we see no shame in that. Our inability to play the violin—or perform any other task—is usually only a reflection of our never having had an adequate opportunity to learn how. Similarly, most people have never had the opportunity to learn how to love.
- The failure of other people to love you doesn't make *you* bad either. When other people don't love you, they're saying little about you, only making a declaration about their own inability to love.
- Just because they don't love you in the moment they're angry or critical or selfish doesn't mean they *never* love you. The ability we all have to love waxes and wanes with variation in a number of factors.
- Just because someone doesn't know how to love you now doesn't mean he or she can't learn. Once we learn about Real Love, there is great hope for the achievement of happiness and great relationships.

In the space on the next page discuss what this realization—that with their behavior the people around you are often telling you that they *don't* love you, at least in those moments—could mean for you.

Possible examples might include or be similar to the following:

- I've been frustrated for so long that my husband claims to love me, but then a lot of the time he is so critical and angry. Now I see that on those angry occasions, he really *isn't* being loving. Instead of being offended by that, I need to understand that sometimes the burdens he carries—often quite invisible to me—make it impossible for him to be loving. He's just not *able* to love me, so at times like that it's crazy for me to push him to be more loving. He doesn't have it to give.

- All the confusing situations in my relationships—past and present—make sense now. In the past I tried to make sense of the contradiction of people's behaviors and their words. I see now that I just need to *believe* their behavior and pretty much ignore the words they speak.

- When people tell me with their behavior that they're not loving me in a given moment, I need to just accept that and not insist that they be different.

- All these years I believed my mother when she told me she loved me, but I was confused by her always criticizing me and controlling me. Finally I understand. She has *not* loved me. That's no accusation of her, just an enormous revelation for me. Now I can understand why I have behaved as I have for most of my life. I have been so angry and manipulative with people almost my whole life, and now I understand that I've just been empty and afraid because I never felt loved. All these years I've been trying to fill my emptiness and protect myself. It's a relief to solve the mystery.

All of our lives most of us have avoided the possibility that certain people don't love us, but finally accepting the truth has enormous advantages. With an understanding of the truth, however unpleasant it might be initially, we can:

- eliminate the confusion and frustration that have haunted us for so long. Again and again I have seen in relationships that people are often as hurt by not *understanding* the behaviors of others as they are by the behaviors themselves.
- finally change the destructive patterns that we have been repeating. When we don't understand a problem or mistake, we're virtually guaranteed to repeat it. We may not like facing the truth of the problem, but, in the words of Jesus, "the truth will make us free." (John 8:32) The momentary discomfort of letting go of old illusions is a tiny matter when weighed against the enormous benefits of finally learning the truth and experiencing the freedom and power that accompany that knowledge.
- begin to take the steps to *find* the Real Love we have been missing. Most of us spend our entire lives trying to get love from people who don't have it to give, trying to squeeze blood from a turnip. Once we face the truth that certain people simply *can't* love us, we can turn our efforts to finding love from those who *can* love us.

So what is the truth? What is love, really? That's the subject of the next section.

THREE, 18:43 - 19:42   Real Love
CD Track Three, 0:43 - 1:43

It's Real Love when I care about *your* happiness without wanting anything from you in return. It's Real Love when you care about *my* happiness without wanting anything from me.

This is a very important definition of love. Without it, most of us have been lost and confused all our lives, individually and in our relationships.

First let's take notice of what Real Love is *not*. It is not:

- the feeling of satisfaction we get from people who give us exactly what we want.
- the feeling of importance and worth we get when people flatter us.
- the exhilaration of sex.
- romance.
- the approval we get from people when we do what they want.

Real Love is a *decision* to care about other people whether they return the consideration or not. Real Love is a choice, an action.

Paul explained Real Love to the Corinthians when he wrote:

Love is always patient and kind, never jealous or proud or rude or selfish. Love doesn't take offense and isn't easily provoked. Love takes no pleasure in other people's faults, rejoices in the truth, bears all things, believes and hopes and endures all things, and never fails. (1 Corinthians 13:4-8)

It is critical that we have a clear understanding of Real Love, because without it:

- we simply will not know how to find the one element most essential to our happiness.
- we won't be able to give to those around us what they need most, thereby making loving relationships impossible.
- we'll be forever confused by the conflict between what love *is* and what people claim that it is.

So now we have a definition of Real Love. But let's be practical. How can we really *know* whether we're caring about someone's happiness without having an expectation of some return for ourselves? How can we know whether other people are really caring about *us* and not themselves?

Fortunately, Real Love can be distinguished from everything else by the presence or absence of two characteristics: disappointment and anger, which are the subjects of the next section.

THREE, 19:42 - 22:17   Disappointment and Anger
CD Track Three, 1:43 - 4:18

For ease of discussion, I won't keep referring to both disappointment and irritation. I'll talk only about irritation and its synonyms: anger, frustration, annoyance, and so on. Disappointment and anger are just different places on the same spectrum, so separating them serves no function. I'll make that point more clearly in a moment.

We also need to be clear about what the word *anger* means. Most of us can admit to being angry when it's undeniable—when we're screaming, our faces are red, and we're throwing objects across the room. If we acknowledge anger only we're in its volcanic stages, however, we're missing its terrible effects in far too many circumstances. Anger includes all of the following conditions:

- Rage
- Irritation
- Impatience
- Annoyance
- Frustration
- Disappointment
- Aggravation
- Feeling provoked
- Feeling bothered

We like to hide our anger by disguising it with clever words, like some of those above. We like to say, "No, I'm not angry. I'm just frustrated," because deep down we know that anger is selfish and unloving.

I Don't Love You

What I just said—about anger being unloving—is one of the most difficult concepts for people to understand and accept as they begin their study of Real Love, but I promise you that if you will:

- continue watching or listening to the seminar,
- read and complete this workbook, and
- keep your mind open,

you'll change the rest of your life.

An understanding of anger need not be complicated. In the video or audio recording of the seminar, review the example I gave of the man who made a mistake at work (in the *audio* recording, when I used the word *you*, I was addressing a man in the audience). As I lovingly, patiently described how he could have made different choices, how did you feel? Did you feel threatened or uncomfortable? Or did you feel safe? Although you may not have been able to see his face, I can tell you that he was quite comfortable, not the least bit threatened.

Now, in the space below take another moment and describe how *you* would have felt had I approached you in the same way about a mistake you'd made. If I came to you with the same gentle tone and manner, how would you have felt?

- Afraid OR calm?
- Criticized OR supported?
- Discouraged OR eager to try the new approach I described?
- Resentful OR willing to work with me toward the accomplishment of a common goal?

Now, by way of contrast, how did you feel when I changed my approach—when I raised my voice and sputtered with exasperation about the mistake the man in the audience had made? Quite a different experience, wasn't it? What you couldn't directly perceive from the video or audio recording was that the instant I changed my tone of voice—as well as my posture, facial expression, and choice of words—the entire audience that was present at the filming *froze*. No one moved. Some even held their breath. They were *afraid*, even though the example was hypothetical and didn't involve any of them directly. It's not difficult to imagine how you would feel if I approached you in that manner in real life about a mistake you actually made.

If I could choose only one thing for you to remember from this entire seminar and workbook, it would be this:

Every time you're angry (or impatient or disappointed or irritated or frustrated) as you interact with another person—be it a spouse, child, co-worker, or whomever—that person hears you say only four words: "I don't love you."

Let me re-state that in an abbreviated way: Every time you're angry, the people around you hear you say only, "I don't love you." If you have any doubt about the truth of that statement, I suggest that you do two things:

- Pick anyone you'd like, vent your anger on him or her, and watch that person's face.
- Reflect on how *you* feel when people are angry at you.

When I'm angry at you, my concern is for *me*. I'm thinking and saying with my words and behavior:

- Look what you did to *me*.
- Look at what you should have done for *me*.
- You have dared to inconvenience *me*.

When I'm angry—when my concern is for *me-me-me*—there is no way in the world that you could feel my unconditional concern for you. None. Because I am not unconditionally concerned about you, and you know it.

God has left no doubt where He stands on the issue of anger. It is not compatible with being loving or living a Christ-like life. He has said Himself, and through his prophets and apostles:

- From long ago, you have heard it said that you shall not kill, and whoever kills will be in danger of judgment. But I say unto you, that whoever is angry with his brother, or calls him a fool, will be in danger of hellfire. (Matthew 5:21-25)

- Let nothing be done in contention or selfishness, but in humility let everyone regard others as more important than themselves. (Philippians 2:3)

- Now you must completely avoid all these: anger, rage, ill will, evil speaking, filthy communication. Don't lie to one another, having eliminated your old self with his old ways, and having taken on your new self, which is made new in the image of the Creator. (Colossians 3:8-10)

- Speak ill of no man, avoid quarreling, and instead be gentle, showing kindness to all men. (Titus 3:2)

- Live in peace with all men, and in holiness, without which no man shall see the Lord; watching carefully so that no one fails to partake of the grace of God, so that no root of bitterness will spring up to trouble *you* and poison many. (Hebrews 12:14-15)

- So, my beloved brethren, let every man be swift to hear, slow to speak, slow to anger, for the anger of man does not accomplish the righteousness of God. (James 1:19-20)

- Finally, all of you be of one mind, having compassion for one another. Love as brethren, be tender-hearted and courteous. Don't pay back evil for evil, or insult for insult: but on the contrary, pay back both evil and insult with blessing. For this is your calling, that you should bless and inherit a blessing. For he that will love life, and see good days, let him keep his tongue from evil, and his lips that they speak no lies. (1 Peter 3:8-10)

In our society—and in most of our individual lives—anger is so common that we have come to accept it as normal. It's become virtually a background noise that we scarcely notice anymore. When *everyone* is doing something, we reason—mostly unconsciously—how in the world could it be wrong? In view of what you have read and heard here, however:

- in the audio or video recording of the seminar,
- in the workbook, and
- in the Bible verses above,

are you willing to modify your view of anger? In the space below, describe what you have learned and how you see anger differently now.

In the space on the next page discuss some occasions or relationships in your life where someone expressed their anger at you, and then answer the following questions about these occasions or relationships:

- Did you feel loved in those moments?
- Did you feel closer to that person?
- How did those angry moments affect your relationship?

Now consider this: If *you* dislike the effect of *other people's* anger, is it possible that *other people* don't like the effect of *yours*? In the space below discuss some occasions or relationships in your life where you have wondered why someone withdrew from you or where your relationship suddenly soured. Then honestly consider whether that change might have had something to do with *your* being angry at that person. Is it possible that your relationship changed because with your behavior—your disappointment, your impatience, your irritation—you clearly communicated that you didn't love him or her?

We must learn to identify our anger and realize the selfish and destructive effects it has on us and on the people around us. When you're angry, say this to yourself: "I am not being loving. I'm being selfish." Now look back on the occasions when you have been angry and say, "I was not loving. I was being selfish." This is not a condemnation. You're simply identifying what you've been doing for the purpose of making wiser choices. We'll talk much more about this in Module Two.

The Test: Identifying Real Love vs. Imitation Love

Imagine someone in your life whom you *want* to love unconditionally. Now further imagine that you actually *do* feel unconditionally loving toward that person. You care about his or her happiness more than anything in the world.

Now imagine that you're describing to this person a mistake he's made. Caring primarily about *his* happiness, would you be angry as you described the mistake, or would you calmly describe the mistake in a way that would benefit *him*—simply so he could avoid the mistake and be happier himself? The answer is obvious, is it not?

Now, in the space below describe the last time you were disappointed or angry at someone for making a mistake that inconvenienced you. Describe how you see your disappointment and/or anger as it functioned in that situation. Did your irritation benefit the other person? Was it loving? Was it selfish?

Considering the criteria we have discussed thus far for identifying Real Love, how consistently have you received Real Love from other people? How consistently have you *given* Real Love to others?

The Foolishness of Anger

I have now heard hundreds of people defend their anger, claiming in various ways that anger is sometimes necessary. To be sure, anger is often the only choice we see, but it is never necessary and never the best choice.

To further illustrate this point, suppose I give you a Shakespearean sonnet to memorize in the next twenty minutes. And I give you two choices about how you might accomplish this task:

- You could learn the sonnet while I sit in the room, silently supporting you.
  OR
- You could study while I'm screaming in your ear and slapping your face.

Is there any question about which choice you'd make? No one learns better while being attacked or threatened, which is the effect of anger. We choose anger not because it's the *best* choice as we interact with others—it's clearly not—but because it's the *only* choice we know in many circumstances. We haven't learned a better way yet.

With the understanding you just acquired, describe in the space below some occasions where you thought you were using anger to motivate someone to accomplish something positive but later discovered that you were having mostly a negative effect on that person's behavior.

Possible examples might include or be similar to the following:

- My son just wouldn't do his homework. The only way I could get him to do anything was to get mad at him, but when I did that he became increasingly sullen and rebellious. I'm not sure the anger was worth it.
- When my wife doesn't want sex, I get mad, but all that does is make her want sex even less.
- When my husband doesn't spend time with me, I nag him and get irritated, but then he just withdraws even more.
- When my neighbor says something snippy at me, I defend myself and get angry, but then the conversation goes badly every time.
- When my daughter didn't keep her curfew, I got really angry, but that just led to shouting matches and really terrible scenes.
- I get mad at my boyfriend when he doesn't listen, and then he tunes me out completely.

In the moments we're angry, we are *not* loving. We are concerned about our own interests. We must absolutely give up saying things like, "I'm mad at you, but I still love you." Such expressions only keep us from facing the truth ourselves and cause confusion in the minds of others.

We also claim to get angry at other people "for their own good," especially in the case of our children. Let's get rid of that notion now: Do you like it when people get angry at *you*? So how could you possibly claim to use anger for the benefit of someone else?

CHAPTER FOUR
Meditation

FOUR, 22:17 - 26:16 Feeling Loved
CD Track Four, entire track

Doing your best to avoid intellectualizing the experience, in the space below and on the next page discuss what it *felt* like for you to be in the village described in the meditation.

- Were you even able to imagine what it would be like to be among people who could love you in that way?
- How did it feel as you told them the story of your life?
- How did you feel as they accepted you as one of their own, without hesitation?
- How did you feel as you left the village and the valley behind?

CHAPTER FIVE
The Effect of the Lack of Real Love

FIVE, 26:16 - 26:50   The Effect of Feeling Loved
CD Track Five, 0:00 - 0:34

Consider in greater detail how you felt while you were in the village, and describe your feelings in the space below and on the next page.

- Did you feel any inclination to feel angry at those people, or lie to them, or withdraw from them?
- Did you feel any inclination to feel angry at *anyone*, even the people you know out here in the real world?
- What would you give to be able to feel like that all the time?

Think about what I say in the seminar: "Love does that to anger." When people feel unconditionally loved, they simply *lose* their anger. Anger cannot survive in the face of Real Love.

The apostle John taught that same principle when he said, "There is no fear in love, but perfect love drives out fear." (1 John 4:18)

Every day we tend to blame other people for our irritation.

- When we get mad in traffic, it's because of those "stupid drivers."
- When people are late and make us wait, that "makes" us mad.
- When people fail to do as they've promised, they "irritate us."
- When our children don't do as they're told, they "provoke us."

In the space below describe some occasions or relationships where you have blamed circumstances or other people for your anger:

In our society, it is almost universally accepted that other people have the ability to make us angry with their behavior. But consider what happened in the village above. Although all the people in the real world remained unchanged, when you were surrounded by Real Love from the people in the village, your anger at all people either disappeared or greatly diminished.

This is absolute proof that other people do not make us angry. The logic is straightforward:

- When you were in the village, you lost your anger because you had enough *what*? Real Love.
- In the presence of sufficient Real Love, anger decreases or disappears.
- What, then, is the real cause of anger? That we *don't* feel loved. It really is that simple, and we'll discuss this subject much more in Module Two.

In the space below describe some of the people in your life toward whom you frequently experience anger, perhaps using some of your examples from the on the previous page. Now imagine what it would be like if you were constantly filled with the feeling you experienced in the village. Can you picture in your mind how differently you would react to those people?

The feelings you experienced in the village—utter peace and contentment—are much more than a metaphor or fairy tale. Jesus talked about the reality of such feelings when He extended to us this *promise*: "I leave peace with you. I don't give you the kind of peace the world gives, but my peace. Don't let your heart be troubled or afraid." (John 14:27)

There really is a simple path by which you can replace all the fear, anger, and frustration in your life with how you felt in the village. That feeling of peace and happiness is worth everything we could ever do to achieve it, and I promise you that as you learn the principles in *The Essentials of Real Love* and in the *Workbook*—and as you apply them in your life—you will find the love and happiness you briefly experienced in the meditation.

The Savior captured the worth of Real Love in a parable He told about the kingdom of heaven:

> The kingdom of heaven is like a merchant who was looking for high-quality pearls, and when he found one of great value, he sold everything he had to buy it. (Matthew 13:45-46)

In the space on the next page, make a written personal commitment that you'll do whatever it takes—for as long as it takes—to achieve this condition, which has been promised by Christ and is described in *The Essentials of Real Love*. Why a written commitment? The more concrete a commitment we make to do anything, the more likely we are to keep it and accomplish what we have planned to do.

- Are you willing to sacrifice your pride and take a new and brave look at the nature of the disappointment and anger in your life?
- Are you willing to invest the time and energy required to gain a thorough understanding of the principles of Real Love?
- Are you willing to practice the principles of Real Love long enough to experience the feelings you had in the village of the meditation?

FIVE, 26:50 - 28:37   The "Love" We Actually Received
   CD Track Five, 0:34 - 2:50

Now that we know what Real Love looks like, and what it feels like, let's compare that to what most of us have actually received, beginning in childhood.

As you answer these questions, remember that no one is being *accused* of anything. There is no blaming here. What we're striving for is simply a greater understanding of how the foundations of our lives were built, because with that knowledge we can make more effective strides in our personal growth and in our relationships.

If you're like most people, when you were a child, and you:

- got good grades,
- kept your room clean,
- succeeded in athletic competitions, or
- obeyed your parents,

what kind of reactions did you see? If you were lucky—and you weren't just ignored—you saw the following kinds of positive reactions, which most of us live for:

- Smiles
- Gentle tones of voice
- Kind words
- Pats on the head
- Being held up as the "good child" or even the "perfect child" to others

Describe here some of the signs of approval or acceptance you received as a child from others when you were "good."

It was from these behaviors that we got the feeling that we were loved. Unfortunately, things changed dramatically when our behavior changed. When we:

- cried,
- made too much noise in the car,
- fought with our sister,
- spilled milk all over the living room table,
- failed to do our homework,
- dragged dog poop across the living room carpet,
- embarrassed our parents in public,
- got out of bed for the fifth time in one night,
- got bad grades,
- wrecked the family car,
- stayed out way past our curfew, or
- teased our little brother,

what happened then? Did we hear the kind words and gentle tones? Fat chance. Did we see smiles on the faces around us? Hardly.

Describe below what you remember from your childhood as you made some of the mistakes listed above. Name some of your "bad" behaviors that were different from the above list. On those occasions, what were the reactions of your parents? Other family members? Teachers? What did they say? What did they do? How did their faces look? How did they sound?

On the occasions when we made mistakes and those mistakes were followed by a dramatic change in the behavior of the people around us, there was only one lesson we could have learned:

When you're "good," I love you; when you're not, I don't.

Although no one *meant* to communicate that message, it was nonetheless conveyed with great power and clarity, and we felt it right down to the marrow of our bones. People loved us more when we did what they liked, which is the very essence of *conditional* love—not Real Love at all—and yet we were told by these same people that they truly loved us. How confusing it was for us.

Discuss below how you felt as you made the numerous mistakes of childhood and then experienced the strong disapproval of the people important to you. Again, remember that there is no accusation or blaming here, only an intent to learn something about the foundations that other people built for our lives during our childhoods.

The message we heard as children—that love is conditional— has continued virtually without interruption for us as adults. In the space below discuss how you have been treated as an *adult* as you have made mistakes. Discuss below specific examples of how your spouse, boyfriend, girlfriend, parents, friends, children, co-workers, boss, and others behave toward you now when you:

- are late.
- don't give them the attention they demand.
- fail to fulfill the other obligations they heap upon you.
- are tired and cranky and need some love and support yourself.
- make mistakes at work.
- just don't feel like having sex.
- spend too much money.
- don't spend enough money on them.
- otherwise fail to meet their unending expectations.

When you make these "mistakes," are you greeted with the kind of complete acceptance and unconditional love that you experienced in the village during the meditation on page 59? If not, you're getting the same conditional love as an adult that you almost certainly received as a child.

Why do we need to recognize and discuss these evidences of conditional love? Why not just let the past go? Because we need to see the *effect* that all that conditional love has had upon us, from childhood to the present. With that understanding, we can de-mystify so much that has baffled us to this point, and then we'll have the knowledge and power to change and grow in the ways we'd like.

Our Parents

Discuss in the space below the possibility that your own parents did not sufficiently love you unconditionally. Give examples of their loving you conditionally.

This is an important realization, because the vast majority of us did not experience a consistent pattern of Real Love early in our lives, and we must understand and accept that fact before we can understand the roots of the difficulties we're having now with our marriages, our children, our jobs, and so on. Your frustration and anger with anyone in the present are almost always founded on a profound unhappiness that began with insufficient Real Love in childhood.

We commonly quote the verse in Proverbs which reads, "Train up a child in the way he should go, and when he is old, he will not depart from it." (Proverbs 22:6) Rarely, however, do we consider the natural corollary to this verse, which would read, "Train up a child in the ways he should *not* go, and when he is old, he will not depart from them." What we experience in childhood usually sets the tone—often the entire pattern—for the rest of our lives. If we are not given sufficient Real Love during that critical time, we are virtually guaranteed to experience lives of emptiness and fear, with the accompanying Getting and Protecting Behaviors.

It will be easier to accept and talk about the conditional love of your parents if you also realize that they loved you *as well as they could*. If they failed to love you unconditionally it was only because *they* didn't receive the Real Love *they* needed either. We can't give what we don't have. Despite our understanding and acceptance of their behavior, however, the effect of their not loving us unconditionally remains. Anything other than Real Love is never enough and leaves us painfully empty. Parents have a huge responsibility for the unhappiness in our lives, and we need to talk about it—not to blame them and not to make excuses for our behavior and feelings in the present, but to *recognize* the effect that a lack of Real Love has had on us. We need an understanding of the past to make sense of the present and to give us the power to meaningfully address changing the future. We also must realize that changing our lives is now entirely *our* responsibility.

FIVE, 28:37 - 30:17   The Effect of a Lack of Real Love
CD Track Five, 2:34 - 4:02

Real Love isn't just another important element that contributes to our happiness. It's *the* factor most important in determining our emotional well-being. We can no more be happy without Real Love than we can thrive physically without air and water.

Without Real Love, then, we eagerly reach out for whatever will make us feel better in the moment, as I did in my seminar example with Mrs. Woods.

Unless you're different from almost everyone around you— easily 98%—you too have spent a great deal of your life working to get other people to think well of you. In the space below discuss what qualities you tried to achieve as a child, qualities that people praised you for, qualities that made you feel worthwhile and "loved."

Possible examples:

- Cute
- Quiet
- Clean
- Pretty
- Responsible
- Reliable
- Smart
- Cooperative
- Grateful
- Helpful
- Athletic
- Strong

Talk about what you did in order to hear those descriptive words from the people who "loved" you.

Then describe some occasions when you failed to demonstrate those qualities—when you disappointed the people around you. How did they behave? What did they say? How did you feel? Did you still feel worthwhile? Valued? Loved?

What we learn as children we tend to repeat as adults. In the space below discuss what qualities you now work to possess, qualities that people praise you for, qualities that make you feel worthwhile and "loved."

Examples:

- Intelligent
- Hard working
- Handsome
- Beautiful
- Helpful
- Good listening
- Clever
- Witty
- Powerful
- Strong
- Physically fit
- Organized
- Cooperative

Notice the strong similarities between this list and the one you generated on page 70 for when you were a child. It should be no surprise that we tend to repeat as adults the behavior patterns we learned as children.

FIVE, 30:17 - 31:14   Our Need for Approval
CD Track Five, 4:02 - 5:00

As I describe our willingness to change who we are in order to win the approval of others, many people protest, "I don't do that. I remain true to myself."

We don't like to admit how much we need the approval of others, nor how readily we're willing to sell ourselves to get it. To help you see how you might be doing this, in the space below discuss whether you:

- get nervous before and during some discussions.
- sometimes search anxiously for the "right words" to say as you talk with people.
- worry that what you're about to say won't be well received.
- are looking for a certain outcome from a conversation or interaction.
- dread speaking in public.
- change the way you speak with certain people.

If your answer to any of these questions is *yes*, you're either changing who you are to please people, or you're *preparing* to do so. In this regard, you're in a very large club. It was a well-established practice in the time of Christ, as we learn in this verse:

Among the leaders of the Jews many believed in Jesus, but because of their fear of the disapproval of another group of Jews they did not admit their belief, because they loved the praise of men more than the praise of God. (John 12:42-43)

For thousands of years we human beings have been eager to change our beliefs in order to win the approval—or at least to avoid the disapproval—of those around us.

FIVE, 31:14 - 32:41   Buying Love
CD Track Five, 5:00 - 6:20

Saying and doing the right things so that other people will think well of us is so common in our society that it's not even remarkable. Virtually *everyone* does it. So how could it be bad? Isn't it a good thing to want to create a good impression of ourselves?

As described in the seminar, the moment I do *anything* to earn your approval—assuming that I actually get it—I have *bought* your approval. I've *purchased* your acceptance and love, just as surely as if I had paid you in cash.

And that explains much of why we often feel unloved and alone. When we buy love, we cannot feel genuinely accepted and connected. No matter how much love we buy, we still feel alone. In fact, let's assume for a moment that you are actually loving me unconditionally. If I'm manipulating you for approval, however, I still can't *feel* the Real Love you're giving me. Because of my manipulations, I can conclude—mostly unconsciously—only that the love I'm receiving is purchased. Although you're giving me Real Love, I will *feel* Imitation Love.

Jesus understood the pitfalls of earning the approval of others, and He spoke about it on more than one occasion:

Be careful not to do your good deeds so that others will see you, or you will have no reward from your Father in heaven. So when you do your good deeds, don't make them loudly known, as hypocrites do, so they can have the praise of men. I tell you, such men have their reward. But when you do your good works, don't even let your own left hand know what the right is doing, so your good deeds will be kept secret, and your Father who sees in secret will reward you openly. (Matthew 6:1-4)

If we "do our good works so others will see us," we "have our reward," which is Imitation Love in the form of praise. But as we earn the love of others, we can't feel the Real Love available from men *or* God. God's love is available to all of us, but if we're trying to earn it, we can feel His love only as a reward for what we have done. If, on the other hand, we make no effort to be recognized as we serve and love, our "Father will reward us openly." In other words, we will finally *feel* the life-giving power of His love.

In our defense, without Real Love it is virtually inevitable that we will try to earn some kind of approval. How could we not? The emptiness and pain of not feeling loved are just intolerable.

In the space below and on the next page discuss some ways—or evidences—that you try to earn the approval of others, or at least avoid their disapproval. Your answers might include:

- I smile a lot, not because I'm feeling happy at the time, but because I know people like it better when I appear to be happy around them.
- When I dress up to go out, I often ask people, "How do I look?"
- When I make a mistake, I always glance around me quickly to see if anyone noticed what I did.
- In class, I'm very reluctant to raise my hand, because I don't want to make a mistake in front of everybody.
- When I do something well, I'm disappointed if people don't notice and say something.
- I'm offended when people don't appreciate what I do for them.

CHAPTER SIX

Imitation Love—Praise

**SIX, 32:41 - 34:11 Buying Imitation Love in the Form of
    Praise
    CD Track Six, 0:00 - 1:31**

Imitation Love is anything we use as a substitute for the Real Love we need, and praise is one form of Imitation Love. As we discussed above, however, we have to *buy* praise with our behavior, and for that reason alone praise can never make us feel loved.

As a young man, I excelled in many areas, and I could never understand why the praise I received for my accomplishments felt so hollow. I remember once playing the piano before a thousand people, and after the performance they clapped and cheered, and many people came up to personally congratulate me. And yet, despite all that praise, I just wanted to run away. Already I was sensing—although I couldn't have put it into words—that I was trapped in a position where I had to buy their praise and affection, so it felt worthless.

Describe some occasions in your life when you have received praise for performing well, only to discover that it just didn't feel as good as you had hoped it would.

Does this mean that all praise is bad? That we shouldn't ever compliment another person? No, and we'll talk more about that shortly.

SIX, 34:11 - 34:22 Praise Doesn't Last
CD Track Six, 1:31 - 1:42

We've all experienced the exhilaration of praise, and we've also realized how briefly the satisfaction lasts. Pitiful.

And just in case we wondered about the durability of the praise of men, the Lord made it clear where our self-proclaimed greatness fits into the eternal scheme:

I will bring to nothing the understanding of those who think they know a lot. So to those who think they know a lot—who enjoy the praise of others for their knowledge—I say, next to God, who is wise? Who is capable of teaching or debating? Hasn't God made the knowledge of this world into nothing? (1 Corinthians 1:19-20)

SIX, 34:22 - 36:41 The Addiction of Praise
CD Track Six, 1:42 - 4:02

In the seminar, I tell the story of the comedian who required more and more praise, and eventually no amount was enough. Praise and all the other forms of Imitation Love become addictions. You're addicted to something when:

- you have to have more and more of it to feel a sense of satisfaction.
- you experience great discomfort when you can't have it right when you want it.
- you become desperate or angry when it's taken from you.
- you're willing to go to great lengths—sometimes even do questionable things—to get it.

We tend to avoid the word *addict* as applied to ourselves, but we need to acknowledge the truth of it. In the space on the next page discuss the evidence in your life that you are addicted to praise.

Examples:

- Before I leave the house, I spend quite a bit of time ensuring that I look good.
- I often make sure that other people notice my accomplishments.
- When people fail to see the good I've done, I become irritated.
- I sometimes work to get more credit for a success than those around me get.
- I kiss up to the boss.
- I enjoy hearing my name mentioned in association with a successful venture.
- I love seeing my name in print.
- I keep my ears open for what other people are saying about me.
- I enjoy people seeing me as sexually desirable, and I devote considerable time and effort to enhancing my appearance.
- I get a real sense of worth from my accomplishments in school and at work, and when I'm having problems there, I get discouraged or angry.

- I like it when people know how much money I make.
- I take credit for the work others do.
- I drive a car I can't afford.

As you realize these things about yourself, don't condemn yourself. You're just gathering *information*, so you can begin to make decisions that will lead to greater happiness in your life.

SIX, 36:41 - 39:04 Praise Isn't Really About You
CD Track Six, 4:02 - 6:23

In the seminar, I give two examples of praise being selfish: the boss giving a compliment at work and a man saying, "You're so beautiful" to a woman. We spend a lot of our lives earning praise from people who are simply *using* us. Is it really worth it? We acquire all that praise—or any form of Imitation Love—and believe that we have what matters. We believe ourselves rich in the things of the world, and Jesus spoke directly to that illusion:

But woe unto you that are rich, because you have had your time of happiness. Woe unto you that are full, because you will be hungry. Woe unto you that laugh now, for you will mourn and weep. Woe unto you, when all men will speak well of you, because their fathers did the same to the false prophets. (Luke 6:24-26)

In the space below discuss some examples of where you have offered selfish praise to others.

Examples:

- I tell my girlfriend all the time how great she looks. Now, she *does* look good, but part of the reason I tell her that is because I know she gets mad when I *don't*.
- I compliment my boss because he treats people differently when they do that.
- I praise my wife's cooking partly because it *is* good, but also because when I praise her she tends to put more effort into doing it again, and I like that.
- When my son cleans his room, I praise him. Part of me does it because I want to encourage him to be responsible—which is a trait he needs—but I also do it because I want him to keep the room clean for *my* benefit. I hate it when his room is messy.
- One of the reasons I tell my wife she's beautiful is that I've learned that then I'm more likely to get sex.

SIX, 39:04 - 41:38   We're Trained to Earn Praise
CD Track Six, 6:23 - 8:57

From the time we're small children, we're actually *taught* to earn the praise of those around us. The first time someone smiled at us for being "good" and frowned when we were "bad," we began the lifelong education in buying praise.

But the moment we "put our best foot forward" and earn praise, we begin a deception that can only cause problems. To illustrate this concept, suppose that I work hard to create a great first impression with you, and you indicate that you like me. Now I can conclude only that you like me *because* of those positive characteristics I worked so hard to display. Now I can assume only that I will have to *keep* working hard to impress you, or you'll no longer have those reasons to like me. What an exhausting situation.

We see this process played out pointedly in the act of falling in love. Two people put on the best show they can, and for a while that actually seems to work. They love being with someone who has such great qualities. But eventually we can't hide the fact that there is more to us than our best foot, and when the lie is revealed, disappointment and a sense of betrayal are natural.

As I counsel with couples whose relationships are in trouble, it's very common for one or both parties to say something like, "He used to be so romantic and thoughtful and attentive. But now he's changed." No, he hasn't changed. He's just tired of the effort required to show only his best foot. You're finally seeing *the rest* of who he has been all along. But don't blame him. You were putting your best foot forward too. And, frankly, you *wanted* to believe that his best foot represented all of him. It was a mutual deception, in which both of you participated eagerly.

On the next page describe a relationship where you put your best foot forward and created an impression that you found difficult to keep up. And then what happened to the relationship?

SIX, 41:38 - 44:13   Why We Keep Buying Love, and Why It Can't Work
CD Track Six, 8:57 - 11:34

So if the results of earning praise—earning "love"—are so uniformly disastrous, why do we keep doing it?

- In the absence of sufficient Real Love, the emptiness and pain are intolerable, so we feel compelled to do whatever we can to minimize that discomfort. Buying Imitation Love is one way to reduce our pain, however briefly.
- Almost every human being around us is doing the same. When everyone is doing something, we tend to do that same thing ourselves, without question. Earning Imitation Love is so common that it's not even noticed.

Wanting to create a good impression seems to many people like such an innocent thing. "It's only natural that we'd want to look our best," they say. Let me share a passage from the book, *Real Love in Dating*:

Imagine that you read an advertisement in the paper that states, "Best apples you've ever eaten." Rushing down to the store, you find on display the most beautiful apples you've ever seen. The store clerk offers you a slice of one of the apples, and you discover that they taste every bit as good as they look. You buy an entire bushel and load them in the car. At home you eat nearly a dozen of the apples in the first couple of days, and you pat yourself on the back that you saw that newspaper advertisement. You even tell your friends about your good fortune. On the third day, however, after eating through the upper two layers of apples, you discover that all the rest of the apples are soft and old, and many are rotten.

Rushing back to the store, you confront the clerk about the rotten apples, saying, "You promised that these would be the best apples I'd ever eaten."

"But the apples on top *were* the best you'd ever eaten," says the clerk. "Am I right?"

"Well, I guess they were," you say, "but that's not the point. You lied to me."

"I did not lie," says the clerk. "I gave you the best apples you'd ever eaten, just as I promised."

"What about the rotten apples?" you protest.

"I delivered exactly what I promised," says the clerk. "I didn't tell you about the rotten ones, because then I knew you wouldn't buy the whole bushel—and you didn't ask me about them, either. You were happy enough when you bought them. It's not my fault that you didn't look through the bushel to see if it was the same on the bottom as the top."

It's quite obvious that the clerk lied to you—he completely misrepresented his product—but he did nothing different from what most of us do on a first date. Two people on a first date are engaging in a best foot festival, with each party diligently putting on a show of his or her best characteristics. On the surface, that might appear commendable, but look at the eventual consequences of people putting their best apples on top. They both believe that the other person's best foot—his or her best apples—accurately represents who that person really is, and that's where the problems begin.

After two people successfully establish a relationship based on their best foot, they eventually discover that their partner is a lot more than his or her best foot—that, metaphorically, there is also the other foot, bad breath, and numerous other imperfections—and the resultant disappointment can be overwhelming. Both partners feel deceived, cheated, and betrayed, and it's understandable that they vent their frustration on their partner. "After all," they reason—silently and aloud—"I used to be happy in this relationship, but now I'm not, so you must be withholding the happiness you once gave me."

When a relationship goes bad, our natural conclusion is that *our partner* has failed us in some way, breaking the unspoken contract we've made together. But the real reason relationships fail is that from the beginning we establish the relationship on something less than the complete truth about ourselves. Expectations are created, and when those are not met—when the truth comes out about who we are, and who our partners are—we feel as though our dreams have been crushed.

Relationships fail because we create them on a foundation lacking the one ingredient—Real Love—most essential to happiness and fulfilling relationships. Without sufficient Real Love, neither partner has the tools to create a healthy and mutually rewarding relationship. Without enough Real Love, the foundation of any relationship will be fatally flawed, and no amount of time, effort, and worry spent on the windows, doors, and carpets will ever create a healthy relationship. *With Real Love, nothing else matters; without it, nothing else is enough.* We'll talk more about the proper foundation of a relationship, as well as the foundation for our lives, on pages 108-9.

SIX, 44:13 - 46:07   Other Forms of Praise
CD Track Six 11:34 - 14:26

Flattery is an obvious form of praise, but there are others:

- Gratitude. Do you get a sense of worth when people are grateful to you for the things you do for them? Are you disappointed when people are *not* grateful for the things you do?
- Respect. When people can't have the Real Love they need, they often settle for demanding respect, which is a combination of praise and power.
- Sex. In our society, being sexually attractive is one of the ultimate forms of praise.
- Money. The more we have, the more highly people tend to think of us.
- Acceptance. It's only natural that we would conclude that if people accept us, we must be more worthwhile.

Discuss below how you have used the forms of praise above—receiving them and giving them—as well as others you might think of.

CHAPTER SEVEN
Imitation Love—Power, Pleasure, Safety

SEVEN, 47:05 - 48:29 Imitation Love in the Form of Power
CD Track Seven, 0:00 - 1:24

Discuss what you learned from this segment:

- What is power?
- Why do we abuse it?
- Why do we crave it?
- Why do we become frightened when we feel powerless?

Power is a seductive form of Imitation Love, and it has caused a great many of us to go astray. Satan demonstrated his knowledge of the attractiveness of power when he tempted Christ in the wilderness. In two of the three situations described, he tempted Christ with power:

> After Jesus fasted in the wilderness for forty days and forty nights, the devil came to him and said, If you are the Son of God, command that these stones be made bread. After Jesus refused, the devil took him to the top of the temple in Jerusalem and said, If you are the Son of God, throw yourself down, for it is written, He shall give his angels charge concerning thee: and in their hands they shall bear thee up, lest at any time thou dash thy foot against a stone. Again Jesus refused, so the devil took him to a high mountain and showed him all the kingdoms of the world, and said, I will give you all this if you will fall down and worship me. On this last occasion, Jesus banished Satan from his presence. (Matthew 4:1-11)

In the second scene, Satan taunted Jesus ("If you are *really* the Son of God") to demonstrate and thereby prove his power, while in the other ("I will give you all this") he simply offered power to Jesus.

We get a feeling of power from so many things we do:

- Anger
- Controlling
- Making people feel guilty
- Hurting people—with anger, criticism, sarcasm
- Withholding affection

In the space on the next page discuss some of the ways you get a sense of power from the people around you in order to fill the emptiness in your life and to protect yourself from pain.

Examples:

- In conversations, I often insist on being right instead of really listening to what other people are saying.
- I get angry pretty often, to get people to do what I want.
- I often correct my husband when he speaks, even over little mistakes he makes.
- I tend to control the behavior of my children more than I need to, making comments about what they wear and what they do far past the age when they really need or want to hear what I think.
- I like to be the center of attention.
- I like to be in charge.
- I love to shop. When I'm spending money, and clerks are swirling around me, I feel important.
- I don't like to be told what to do.
- I bully employees.
- I use sex—or at least my sexual attractiveness—to get men to do what I want. I've done that for a long time.
- When people don't do what I want, I make them feel guilty.
- I often make critical comments about other people's mistakes.
- I like things done *my* way.

- When I get angry at my husband, he's afraid *not* to do what I want.
- When my children don't do what I tell them to do, I get irritated, and then they respond more quickly.
- I fire employees who annoy me personally.
- I get a sense of importance from having a lot of money.
- I physically intimidate my wife and children.

Knowledge can become one form of power—since we tend to think ourselves great when we know a lot—and Paul wrote to the Corinthians about the relative values of knowledge and love:

Knowledge makes people proud, but love builds character. And if any man thinks he knows something, he doesn't know what he really should know. But if a man loves God, God knows him. (1 Corinthians 8:1-3)

SEVEN, 48:29 - 49:39   Exercising Power over Our Children
CD Track Seven, 1:24 - 2:32

As I indicate in the seminar, perhaps the most common abuse of power on the planet is the control parents exercise over their children. There is rarely intentional malice involved in this, but when parents don't feel unconditionally loved, they'll use whatever form of Imitation Love is handy. We often find it difficult to control the behavior of other adults, but children are quite another matter. Children are weaker, more malleable, and easier to control, and it's only natural that we would tend to control them.

Many of us resist the notion that we use our children in this way—it's not a pretty thing to see, after all—but our use of power becomes much easier to identify when we look at how we behave when our control is *taken* from us. In the space below and on the next page discuss the answers to the following questions as they apply to the present (if you have children at home now) or the past.

- When my children don't do what I tell them—or ask them—do I become irritated?
- When my spouse disagrees with how I'm handling a situation with the children—or even takes the situation over—do I become annoyed?
- When my children are disrespectful, do I become frustrated or angry or controlling?
- When my children don't listen to my advice, do I become more insistent?

If your answer to any of these questions is *yes*, you're demonstrating a reluctance to have power taken *from* you, which is no different from seeking power.

God knows the negative effect of our pursuing the power of the world, and He has spoken in wisdom against that course:

> God has chosen what the world calls foolish to shame the wise, and God has chosen the weak things of the world to confound the things which are mighty. And God has chosen the lesser things of the world and things which are despised and things which seem to be nothing to bring down the things that seem to matter, so that nothing of the world can be proud in his presence. (1 Corinthians 1:27-29)

The Lord takes an especially dim view of those who exercise power over children:

> Whoever will bring harm to one of these little children, it would be better for him to have a large stone hanged about his neck and be drowned in the depths of the sea. (Matthew 18:6)

SEVEN, 49:39 - 51:15   Imitation Love in the Form of Pleasure
CD Track Seven, 2:32 - 4:09

In the absence of sufficient Real Love, pleasure—in its many forms—can become a very welcome distraction from our pain. In the space on the next page discuss how you use pleasure as a distraction and substitute for Real Love.

Examples:

- I love looking at women and fantasizing about having sex with them.
- I love the excitement of driving fast.
- I eat more than I should.
- I play video games/watch television for hours when I know I could be doing much better things with my time.
- I push my wife to have sex, even when I know she isn't interested.
- I enjoy the "buzz" I get from drinking a couple of beers after work.
- I gamble regularly.
- I look at pornography regularly.
- I really enjoy shopping, whether I can afford it or not.
- I'm always looking for the next thrill: mountain climbing, scuba diving, whatever.
- I use drugs recreationally.

There's no doubt that pleasure *feels* good, but the rewards are so very fleeting, as described in Proverbs:

> He who loves pleasure will be a poor man. He who loves wine and oil will not be rich. (Proverbs 21:17)

Also:

> The Lord says, I will put a curse on those who trust in mere human beings, who depend on mere flesh and blood for their strength, and whose hearts have turned away from the Lord. They will be like a shrub in the desert. They will not experience good things even when they happen. It will be as though they were growing in the desert, in a salt land where no one can live. (Jeremiah 17:5-6)

The *Forms* of Imitation Love Are Not Always Harmful

I am *not* saying that all pleasure is a form of Imitation Love. Pleasure becomes Imitation Love only when it's used as a substitute for Real Love. Unfortunately, because the vast majority of us feel a great lack of Real Love, pleasure is used as a form of Imitation Love most of the time.

Without Real Love, pleasure creates only a temporary satisfaction. It cannot make us happy. In the presence of Real Love, however, pleasure can become a delightful *addition* to the joy that unconditional love brings. When two people enjoy a relationship founded on Real Love, for example, sex is a fun and profound *expression* of love and adds to the joy they share. Such people do not use sex compulsively, however, nor do they use it in the hope of *creating* a genuine depth in their relationship.

How can you tell whether you're using pleasure as a form of Imitation Love? In the presence of Real Love, the pursuit of pleasure is casual and relaxed. Without enough Real Love, people pursue pleasure addictively:

- They can't do without it. The loss of any form of pleasure is a huge blow.
- They need more and more.
- They're always moving from one form of pleasure—hobbies, pastimes, items to purchase, travel destinations, adrenalin rushes—to the next.

SEVEN, 51:15 - 52:29   Imitation Love in the Form of Safety
CD Track Seven, 4:10 - 5:24

The French philosopher Marcel Proust once said, "To kindness, to knowledge, we make promises only; pain we obey." There are few conditions as painful as not feeling loved, and when we don't feel loved, we'll do almost anything to avoid adding to our pain. Safety—the relative absence of pain or threat of pain—becomes our primary goal.

In the space on the next page describe how you use safety as a form of Imitation Love:

Examples:

- Would you describe yourself as shy?
- Do you avoid situations where you could look foolish?
- Do you say you have a "good" relationship with your husband, when the truth is, you've just learned not to push each other's buttons? Do you feel genuinely loved, or do you just feel relatively safe and comfortable?
- Are you qualified for a much better job but stay in the same one because you can't stand the thought of going out there and being rejected?
- Do you leave relationships when they get difficult?
- Do you emotionally withdraw from relationships?
- Have you withdrawn from dating for fear of getting hurt again?
- Do you avoid supervisory positions because of a fear of failing?

- Do you avoid having conversations with your spouse about the difficult issues that hang in the air?
- Do you use alcohol or drugs as a way to achieve relief from tension?
- Do you tend to control people and situations in order to feel safe from uncertainty and possible threats or harm?

Despite all the safety we might gather to ourselves, however, it can never make us happy. In fact, the idea of compete safety is just an illusion, as the Lord illustrates with this passage:

The disciples came to Jesus and asked, what *shall be* the sign of your coming, and of the end of the world? And Jesus said, you will hear of wars and rumors of wars. Nation will rise against nation, and kingdom against kingdom: and there will be famines, and pestilences, and earthquakes, in divers places. All these are the beginning of the sufferings. Then they will deliver you up to be afflicted, and will kill you: and you will be hated of all nations for my name's sake. And then shall many be offended, and shall betray one another, and shall hate one another. And many false prophets shall rise, and shall deceive many. And because iniquity shall abound, the love of many shall wax cold. (Matthew 24:3-12)

In this passage, Jesus is explaining to us that the day will come when there will be no such thing as physical or external safety—there *will* be wars, famines, earthquakes, afflictions, death, offense, deception, and betrayal—but we can always prepare ourselves spiritually to be surrounded by peace and strength no matter what is going on around us, as illustrated by these verses:

- Troubles are all around us, but we're not worried. We are bewildered but not in despair. We are persecuted but not abandoned, thrown down but not destroyed. (2 Corinthians 4:8-9)

- The peace of God, which is beyond all understanding, will keep your hearts and minds through Christ Jesus. (Philippians 4:7)

SEVEN, 52:29 - 52:56   The Epidemic of Imitation Love
CD Track Seven, 5:24 - 5:50

As most people learn about Real and Imitation Love, they are stunned to realize just how often they use Imitation Love. Little wonder that they would be surprised. The use of Imitation Love is so common that we have come to accept it as normal. When a given behavior is almost universal, we don't question anymore whether there's something wrong with it.

Some people have even protested to me that the use of Imitation Love is just "natural." Yes, actually, it is natural, but so is snake venom, and both are still deadly. Paul spoke about the effects of the "natural man":

The natural man doesn't receive the things of the Spirit of God, because they are foolishness to him. He can't understand the things of the Spirit, because they are spiritually understood. (1 Corinthians 2:14)

We must identify our use of Imitation Love, because only then can we begin to make choices that will lead to the lifegiving effects of Real Love.

CHAPTER EIGHT
The Power of Understanding Imitation Love

EIGHT, 52:56 - 54:43   The Need to Understand Imitation Love
CD Track Eight, 0:00 - 1:47

Although Imitation Love is everywhere, and its effects on our lives are overwhelming, the more we understand it, the greater our power becomes to abandon it and move on to Real Love.

George Santayana said, "Those who cannot learn from history are doomed to repeat it." The same is true of our *personal* histories. If we don't understand how past events have affected us and *why* we behave as we do now, we are absolutely doomed to repeat the same old unproductive patterns that have brought us so much unhappiness to this point.

In the space below discuss a form of Imitation Love—or combination of several forms—that you have used repeatedly in your life. With each use you experienced some reward, but it never produced the happiness you were looking for. With your present understanding of Real Love, can you see why your use of Imitation Love was never genuinely productive?

As you do this exercise, consider the words of Jesus on the subject:

- Don't store up for yourselves earthly treasures, where they get rusty and moth-eaten, and where thieves break through and steal. Instead store up for yourselves treasures in heaven, where there are no moths or rust to spoil them, and where thieves do not break through or steal. (Matthew 6:19-20)

- A man came to Jesus and asked, What good thing shall I do, that I may have eternal life? And Jesus said, keep the commandments. The man asked, which of the commandments? After Jesus described several of the ten commandments, the man said, I kept all these since I was young, so what am I still missing? Jesus said, If you want to be perfect, go and sell your possessions and give to the poor, and you will have treasure in heaven: and come and follow me. But when the young man heard this, he went away sorrowful: for he had great possessions. Then said Jesus to his disciples, A rich man shall hardly enter into the kingdom of heaven. (Matthew 19:16-23)

- So after you have found God, or have been found by Him, how can you turn back to the weak and ineffective things that will imprison you again? (Galatians 4:9)

- Don't love the world or the things in the world. If a man loves the world, the love of the Father is not in him. Because everything in the world, the lust of the flesh, and the lust of the eyes, and the pride of life, is not of the Father, but is of the world. And the world will disappear, with all its lusts, but whoever obeys the will of God will live forever. (1 John 2:15-17)

The Lord describes Imitation Love such that we can identify it clearly. Imitation Love is:

- the treasures of the earth.
- the things that can be destroyed or taken.

- riches or whatever thing we have our heart set on.
- weak and ineffective.
- the lust of the flesh.
- pride.

It is important that we understand God's *motivation* in speaking to us about Imitation Love. He wants us to avoid its many forms not because He is personally annoyed when we don't, but because these riches the world has to offer simply have no value and will all disappear like so much dust or garbage. Because He *loves us* as our Father, He wants us to avoid the tragic mistake of literally exchanging our lives—our time, effort, and resources—for "riches" that are nothing but a lie. He wants us to know, in fact, that if we are not willing to give up our love for these deceptions, they will destroy us. They will keep us from the pursuit of that which can give us genuine happiness.

EIGHT, 54:43 - 56:42   Assessing Imitation Love, the Basis for Relationships
CD Track Eight, 1:47 - 3:46

Without enough Real Love, it is a certainty that we will look for as much Imitation Love as we can find, and we'll be attracted to those people who will give us the greatest supply. Our motivation is not primarily malicious; it's just a matter of survival. Once we are immersed in Imitation Love, however, we become very confused and distracted by its pleasure, as Paul taught the Corinthians here (with my editorial comment added):

> The natural man (which describes how we are when we're empty and afraid and using Imitation Love in a vain attempt to fill up our emptiness) doesn't receive the things of the Spirit of God, because they are foolishness to him. He can't understand the things of the Spirit, because they are spiritually understood. (1 Corinthians 2:14)

This, of course, is one of the reasons God has told us to avoid these treasures of the world, because they confuse us and render us incapable of listening to the Spirit. Then we're truly lost.

God wants us to always be aware of the difference between the things of the Spirit and the things of the world:

> The deeds of the flesh are obvious, including adultery, sexual sins, uncleanness, indecency, the worship of idols, witchcraft, hatred, contention, jealousy, anger, conspiracies, heresies, envyings, murders, drunkenness, partyings, and so on. And as I have said before, those who do such things shall not inherit the kingdom of God. But the fruit of the Spirit is love, joy, peace, patience, gentleness, goodness, faith, kindness, and self control. There is no law against these qualities. (Galatians 5:19-23)

In the space below and on the next page discuss some people in your life for whom you have felt an immediate attraction—not just sexual, but an overall attraction. This would include boyfriends, girlfriends, spouses, friends, family members, co-workers. Now list the *reasons* you were attracted to these people. Following are a few examples of qualities in people that tend to attract us to them:

- Physically attractive. This is a proven, powerful quality that attracts people to one another.
- Intelligent
- Witty
- Wealthy
- Powerful
- Accepting, kind
- Reliable
- Hard-working
- Adventurous
- Entertaining
- Optimistic

Notice that in most cases these are qualities that benefit *you*, that potentially give you Imitation Love in the forms of praise, power, pleasure, and safety. Of course, other people are attracted to *you* for the same qualities, and now we have two people in a given relationship who are each expecting one another to make him or her happy with Imitation Love. It's a formula for disaster that we see repeated with painful consistency.

Let me add that the qualities above are not by themselves flaws. In fact, people who have those qualities—intelligent, hardworking, and witty, for example—in addition to Real Love are happier than other people. The qualities listed above are harmful only when used as substitutes for Real Love.

We can assess the potential for Imitation Love in another person with remarkable speed and accuracy. Usually in just a few minutes—often seconds—we can determine from words, tone of voice, posture, facial expressions, and other clues whether the person we're talking to is likely to be:

- critical or accepting (a source of praise, power, safety).
- controlling or submissive (power and safety).
- sexually conservative or liberal (praise, power, pleasure).
- slow or intelligent (pleasure, power, safety).
- dull or witty (pleasure).

In the absence of Real Love, we tend to "like" the people who have more to give us, and we'll tend to choose an association with them.

Honestly describe a friendship you have. Describe below how a mutual exchange of Imitation Love may have contributed to the way it began and grew. Now describe how you believe trading Imitation Love has caused problems over time.

CHAPTER NINE
Falling in Love

NINE, 56:42 - 59:45   Falling in Love
CD Track Nine, 0:00 - 3:03

In the absence of sufficient Real Love, our pursuit of Imitation Love is not a casual affair—it's desperate. We eagerly search for all we can get, and one obvious way to increase how much we get from people is to give it to *them*.

As described in the seminar, we unconsciously give bits of Imitation Love—a dollar at a time—to people everywhere we go. When we find someone who gives us far more in return than everyone else, we tend to "fall in love" with that person. We do this not only with exclusive intimate partners—boyfriends, girlfriends, and spouses—but with *anyone* who gives us a great rate of return on our investment. We fall in love with co-workers, bosses, friends, and certain family members. Yet another example is parents who have a favorite child, despite their claims to the contrary. Why do they show that favoritism? Because one child returns more Imitation Love to the parent than the other children, and the parents naturally enjoy that—and reward it.

Is there any feeling quite as exciting as falling in love? Wow, what a thing it is to find someone who gives us great gobs of Imitation Love. But then the effects of Imitation Love wear off—they always do—and we're left with our hopes dashed and our dreams crushed, and the subsequent sense of disappointment and betrayal is monumental.

In the space below describe a relationship where you were in love—with a boyfriend, a girlfriend, a spouse, a co-worker, and so on.

- Can you see how the relationship began because of a "relatively equal and abundant exchange of Imitation Love?
- Were you baffled when that glorious, exciting relationship fell apart?
- Now do you understand what happened?

This notion that falling in love is a form of Imitation Love actually has a growing basis in physiology. Studies have shown that the same areas of the brain are active—and the same neurochemicals are being generated—both when we are in love and when we are gambling or addicted to drugs.

Falling in love can be so exciting that we often tune everything else in life out. The common expression is that "love is blind," or at least the pursuit of *Imitation Love* is. Paul demonstrated an understanding of the confusing or blinding effects of pursuing the excitement of the various kinds of Imitation Love when he wrote:

I testify in the Lord, that from now on you should not walk as others in the world walk: in the pride of their minds, with their understanding darkened, being separated from the life of God through their ignorance, because of the blindness of their heart. Being past feeling, they have given themselves over to lusts, to greedily act in unclean ways. (Ephesians 4:17-19)

As we pursue the excitement of Imitation Love, we:

- become blinded to what is real and true.
- become separated from the things of God.
- become unable to feel the things of the Spirit.
- are given over to natural lusts, to greedily act in unclean ways.

God has spoken many kind words of warning regarding this path, saying:

- Set your desires on things above, not on things of the earth. (Colossians 3:2)

- Whoever is rich will fall into temptations and traps and many foolish and harmful lusts, which drown men in destruction and damnation. For the love of money is the root of all evil, and in the process of lusting after it, some have been led away from the faith and pierced with many sorrows. But you, O man of God, avoid these things; and follow after righteousness, godliness, faith, love, patience, gentleness. (1 Timothy 6:9-11)

- Women should clothe themselves modestly, with restraint and soberness, not with braided hair, or gold ornaments, or pearls, or expensive clothing. (1 Timothy 2:9)

NINE, 59:45 - 1:00:44   Marriage and Imitation Love
CD Track Nine, 3:03 - 4:02

When we've been without sufficient Real Love our whole lives— and when we're not getting a very good income of Imitation Love, either—finding someone who gives us a great deal of Imitation Love is earth-shaking. We want to *keep* that person in our lives. We want a verbal and written *guarantee* from him or her that reads or sounds something like the following:

> I promise to continue supplying you with all the Imitation Love I have (of course he or she doesn't *realize* it's Imitation Love) and to make you happy for the rest of your life.

And *that* is how most of us see a marriage contract, as a way to guarantee a reliable and endless supply of Imitation Love—and "happiness"—from one person for ourselves. Of course, Imitation Love can't ever produce genuine happiness, so the entire contract is virtually certain from the beginning to produce misery for both partners.

If you're married, discuss below and on the next page *why* you married your partner. This will require considerable honesty on your part. Do you see how a supply of Imitation Love might have played a part in your selection of a partner?

The Lord understands how we tend to choose our partners. He therefore recommended that we use more spiritual principles upon which to found our marriages:

> Men should love their wives as they love their own bodies. He who loves his wife is only loving himself, because no man hates his own body, but instead he nourishes and cherishes it, just as the Lord nourishes and cherishes the church, because we are members of his body, his flesh, and his bones. For this purpose shall a man leave his father and mother and be joined with his wife, and the two shall be one flesh. This is a great mystery, but I speak also concerning Christ and the church. Nevertheless let every one of you love his wife as himself; and the wife respect *her* husband. (Ephesians 5:28-33)

If you're not married, but you want to be, discuss below what you're looking for in a partner. Again, be honest. Like most people, are you looking for characteristics—like those on page 99—that will give you an abundant supply of Imitation Love?

The Real Meaning of "I Love You"

When we don't have sufficient Real Love, "I love you" really means this:

- I really, really like how **I** feel when I'm around you.
- I *need* you.
- I expect you to keep making *me* feel good.
- I hope you will love *me*.
- I do care about your happiness somewhat. I'm not entirely selfish.

Discuss below some occasions and relationships where you have said "I love you" with some of the above motivations.

NINE, 1:00:44 - 1:03:29   Why Relationships Fail
CD Track Nine, 4:02- 6:47

All over the world marriages are failing—or have already failed—by the millions. And when each marriage fails, the feelings are very strong:

- Confusion. "How in the world could this have happened? We were so in love. How could we have traveled such a great emotional distance, from being in love to this?"

- Huge disappointment. "The joy of marriage was perhaps the greatest dream of my life, and now that dream is dead."
- Anger. "How could you have done this to me?"
- Betrayal. "You promised to love me forever. You promised. And now you're leaving?"
- Frustration. "I did everything I could to make this relationship succeed, and nothing worked. What could I have done differently?"

The combination of these feelings is intolerably painful. Moreover, when something has gone drastically wrong, we've been trained that someone *must* be blamed, and in a relationship there are usually only two options we can see. We consider—silently and aloud:

- Maybe it's my fault. This choice makes no sense, though, because **I** have done everything I possibly could to make this relationship work. How could it be *my* fault?

- It's my partner's fault. Ah yes, this makes *much* more sense. My partner promised to make me happy, and at one time he or she did. But now I'm miserable, and my partner's behavior has changed, so it *has* to be his or her fault.

Of course, our partners are going through the same reasoning, which means that two people are both concluding—supported by mountains of evidence—that it has to be the other person's fault. This approach uniformly works poorly. It should be noted, for the sake of completeness, that some people actually blame *themselves* for everything that goes wrong in a relationship. That's not healthy either.

Jesus said a lot about our blaming other people, including this:

Do not judge others, and God will not judge you. Do you condemn others, and God will not condemn you. Forgive others, and God will forgive you. (Luke 6:37)

Everything changes for us when we understand that most relationships—including marriages—begin without enough of the one ingredient most essential to success; they are based on a foundation of Imitation Love. The confusion about why relationships fail is now gone. Now we understand that there's nobody to *blame* when a relationship fails. Relationships fail because both partners were unprepared from the beginning to participate in a mutually loving experience.

With that understanding we can stop the utter futility of the endless blaming, and then we are free to concentrate on the only sensible solution, which is to find the Real Love that both partners have needed all along. Christ taught this when He said,

> Whoever hears and does what I say is like a wise man who built his house on a rock, and then when the rain fell, and the floods came, and the winds blew and beat upon that house, it didn't fall, because it was built upon a rock. But whoever hears me and doesn't do what I say is like a foolish man who built his house on the sand, and when the rain fell, and the floods came, and the winds blew and beat upon the house, it fell, and the fall was great. (Matthew 7:24-7; Luke 6:47-49)

Suppose your relationship is failing, or perhaps it has already failed, and let's compare your relationship to a house—much as Christ compared our lives to the building of a house. During and after the failure of a relationship, there's a natural tendency to create a drama over the crisis and to point fingers of accusation about each crack in the wall, each broken window, and each leak in the roof. But what a waste that is. It's also a waste to make repairs for each of these problems until you first identify the central cause. The truth is, in a failing or failed relationship you had long ago built the foundation on sand, so when the rains and winds came, it was inevitable that eventually the house would begin to fall apart, and now you're living with the consequences of your original foundation.

That *could* seem discouraging to admit that the foundation itself is flawed, but it's actually an enormous relief and source of hope. Why? Because now you both understand everything that's happened, and you know exactly what needs to be done. You need to get to work doing whatever it takes to put a foundation of rock under the house, under your relationship. And what is the rock? The Rock is Jesus Christ, along with the love He offers to us and through us:

- Christ is a living stone, rejected by men but chosen and precious to God. He is the most important stone in the foundation, chosen and precious, and whoever believes on Him shall not be put to shame. To you who believe He is precious, but to those who are disobedient and who reject him, He becomes a stone over which they will stumble and a rock that will injure them. (1 Peter 2:4-8)

- God is love. (1 John 4:16)

In the space below and on the next page discuss some of your relationships that have gone badly—not just with a spouse or boyfriend or girlfriend, but with friends, co-workers, and family members.

- What feelings did you experience as the relationship began to fail? Did they include some of those listed earlier in this section on pages 106-7?
- Were you angry at your partner?
- Did you blame your partner for the failure of the relationship?
- Did you talk with other people about your partner in a negative way?
- Did all that blaming *ever* make you happy?
- Would you like to be free of all the anger, blaming, and confusion?

NINE, 1:03:29 - 1:05:38   The Pattern of Imitation Love
  CD Track Nine, 6:47 - 8:55

During the course of a lifetime, we have all developed certain patterns of Imitation Love that we prefer to give and receive. Usually, we learned these patterns in childhood, although as adults we may have modified them to some degree.

Imagine, for example, that you're a child.

- Your parents demand respect from you (*power* for them).
- You earn their approval by being obedient and cooperative (*praise* for you, *power* for them).
- You avoid doing anything that would earn their displeasure (*safety* for you, *power* for them).
- Because it's easy and because with this approach your parents get you to like them (*praise* for them), for long periods they allow you to entertain yourself with television, video games, and other forms of recreation (*pleasure* for you), without teaching you responsibility (*safety* for them).

From these experiences you learn a pattern of behavior that earns a certain combination of praise, power, pleasure, and safety—for you and for your parents and others in positions of authority. You become *comfortable* with this pattern. It's familiar and predictable.

For the rest of your life, you naturally learn to seek out the association of people who give and receive Imitation Love in combinations similar to those used by your parents. Why? Again, because these patterns are familiar and predictable. That's why so many of us marry a partner who is similar in many ways to one or both of our parents. We marry someone who trades in a combination of the forms of Imitation Love similar to the trading combinations we once used with our parents and others in our childhoods.

In light of what you have learned about Real and Imitation Love, in the space below and on the next page discuss some of your closest relationships: boyfriend, girlfriend, spouse, friends. Ask yourself, among other questions:

- Can you see a similarity between these people and the people who influenced you early in life (usually your parents)?
- Can you see how you are attracted to people who offer a certain combination of the forms of Imitation Love?
- Can you actually describe that combination? Can you see that you prefer a larger portion of praise, for example, and lesser portions of power and safety?

CHAPTER TEN
More about Imitation Love

TEN, 1:05:38 - 1:06:17   Mid-Life Crisis
CD Track Ten 0:00 - 0:39

Do you know people who have experienced a mid-life crisis? In the space below and on the next page discuss what you can see now in their behavior.

- Do you see how they were trying to find happiness with Imitation Love?
- Do you see how in many cases they *appeared* to be successful or happy, often for many years, because they simply had enough income in Imitation Love?
- Discuss how they attempted to make up for their failure in finding happiness with one form of Imitation Love by switching to another form.

Perhaps you have experienced a crisis like this yourself. If so, discuss the answers to these questions in terms of your own experience in the space below.

The apostle James talked about the enormous sense of disappointment that can result when we realize that our pursuit of happiness through Imitation Love has been in vain.

Now, you men who are rich in the eyes of the world, weep and howl for the miseries that will come upon you. Your riches are rotten, and your clothing is motheaten. Your gold and silver are rusted, and their rust will be evidence against you and will eat your flesh like fire. (James 5:1-3)

TEN, 1:06:17 - 1:07:18 Definition of Happiness
CD Track, 0:39 - 1:42

While we're in the process of looking for happiness, it's critical that we understand what genuine happiness is. Otherwise, we'll spend our entire lives devoted to the pursuit of an illusion.

In the space below and on the next page, discuss what we've learned about what happiness is *not*: Among your answers you might consider that happiness is not:

- romance.
- sex.
- entertainment.
- the absence of crises.
- comfort.
- excitement.
- controlling other people.

The apostle John helped us understand what happiness is not when he said:

> Don't love the world or the things in the world. If a man loves the world, the love of the Father is not in him, because everything in the world, the lust of the flesh, and the lust of the eyes, and the pride of life, is not of the Father, but is of the world. And the world will disappear, with all its lusts, but whoever obeys the will of God will live forever. (1 John 2:15-17)

TEN, 1:07:18 - 1:08:23 The Laws that Govern Happiness
CD Track Ten, 1:42 - 2:45

We've already discussed the fact that genuine happiness is a result of receiving and sharing Real Love. In addition, if we want to know peace, freedom, and joy, we must live according to the natural laws that govern those qualities, and in later modules we'll be discussing these in detail.

CHAPTER ELEVEN
Module Summary

ELEVEN, 1:08:23 - 1:10:10
   CD Track Eleven, entire track

MODULE TWO

CHAPTER ONE

ONE, 0:00 - 2:50   More about Imitation Love
CD Track One, 0:00 - 2:50

Notice that in the seminar I say that praise is not always a bad thing; it's negative only when used as a substitute for Real Love. When people don't have sufficient Real Love in their lives, however, the use of praise as a form of Imitation Love is unavoidable. Ask yourself:

- Do you get a sense of worth when people praise you? Almost everyone does.
- When you do something worthwhile and nobody notices, are you disappointed?
- When people criticize you, do you feel hurt or threatened or angry?
- When you praise other people, do you expect their appreciation or acknowledgment in return?

If your answer to any of these questions is *yes*, the likelihood is very high that you need praise as a form of Imitation Love—and that is hardly unusual. When people have sufficient Real Love, they regard both praise and criticism as merely pieces of *information*. They neither *need* the praise nor *fear* the criticism. With Real Love— the greatest treasure of all—everything else pales by comparison.

In the following parable Jesus illustrates the relative value of all forms of Imitation Love—including praise—compared to the riches of God, which include love.

Jesus said, A rich man had an abundant harvest and thought, What shall I do, because I won't have room to store it all? I will pull down my barns, and build larger ones for storing my crops. And I will say to my soul, You have great wealth laid up for many years, so relax, eat, drink, and be merry. But God said to him, You fool, tonight you die, and then who will own all your possessions? And so it is with anyone who stores up treasure for himself but is poor in the sight of God. (Luke 12:16-21)

No matter how much of the treasures of the world we accumulate—a harvest of goods, the praise of others, money, whatever—we are foolish to store it up in hope that it will make us happy. As Jesus asked, when we die, who shall own it all?

CHAPTER TWO
Getting and Protecting Behaviors

TWO, 2:50 - 3:53   Introduction to Getting and Protecting Behaviors
CD Track Two, 0:00 - 1:03

In the short term, there are no motivations more powerful than emptiness and fear. We respond to these feelings quickly and predictably. God certainly recognizes the influence of fear in our lives, as evidenced by the fact that in the Bible:

- the word *fear* is found 847 times, including its variations—afraid, tremble, dread, dismay.
- the phrase, "Be not afraid" is found 103 times, including its variations—"Be not afraid" and "Be not dismayed."

In the space on the next page discuss your experiences with fear. Be specific. You have experienced these fears with whom? Discuss examples. Following are a few examples of some general fears to provoke your discussion of general and more specific fears.

- Fear of being abandoned
- Fear of criticism
- Fear of being laughed at
- Fear of being rejected
- Fear of illness
- Fear of failure
- Fear of physical injury
- Fear of death
- Fear of never being loved
- Fear of not having enough money
- Fear of failure in career
- Fear of commitment
- Fear of public speaking

While you are consumed by fear, what's it like for you? Discuss this in the space below.

- Are you happy?
- Are you thinking about the well being of others?
- Do you think clearly?
- Do you make your best decisions?
- Do you feel paralyzed?
- Do you feel connected to God?

The motivation of fear is absolutely compelling, and the effect is not positive. When we're afraid, we respond automatically with the Protecting Behaviors, all of which have terribly destructive effects on us personally and in our relationships.

God knows the destructive effects that fear has on us. Hence the 103 admonishments in the Bible that we should not fear, including the following:

- Fear not, little flock, for your Father is pleased to give you His kingdom. (Luke 12:32)

- Jesus said, even the hairs on your head are all important to the Father, so fear not. (Matthew 10:30-31)

Now discuss your experiences with emptiness—a serious lack of food, water, attention, praise, affection, pleasure, or anything else. Again, how does emptiness affect you? When we're empty emotionally, we reach out to fill the emptiness by using Getting Behaviors.

TWO, 3:53 - 7:02 Lying as a Protecting Behavior
CD Track Two, 1:03 - 4:12

In the absence of sufficient Real Love, every morsel of conditional approval becomes very important to us. The thought of losing any of that approval becomes terrifying, and in the short term lying is one effective way to prevent the loss of approval. We learned to lie as small children, and when that proved successful we continued the pattern as adults.

Because we lie to protect ourselves from pain—usually the threat of not feeling loved in some way—we can easily justify doing it, in most cases without even thinking about it. And, because almost all of us lack sufficient Real Love, we're in a state of low-level, unrecognized pain and fear most of the time. On top of that baseline pain, events are occurring around us almost constantly that create the possibility of our being hurt even more in some way.

So here's the situation: First, lies are easily justified when we're in pain or threatened with pain. Second, we're in a state of pain and fear almost constantly. Considering those two factors, it should be no surprise that lies are so common that we hardly even realize we're telling them. To confirm that suspicion, several years ago one study demonstrated that on average people tell more than 400 lies a day.

In the space below describe how you use lying as a Protecting Behavior:

- Do you often make excuses for your mistakes?
- Do you often say what other people want to hear?
- Do you blame other people for mistakes *you* made?
- Do you let other people have their way mostly because you're afraid they won't like you if you resist them?
- Do you withhold your opinion for fear that you'll be criticized?
- Do you refuse to admit or confess a mistake for fear of disappointing someone?

TWO, 7:02 - 7:37 Lying as a Getting Behavior
CD Track Two, 4:12 - 4:47

Any time we do anything at all to win the approval of other people, we are lying. It's rarely intentional, but it's still lying. When I use the word *lying*, I'm making no condemnation. I'm simply describing our behavior, so we can understand what we're doing and begin to make far more productive choices.

Discuss below how you use lying as a Getting Behavior:

- Do you "put your best foot forward" so people will think well of you?
- Do you do things for people so they'll like you or feel indebted to you?
- Do you give gifts to people with some expectation of appreciation or gratitude? (You'll answer this question more accurately when you ask how you feel and behave when people are completely unappreciative and ungrateful *after* you have given them a gift.)
- Do you sometimes flatter people so they'll like you?
- Do you love to talk about your accomplishments but avoid talking about your mistakes, flaws, and fears?

TWO, 7:37 - 9:02   The Problem with Lying
CD Track Two, 4:47 - 6:13

So what's the big deal? If almost everybody around us is lying, how could it be that bad? As indicated in the recording of the seminar, when we lie we eliminate the first step—telling the truth—in the lifegiving process of feeling seen, accepted, and loved.

Truth

↓

Seen

↓

Accepted

↓

Loved

When we lie, we can't feel loved, and that is *the* tragedy. Using the space below and on the next page, further discuss some of lies you listed in the previous two spaces—either to get Imitation Love or to protect yourself—or discuss some lies you did not previously list.

- On these occasions when you lied, did you feel *unconditionally* loved?
- Isn't Real Love what you want most? More than the Imitation Love you *might* get from lying to people?
- So, no matter what you got from lying, was it really worth it? With your lies, was it worth paying for the treasures that become moth eaten and rusted and that thieves will steal? (Matthew 6:19-20)
- When you lie, do you feel genuinely closer to the people you lie to?
- Do you feel isolated or alone?
- Do you feel afraid of being caught in your lies? Or of being discovered as a fraud?

Paul understood that in our lies we sow the seeds of our own deaths when he said to the Corinthians,

> The natural man doesn't receive the things of the Spirit of God, for they are foolishness to him. He cannot know them, because they are spiritually understood. (1 Corinthians 2:14)

Love is a fruit or product of the Spirit, and as long as we are lying, we are giving in to the natural or carnal man (Romans 8:6; 1 Corinthians 3:3), who makes use of all the Getting and Protecting Behaviors and who, according to Paul, cannot receive or feel the things of the Spirit—including love. The natural man is separated from the Spirit and is, therefore, spiritually dead.

The Word of God has much to say about the disadvantages of lying:

- Whoever deceives will not live in my house. Whoever tells lies will not stay in my sight. (Psalms 101:7)

- I hate lying and find it disgusting. (Psalms 119:163)

- Lying lips are disgusting to the Lord, but those who speak the truth are His delight. (Proverbs 12:22)

- Adopt a new attitude of your mind and put on a new life, which is created in the image of God in righteousness and true holiness. Put away lying and let every man speak truthfully with his neighbor, because we are all part of the same body. (Ephesians 4:23-25)

CHAPTER THREE
Attacking and Anger

THREE, 9:02 - 12:55   The Destructive Effects of Anger
CD Track Three, 0:00 - 3:53

The use of attacking as a Getting and Protecting Behavior is so common that we often fail to recognize when we're doing it. Any time we push, intimidate, or in any way make people feel anxious or threatened, we are attacking.

In the space on the next page discuss how you use attacking as a Getting and Protecting Behavior. You might include some examples like these below:

- When I don't like what someone is doing, I often frown or raise my voice.
- When my husband or wife makes a mistake, I often respond with a snippy little comment about it.
- When people don't do what I expect, I sigh and roll my eyes.
- When people fail to do what they've promised, I become irritated.
- When my children don't listen, I lean over them and repeat myself in harsh tones.
- When people don't do what I want, I sometimes make them feel guilty and motivate them to change their mind.
- When people get angry at me, I sometimes get them to back down from attacking me by getting even angrier at them and intimidating them.

Now that you understand how selfish and arrogant anger is—from this section and from Module One—discuss in the space on the next page the real reason some of your unpleasant interactions have gone badly. This is a grand opportunity to really apply your understanding of a principle to your own behavior. For example:

- All these years I've been irritated that my wife doesn't want to have sex with me. And what she says is that there's no intimacy in our sex—she doesn't feel close to me. After studying Real Love, suddenly it all makes sense. The moment I'm irritated at her, what she hears is "I don't love you," and then having sex is out of the question. Why would she want to have sex with somebody who doesn't love her? No wonder we've been having this argument for so long.
- I keep talking to my husband about picking up his clothes and other things around the house, but all he does is get defensive. Now I get it. When I talk to him, I'm irritated—I'm saying, "I don't love you"—and then he becomes even more empty and afraid. Then he defends himself because it's the only response he knows.
- I keep saying the same things to my children over and over. I had begun to think they were deaf—I've even told them

they were deaf. But the problem is *me*. Every time I'm angry at them, they hear that I don't love them, and then they can't hear anything else I'm saying.

- My boss keeps resisting my ideas, and now I see why. I'm pushy and aggressive with him, which he feels as an attack. He feels that I don't care about *him*—which is mostly true— and then he doesn't really care what else I have to say.

THREE, 12:55 - 14:19   Anger is Always Wrong
CD Track Three, 3:53 - 5:17

I've heard so many justifications from people for their being angry, but they all crumble to meaningless dust when we consider the overall effects of anger. Our highest purpose of existence is to be genuinely happy, not comfortable or satisfied or excited but the kind of happy we talked about in Module One.

Discuss some of the occasions when you've been angry at the people around you. In these moments have you *ever* felt genuinely happier? Have you felt peaceful? Have you enriched your relationships with anger?

Anger is always wrong because it always detracts from our primary purpose in life. It keeps us from feeling loved, from being loving, and from being genuinely happy.

God has been far from silent on the subject of whether anger is right or wrong:

> From long ago, you have heard it said that you shall not kill, and whoever kills will be in danger of judgment. But I say unto you, that whoever is angry with his brother will be in danger of judgment, and whoever calls another a fool will be in danger of hellfire. (Matthew 5:21-25)

Here Jesus makes the penalties for murder and anger *the same*! How could that be? Surely murder is far, far more serious than mere anger, so how could Jesus equate the two? Because in His day, the Jews—not a bit different from us now—were ever eager to make excuses for their transgressions. With legalistic zeal, they carefully differentiated the seriousness and penalties for moral crimes in such ways that they could come out looking justified and good as often as possible. In this scriptural passage, rather than getting caught up in the human debate—where selfish justification is the goal, not genuine happiness—Jesus throws the entire debate out the window and establishes entirely new criteria for judging both all commandments and all men. This is a legal and spiritual revolution!

First, He establishes that He is come to fulfill the Law (Matthew 5:17). Only in and through Him—and in and through what He is about to teach—do all the laws, rules, guidelines, prophecies, and commandments have any purpose at all. And what is that purpose? How are the laws and commandments fulfilled? It all comes down to love.

- I give you a new commandment, that you love one another as I have loved you. (John 13:34)

- Love *is* the fulfilling of the law. (Romans 13:10)

- For all the law is fulfilled in one word, which is this: You shall love your neighbor as yourself. (Galatians 5:14)

- Bear one another's burdens, and as you do you fulfill the law of Christ. (Galatians 6:2)

Once we understand that love is the *purpose* behind all the commandments, as we've discussed before (Matthew 22:35-40), we can begin to grasp why Jesus would equate anger and murder.

In order to make this point in an unforgettable way, supposed that you were severely allergic to peanuts, to the point that even touching a peanut to your lips would be uniformly fatal. In light of this allergy, which of the following would be worse for you?

- Eating one peanut
- Eating two peanuts
- Taking a bite from a peanut butter and jelly sandwich

Even though the choices have quantitative and qualitative differences, they're all really the same, aren't they? Of course, because they all produce the same result: death. Similarly, even though anger and murder appear to be different on a number of levels, once we see love as fulfillment of all the law, anger and murder are effectively the same, because they both absolutely rule out any possibility of being unconditionally loving and therefore destroy any possibility of being happy, which is our highest purpose in life.

Jesus is teaching us that rather than looking for ways to justify our anger, or to show how we weren't really angry—only annoyed or frustrated—we should just see that anything even remotely like anger—to include frustration, irritation, impatience, or even murderous rage—all has the same deadly effect and needs to be avoided like the death that it is. What a useful perspective this is. It's much easier to avoid *everything* with peanuts in it (spiritually speaking) than it is to quibble over the exact peanut content—the amount, whether they're cooked, how they're cooked, where they were grown, and so on—of every bite that passes our lips.

The Lord has said a great deal about the dangers of anger, and judging from the prevalence of this cancer among us, we can use every word of warning. Review much of what He has said on this subject on page 53. Additional references follow:

- Do not let your anger lead you into sin. Don't let the sun go down upon your wrath. (Ephesians 4:26)

- When the Romans came to take Jesus, one of His disciples fought with a sword to keep Jesus from being taken, and he cut off the ear of a servant of the high priest. Jesus said, Put away your sword, because everyone who uses violence will be destroyed by violence. (Matthew 26:50-52)

- Do all things without complaining and quarreling, so you may be the sons of God, blameless and harmless in the midst of a twisted and foolish world, among whom you shine as lights. (Philippians 2:14-15)

- So clothe yourselves as God's chosen people, holy and beloved, with a tenderness of spirit, kindness, humility, gentleness, patience, bearing one another's faults and forgiving one another if any man has a quarrel against you. Even as Christ forgave you, so must you forgive others. (Colossians 3:12-13)

- We urge you, brothers: warn those who are disorderly, comfort the fainthearted, support the weak, be patient toward all men. See that no one pays back wrong for wrong to anyone, but always follows what is good, both among yourselves, and to all men. (1 Thessalonians 5:14-15)

- If anyone claims to be religious but can't control his own tongue, his religion is worthless. (James 1:26)

- We all stumble in many things, but if a man isn't offensive with his words, he is perfect and able to control himself entirely. We turn the whole body of a horse with a small bit, and with a small rudder we control ships, even though they are large and driven by fierce winds. In a similar way, the tongue is small, but it has great power, just as a little spark can set an entire forest ablaze. The tongue is a fire, and with a flame from hell causes a world of wickedness and sets fire to the course of nature. (James 3:2-6)

- My brothers, don't speak ill of one another. Whoever speaks ill of his brother and judges him, speaks evil of the law and judges the law. And if you judge the law, you are not a follower of the law. There is one lawgiver, who is able to save and to destroy, so who are you to judge anyone? (James 4:11-12)

- Whoever claims to be in the light, but hates his brother, is still in darkness. But whoever loves his brother lives in the light and harms no one. Whoever hates his brother is in darkness and walks in darkness and is lost, because darkness has blinded his eyes. (1 John 2:9)

- Whoever is slow to anger is very wise. (Proverbs 14:29)

- Whoever is slow to anger is better than one who is thought to be powerful; and whoever rules his own spirit is better than one who conquers a city. (Proverbs 16:32)

- A man with good judgment puts off his anger, and it is his glory to overlook transgressions. (Proverbs 19:11)

One justification we commonly use for our anger is that we're *right*:

- Someone has treated us badly. His or her behavior is obviously *wrong* and we are *right* to demand justice.
- In a discussion, we have a solution or proposal that will obviously be beneficial to the other person, or to the company, or the family, or the marriage, but the other person just will not listen. Of course we're angry. We're *right* and other people are not listening.
- We're being falsely accused. The other person is clearly wrong and we are *right*, not only in our claim but in our right to angrily defend ourselves.
- And so on.

In any given interaction, we can always find many things that we're *right* about. But as we emphasize those, we're usually forgetting that our highest priority is to be loving and happy. If we're angry we can't be loving and happy, so we're *wrong*, no matter how else we're right.

Say this out loud: "When I'm angry, I'm wrong." Say it again. Now write it on the blackboard one hundred times. (That was a joke.)

God's Anger

Another justification for anger that I commonly hear is this: "But God gets angry, so how could anger be wrong? And remember how Jesus got angry at the money-changers in the temple when He threw them out?" Does God get angry? That is a reasonable question and deserves an answer—several, actually.

First, there is no mention anywhere in the New Testament that Jesus was ever angry. Specifically, there are two accounts of Jesus causing people to leave the temple, and again, there is no mention of anger. One of those accounts reads as follows:

> Jesus went to Jerusalem and found in the temple people who made money from selling animals for sacrifice. When He had made a whip of small cords, He drove them all out of the temple, poured out their money, and overturned their tables. He said, Take these things out of here and do not make my Father's house a place of business. (John 2:13-16)

No anger is described here. In fact, the record says that after Jesus found these men desecrating the temple, He took the time to sit down and make a whip of small cords, and with that He drove them out. One doesn't fashion a whip in a fit of rage.

Many of us describe this event as an example of anger only because if *we* were in a similar situation—if we were ever in a position where we drove a group of people from a place sacred to us—*we* would be angry. We assign to Jesus the motivations *we* would have had under similar circumstances.

Second, in view of all that God has written—as found on pages 53, 132-3—about the evils of anger, is it reasonable to suppose that He Himself does not live by those principles? Does it make sense that He would require that we live by a standard higher than His own?

Third, it is hypothesized by many that God becomes angry in response to our breaking of His commandments. Considering, however, (1) the great numbers of us on this world and (2) how frequently as a group we break the commandments—billions of times each day—if God becomes angry each time we break the commandments, how could He ever be anything but angry? He describes His kingdom as a place and condition of peace and love. How could that be if He's angry all the time?

Fourth, it is true that in the Old Testament there is considerable mention of an angry God. Remember, however, the context of those references. The people of Israel at the time were like spiritual infants, who rarely paid attention to God's word until He raised His voice—so to speak—and threatened them. God wasn't angry, and therefore unhappy. He simply chose—out of necessity, out of a loving desire to motivate His children—to come across as stern, commanding, even angry. And then, after many hundreds of years of dealing with them in that fashion, Jesus said, "I give you a new commandment, that you love one another as I have loved you." (John 13:34) During and after the mortal mission of Jesus, God comes across quite differently from the God of the Old Testament. Why? Because He finally attended anger management classes and learned to overcome His anger? Hardly. The change in His image was a reflection of a new level of maturity on the part of His people, where they could respond more fully to His love than His sternness, or what the Bible calls his "anger."

If we really want to see God's tendency toward genuine anger, let's examine His reaction toward serious threats—toward insults and pain, for example.

- After all the accusations made of Jesus, He said nothing. And they spit in His face and hit Him repeatedly, mocking Him. (Matt. 26:63, 67)

- There was a terrible agreement among most of the Jewish leaders that Jesus needed to die, and they turned Him over to the Roman governor. The governor wanted little to do with it, but he did ask Jesus a few questions, which He didn't answer. He took his cross to Calvary, without answering the accusations of the masses. (Matthew 27:1-3)

- He was led like a sheep to the slaughter and like a lamb voiceless before his shearer, so he didn't open His mouth. (Acts 8:32)

Guilt about Our Anger

As you identify your anger—as well as your other Getting and Protecting Behaviors—there will be a tendency to feel guilt or shame. Do not indulge those feelings. Instead take the view that as you identify your anger, you're just gathering important *information*, with which you can now make much better choices leading toward the Real Love you want in your life. Shortly we'll be discussing the process of finding that love.

THREE 14:19 - 15:35   Why Do We Keep Using Anger?
CD Track Three, 5:17 - 6:33

Anger is:

- selfish.
- unloving.
- uniformly unproductive in relationships.
- alienating.
- self-destructive.
- incompatible with happiness.

With all these profoundly negative characteristics, why would we persist in having anything at all to do with anger? Why wouldn't we shun it completely and forever as the poison it is?

Because anger is what we've *learned*. From early childhood to the present, we have been given so many examples of anger that we have come to see it as unavoidable, natural, and even desirable. We see that people who are the most successful in motivating others with their anger—and other forms of attacking—are actually *admired*. They are often described as assertive, confident, and aggressive, qualities that are commonly used to describe leaders. Many of them become doctors, lawyers, political leaders, and chief executive officers. We fear such people and, in many cases, we wish we were more like them.

So it's little wonder that when we become empty or afraid, we tend to use anger as a means of protecting ourselves and getting a sense of power. When things become difficult, we don't naturally tend to do what's most effective; we tend to do what we've learned. Again, to paraphrase Proverbs 22:6 as I did on page 69, "Train up a child in the ways he should *not* go, and when he is old, he will not depart from them."

One reason I make this point is to help you not feel guilty as you begin to see the damage you've caused in your own life and in your relationships with your anger. As you study Real Love, you'll increasingly realize that you have hurt a great number of people—some of them badly—with your anger and other forms of attacking. These expressions of "I don't love you" cut deeply. But you must not waste time feeling guilty for your anger. As I've said, you were just doing what you learned. You were not being intentionally harmful or even foolish; actually, you were being a good student of teachers who simply had nothing to give you but examples of their anger.

CHAPTER FOUR
Other People Never Make Us Angry

FOUR, 15:35 - 19:56   Other People Never Make Us Angry
CD Track Four, 0:00 - 4:21

I suggest that you become familiar with the metaphor in the recording of the seminar, the metaphor that:

- compares losing two dollars to the emotional loss we experience when people inconvenience us and fail to do what we want.
- compares having twenty million dollars to having a sufficient supply of Real Love.

- demonstrates how our anger is caused by a longstanding lack of Real Love, not by the individual behaviors of other people in a given moment.

Many people find this metaphor very useful in the times when they're angry. It helps them remember that other people simply are not the cause of their anger. When we can remember that, it's much more difficult to stay angry at people, and without our anger conflicts are not likely to continue.

In the space below describe some times when you've blamed other people for your disappointment or anger. For example:

- I was angry at the boss because he blamed me for something I didn't do and because he didn't appreciate what I did.
- I was irritated at my husband because he didn't do something he'd promised.
- I was angry at my wife because she was late.
- I got angry at the kids when they didn't go to bed on time.
- I was disappointed that nobody in the family said anything after all the work I put into fixing supper.
- I was annoyed when I didn't get what I expected from customer support.
- I get angry at other drivers in heavy traffic.

At the time of these events, imagine how you would have felt if you had been filled with Real Love—if you'd had twenty million dollars. Would your reaction have been different?

FOUR, 19:56 - 20:54   The Two Choices
CD Track Four, 4:21 - 5:19

We simply cannot stop people consistently from taking two dollars from us. We could easily waste our entire lives if we devoted ourselves to controlling people and trying to stop them from:

- hurting us.
- treating us unfairly.
- being unkind.
- saying things about us that are not true.
- inconveniencing us.
- offending us.
- cheating us.
- lying to us.
- yelling at us.
- leaving us.

In fact, many of us do waste our lives in that effort, all the while justifying ourselves by exclaiming that we're "right" and that we've been "wronged" or "treated unfairly." So what? No happiness comes from walking a path where justice is the primary goal. Happiness comes from receiving and sharing Real Love. Over and over you'll be tempted to protect yourself and to right all wrongs, but unless you can do that with unconditional love, you will be stepping into a mire that will suck you in faster than you can imagine. The efforts you devote to finding and sharing Real Love will pay you far greater and longer lasting dividends than defending yourself ever will.

Describe some situations or relationships where you have invested a lot of time and effort to protect yourself and seek justice.

After all that time and effort, did you feel unconditionally loved? Did you feel loving? Did you feel genuinely happy?

I am *not* saying that we should just lie down and be doormats for whoever wants to hurt us. Not at all. In later modules we'll discuss how to say *no* and how to minimize injury to ourselves without feeling like victims or feeling like we're defending ourselves.

CHAPTER FIVE
Acting Like Victims

FIVE, 20:54 - 22:51   Acting Like Victims as a Getting and Protecting Behavior
CD Track Five, 0:00 - 1:55

A victim is anyone who experiences inconvenience, harm, or threat without agreeing to it. It's quite understandable, then, that we often feel like victims, because we really *are* victimized on a regular basis. We are victimized when:

- other people are late and inconvenience us.
- someone says unkind things about us to others.
- a friend is harsh or critical.
- our insurance company inappropriately denies a claim.
- the rain falls on our picnic.
- we're treated with disrespect.
- we're physically/emotionally/sexually abused.
- our children are disobedient, which requires us to stop what we're doing to instruct them once again.
- we're treated unfairly because of our age, sex, race, religion, sexual preference, or any other characteristic.
- we're involved in a car accident that wasn't our fault.
- we're blamed for a mistake we didn't make.

Although we actually are victimized quite frequently, it is still entirely our choice whether we *feel* or *act* like victims. To continue the metaphor from the section above, you can always take two dollars from me—you *can* victimize me—but whether I *feel* like a victim is determined not by your behavior but by whether I have twenty million dollars, and that is a condition I can control. If I have been diligently taking the steps to find Real Love—which we'll discuss in Module Three—and I have twenty million dollars, I will not *feel* victimized even though you might take two dollars—or twenty or more—from me.

In the space on the next page describe some occasions when you have acted like a victim in order to get something you wanted or to protect yourself. You might think of some examples as you answer the following questions:

- Do you sometimes get sympathy from people by drawing attention to what someone has done to you?
- Do you often complain about how things are just not "fair?"
- When you make mistakes, do you often say, "It's not my fault" or "I couldn't help it?"
- Do you often talk about what people should have done for you?
- Do you talk about how people don't appreciate you?
- Do you constantly complain about how you've been disadvantaged because you're a member of some minority group (based on gender, age, sexual preference, race, and so on)?

If you act like a victim, you may be able to protect yourself from pain momentarily, and you may win sympathy from time to time, but you will not feel loved. When you act like a victim, you are manipulating people for attention, and then you cannot feel like the attention you receive was given unconditionally.

CHAPTER SIX
Clinging and Running

SIX, 22:51 - 25:18   Clinging as a Getting Behavior
CD Track Six, 0:00 - 2:27

In the space below and on the next page, describe how you cling to get Imitation Love:

- Do you sometimes say "I love you" to a boyfriend or girlfriend or spouse in hopes that he or she will say something like it in return?
- When you get dressed up to go out, do you say, "How do I look?" In most cases, you're attempting to *get* approval. You're clinging.
- Do you say to your children at bedtime, "Give Mommy (or Daddy) a kiss"?
- Do you compliment people excessively, knowing that then they'll like you more?
- Do you ask your adult children why they haven't called you in a long time?
- Do you sometimes give people gifts so they'll feel grateful or obligated to you in some way? Before you think to say *no*, ask how you'd feel if people were completely *ungrateful* for the gifts you gave.
- When your husband goes somewhere for the evening, do you ever say, "Do you have to go out tonight? We never do anything together."
- When someone is ending a relationship with you, do you tell them how much they'll be hurting you by leaving?

When you cling, you can often get more attention for a moment, but it can't feel like it was given unconditionally.

SIX, 25:18 - 26:12   Running as a Protecting Behavior
CD Track Six, 2:27 - 3:21

In the space below and on the next page describe how you run to protect yourself. In the process answer some of the questions immediately below:

- Do you claim to be shy?
- When a conversation is difficult, do you tend to withdraw and become quiet?
- When you get irritated, do you sulk?
- Do you sometimes have a drink or two after work, just to take the edge off the tension?
- Do you avoid having potentially difficult conversations with people, even when you know the conversation needs to happen?
- At work do you put off writing difficult letters or making phone calls to people you know will be contentious?

CHAPTER SEVEN
The Origin of Getting and Protecting Behaviors

SEVEN, 26:12 - 30:04 Why Do We Use Particular Behaviors?
CD Track Seven 0:00 - 3:52

For reasons outlined in this recorded segment of the seminar, everyone has one or more Getting and Protecting Behaviors they prefer to use over the others. Using the examples from the seminar as a guide, in the space on the next page discuss how you came to acquire your own preferences. For example:

- I was the second child. My older brother was such a dominant personality that I didn't stand a chance as an attacker. He was older, bigger, and more experienced. But I did learn that I could get a lot of attention from being cute and sociable, thereby manipulating people for attention by pleasing them. In other words, I used lying and clinging to get Imitation Love in the forms of praise and safety.
- I can't remember a day when my mother didn't whine for the majority of it. She complained about everything. I hated it, but I'll be darned if I didn't learn to become a victim just like her.

- My father was a real bully, always getting his way by threatening people and yelling at them. As a child, I couldn't begin to compete with him at home, but I did learn that I could attack people at school and other places. I hated it that he treated me like that, but I ended up doing the same thing to other people.
- I was the youngest child. My parents were loud and critical, and so were my older siblings. I didn't stand a chance, so I just withdrew. I was quiet all the time, because I learned that the less I said, the less they bothered me. I've continued to do that all my life.
- My older sister was so smart and successful that there was no way I could compete with her for praise. So I worked to get the sensation of power I felt as I rebelled.

CHAPTER EIGHT
The Power of Understanding Getting and Protecting Behaviors

EIGHT, 30:04 - 32:31   As We Understand Getting and Protecting Behaviors, We can Understand Human Behavior and Understand the Concept of Sin
CD Track Eight, 0:00 - 2:28

It is so important that we understand Getting and Protecting Behaviors—not just as an interesting theory, but to actually *identify* them in ourselves and in the people around us. Why? Because almost everyone around us is using these Behaviors, and if we don't understand them, we'll be forever baffled by so many of the interactions we have with people. We'll also be helpless to know the best courses to take in relationships.

In the space on page 149 describe some behaviors in yourself and others that have previously puzzled you. Now explain them in light of what you now understand about Getting and Protecting Behaviors. Considering the frequency of these Behaviors in ourselves and others, you should be able to do this exercise for pages. Immediately below you can read a few examples of answers to this exercise:

- For years I've nagged my husband to spend more time with me, and all he did was withdraw from me even more. It just didn't make sense to me, but now it does. In the beginning, our marriage was based on Imitation Love, but when that faded away, I became afraid. I used attacking and clinging to get his attention. Of course, that only made him feel even more empty and afraid, so he defended himself by running. Wow, it was so simple all along.
- All my life I've acted like a victim. I've always complained that everything is unfair, people don't treat me right, and so on. No wonder people don't like to be around me. They run from all that whining.

- My wife and I used to have great sex, but over the years she's become more withdrawn. I thought the problem had something to do with sex, but it didn't. I'm seeing now that I've gradually become more and more critical of her—about many things. I didn't realize I was attacking her and that she was hearing me say "I don't love you" over and over again. So she fought me sometimes—attacked me back—but eventually she just pulled away from me (running). That's what she's doing when she doesn't want to have sex with me.

- My children whine all day. I couldn't understand it, but now I see that it's only when they whine—when they act like victims—that I consistently pay attention to them. So I've *trained* them to act like victims. They're just doing what I've trained them to do.

- I've always thought my boss was a real monster. He doesn't appreciate anybody, he's always critical, he's angry all the time. Now I'm seeing that he's just using attacking as a Getting and Protecting Behavior, and he does that only when he's empty and afraid. That big bad monster is just a child who needs to feel loved. It really changes the way I see him.

- I've always had such a temper, and I didn't understand why. The littlest things would set me off. Now I see that when I'm inconvenienced, or when people treat me unfairly, I feel helpless and weak. When I already feel unloved and empty, any little extra inconvenience or unfair treatment is more than I can take. When I get angry, I feel stronger, more powerful, and less helpless.

- My mother is constantly complaining that I don't call her enough, don't visit her enough, don't do anything enough. It was making me crazy, but now I see that she's just empty and afraid, and the only way she knows to get attention is by acting like a victim. She's just lonely and clinging to me.

- My sister has to be right about everything. She thinks she's never made a mistake in her life, and she has some brilliant contribution to offer to every conversation. She's always criticizing people too. That used to intimidate me a lot, but now I see that she wouldn't do all this if she felt loved. She's attacking people so she can get a feeling of power, and she does that only because she feels empty and alone.

On the whole, human behavior really isn't that complicated. Emptiness and fear are at the root of most of the things we do. When we understand that, other people become much less confusing and frightening, and we can be much more productive in our relationships with them. Our own behavior also becomes less confusing, and we can begin to replace anger and confusion with peace and confidence.

As I have read the Bible again and again, I have been consistently impressed with how thoroughly the principles of Real Love are explained by the prophets and apostles, and by the Savior Himself. James, for example, explained two thousand years ago how emptiness is the cause of Getting and Protecting Behaviors. He first asks,

> Where do the wars and other contentions among you come from? (James 4:1)

which is quite similar to asking, "What is the cause of all the Getting and Protecting Behaviors?" since these Behaviors form the roots of all contentions. And then he answers his own question:

> Don't they come from the lusts that are at war within you? (James 4:1)

Getting and Protecting Behaviors are a response to the enormous list of unfilled needs (emptiness or what James calls lusts) within us, all of which are screaming to be filled right now. The competition for all these needs to be filled simultaneously certainly qualifies as a "war."

> You lust but don't have what you want. You kill and desire to have but you don't find what you seek. You fight and war but still you don't get what you want, because you don't ask. You ask and don't receive, because you ask with the wrong motives, so you can satisfy your lusts. You adulterers, don't you know that friendship with the world is against the ways of God? Whoever wants to be a friend of the world is an enemy of God. (James 4:1-4)

This is such an accurate description of Getting and Protecting Behaviors, despite originating two thousand years ago. With Getting and Protecting Behaviors:

- we never quite get our needs met.
- we work harder and harder, to the point in some cases of even fighting and killing.

- we seek with the wrong motives and goals.
- we war against God.
- we become enemies of God.

What a price we pay for these Behaviors.

EIGHT, 32:31 - 33:43   Understanding Our Relationships
CD Track Eight, 2:28 - 3:41

Once we understand human behavior, understanding *relationships* and *interactions* becomes relatively easy. In Module One I say that every time we're angry, we're selfish, and other people hear us say, "I don't love you." It is the same with *all* the other Getting and Protecting Behaviors.

- When you're lying, your primary interest is in whom?
- When you act like a victim, you're focusing on getting something for whom?
- When you cling, you're trying to get something for whom?
- When you run, you're looking for relief of pain for whom?

Notice that the answer is the same for all these questions: *You.* When we're using any of the Getting and Protecting Behaviors, we're thinking of *ourselves*, and our partners *feel that*. So now we can expand what I said earlier about anger: Whenever we use *any* of the Getting and Protecting Behaviors, other people hear us say only "I don't love you." That fact alone explains most of the unproductive interactions we ever have, because after you've said "I don't love you" to someone, how in the world could things go well?

In light of what you have learned thus far from the recording of the seminar, use the space on the next page to discuss some difficult interactions you've had with others. Now explain *why* they went badly. For examples of this kind of interaction, see several of the bulleted items on the previous page. Some additional examples follow:

- Every time my husband and I talk about money, it's a disaster. I always thought it was all his fault, but now I see my part in it. When we talk about money, I act like a victim, I attack him, I don't quite tell the whole truth, and eventually I withdraw from him. I use all the Protecting Behaviors, and in the process I tell him in a hundred ways that I don't love him. So then we're not having a discussion about money anymore. Then he can only protect himself from my not loving him, and it just gets worse and worse.
- My father is very critical and controlling, and then I respond by defending myself. I argue with him and eventually act like a victim. Then he just gets even more critical, and now I see that he's just responding to my not loving him. He's protecting himself and trying to feel worthwhile by getting a sense of power from our interaction.

Two Messages in Every Getting and Protecting Behavior

When someone is using Getting and Protecting Behaviors, it's easy to hear the *I don't love you* message—especially when he or she is screaming at you. What we often miss is the *other message*, the one that uniformly accompanies the *I don't love you*. We usually forget that people use Getting and Protecting Behaviors only because they are empty and afraid, because they don't have enough Real Love in their lives. So the other message they're communicating is this: "I don't feel loved. Please love me."

When someone is angry at us—and therefore screaming "I don't love you"—that can feel quite threatening. In that condition, it's understandable that we'd become focused on ourselves and miss the *please love me* message from our partner. But it's still there, and until we hear it, we will tend to feel threatened by the Getting and Protecting Behaviors of others, and then we'll likely respond with our own unproductive behaviors.

When people don't understand the nature of Getting and Protecting Behaviors, the sequence of events usually goes like this, using Cynthia and John as examples:

- Cynthia says, "The kids have a ton of homework to do tonight, and I'm not getting any help from you." This is an attack. She is clearly saying, "I don't love you," because she is angry and focusing only on *herself*. But she is empty and afraid, so she's also saying, "I need some help. Please help me and love me."
- John is already carrying around the effects of a *lifetime* of not feeling sufficient Real Love, and in that condition the loud "I don't love you" from Cynthia is more than enough to make him feel much more empty and afraid. Then he's in no condition to hear the *please love me* part of her message.
- John responds angrily with, "Oh, right, like you help me with all the things *I* need to do." By attacking Cynthia, John defends himself from *her* attack, hoping to shut her up. He also feels a little less helpless as he experiences the rush of power that comes from anger.

- John's attack also communicates "I don't love you" and "Please love me."
- Cynthia hears the first message but misses the second. Hearing the first message, she feels even more unloved herself and responds with even more anger toward John.
- Now we're back at the top of this sequence, and the entire cycle spirals rapidly downward.

As you can see, when we don't understand Real Love and Getting and Protecting Behaviors, we respond in the worst possible ways to one another. On those occasions we actually *cause* the behaviors we hate. This is taught in the Bible:

- When the Romans came to take Jesus, one of his disciples fought with a sword to keep Jesus from being taken, and he cut off the ear of a servant of the high priest. Jesus said, Put away your sword, because everyone who uses violence will be destroyed by violence. (Matthew 26:50-52)

We use violence to stop violence, we only increase the emptiness and fear of others, who will then react with even more violence to protect themselves.

- God will give suffering and affliction to those who are quarrelsome and disobedient to the truth, who obey wickedness and anger, and who do evil. (Romans 2:8-9)

The above verse describes perfectly what Getting and Protecting Behaviors are—quarrelsome, disobedient, wicked, angry, evil—and what are the rewards of those behaviors? Suffering and affliction, which in great part are a result of the Getting and Protecting Behaviors of others who are responding to those same Behaviors in us. Getting and Protecting Behaviors beget Getting and Protecting Behaviors.

- Because men refused to acknowledge God in their lives, He abandoned them to their own wicked minds, to do those things which are not proper, being filled with all unrighteousness, fornication, wickedness, jealousy, and maliciousness. They were full of envy, murder, contention, deceit, and ill will. They were gossipers, haters of God, proud, boasters, creative in their wickedness, disobedient to parents, foolish, covenant breakers, unloving, stubborn, and unmerciful. And although they know the judgment of God, and that their behavior has a penalty of death, they still persist in their behavior and enjoy the company of people who behave in the same way. (Romans 1:28-32)

Again what a clear description of Getting and Protecting Behaviors, and if we indulge in them, what is one of the worst consequences? We attract "the company of people who behave in the same way," people whose behaviors irritate us constantly.

In the space below, discuss some situations or relationships where people have behaved in ways that were difficult and frustrating for you. Discuss what you see differently about their behavior now. Now can you recognize the "I don't love you" message they were communicating? Can you also recognize the other messages they were sending, like "I feel empty and alone" or "I need to feel loved" or "Would someone please love me?"

In later modules we'll discus some examples of how to respond to this *please love me* message.

EIGHT, 33:43 - 34:55   The Effect of all the Getting and Protecting Behaviors
CD Track Eight, 3:41 - 4:51

As we understand Getting and Protecting Behaviors, we can also recognize the uniform effect they all have, and that gives us even greater power in making decisions about changing our behaviors. Again, let's look at each of them:

Behavior	Why We Use It	The Effect It Has
Lying	So we won't feel empty and afraid	We drive away the people in our lives and feel more empty and afraid
Attacking	So we won't feel empty and afraid	We drive away the people in our lives and feel more empty and afraid
Acting like a Victim	So we won't feel empty and afraid	We drive away the people in our lives and feel more empty and afraid
Clinging	So we won't feel empty and afraid	We drive away the people in our lives and feel more empty and afraid
Running	So we won't feel empty and afraid	We drive away the people in our lives and feel more empty and afraid

Notice a bit of a pattern here? What a terrible irony that the behaviors we choose to protect ourselves cause the very conditions we're trying hardest to avoid. Once we understand that, however, we are better motivated and prepared to avoid these behaviors and take the paths that lead to much wiser choices.

Paul talked about our Getting and Protecting Behaviors to the Galatians, saying:

> The deeds of the flesh are obvious, including adultery, sexual sins, uncleanness, indecency, idolatry, witchcraft, hatred, contention, jealousy, anger, conspiracies, heresies, envyings, murders, drunkenness, partyings, and so on. And those who do such things shall not inherit the kingdom of God. But the fruits of the Spirit are love, joy, peace, patience, gentleness, goodness, faith, kindness, and self control. There is no law against those qualities. (Galatians 5:19-23)

The purpose of this verse is to demonstrate a direct comparison between the results of using the listed Getting and Protecting Behaviors and the results of partaking of the fruits of the Spirit. In order for such a comparison to be meaningful, however, the two results must be *comparable* on an equivalent plane or in a similar sphere. Notice, then, that the fruits of the Spirit essentially boil down to love and other virtues that are found *in this life*, not some far distant time or dimension. A comparison between the fruits of the Spirit and the use of Getting and Protecting Behaviors would not be meaningful, therefore, unless the described results of using Getting and Protecting Behaviors also referred to *this life*, and I submit that that is the case. When Paul says that the consequence of Getting and Protecting Behaviors is exclusion from the kingdom of God, he's describing not just an eventual, spiritual consequence but also an *earthly* and immediate one.

In other words, he is referring to the kingdom of God as it exists on earth. The kingdom of God exists both on earth and in heaven, and there are dozens of verses to support that claim. The following verses speak of the kingdom of God as an earthly condition:

- Daniel 2:44
- Matthew 3:1-3
- Matthew 6:33
- Matthew 13:24-30, 36-43
- Matthew 21:43
- Luke 11:20
- Luke 17:21

The last of these verses is particularly revealing, stating, "Behold, the kingdom of God is within you." It only makes sense that we can't hope to inherit the kingdom of God in the *next life* if we have not previously taken the steps to become its citizens in *this* life. In Galatians 5:19-23 above Paul is referring to the kingdom of God as a condition of the spirit or soul, and he was saying that those who use Getting and Protecting Behavior are incapable of feeling the blessings of that condition: love, joy, peace, patience, gentleness, goodness, faith, kindness, and self control.

In the space below and on the next page, discuss some occasions in your life where you have used Getting and Protecting Behaviors and noticed many of the destructive effects we have discussed. Describe how each of these behaviors has driven people away from you and made you feel even more empty and afraid. For example:

- When I get angry, I feel less empty and afraid temporarily, but I never feel closer to people or genuinely happy.
- When I lie to people, I can often get out of trouble—I can even get people to accept me for a moment—but my lies isolate me. I never feel loved unconditionally while I'm lying.
- When I act like a victim, I like the sympathy I get, but I get tired of manipulating people, and eventually they get tired of my complaining.
- I've run from people and situations all my life. It makes me feel safer, but then I always feel alone.
- I can see that I've used Getting and Protecting Behaviors all my life, but they've never gotten me the kind of happiness I want.

In some of your examples, be specific as to the exact people you have affected with your Getting and Protecting Behaviors.

Also notice that all Getting and Protecting Behaviors have the same end result. I mention this because we have a tendency to condemn the behaviors *other people* use, while making excuses for the ones *we* use. Victims condemn attackers, attackers are disgusted by victims, attackers see runners as weak, and so on. But we need to see them all as equally destructive and lose our criticism of any particular behavior. They're all poison.

Understanding Sin in Light of Getting and Protecting Behaviors

Let's summarize what we know thus far about Getting and Protecting Behaviors:

- They cause us and the people around us to feel even more empty and afraid.
- Because the Getting and Protecting Behaviors make us more empty and afraid, they also inevitably detract in a powerful way from the ability that we and others have to feel loved, loving, and happy.
- Because feeling loved, loving others, and being happy are all fruits of the Spirit (Galatians 5:19-23), anything that detracts from these qualities or abilities would necessarily be against the Spirit, and would therefore be evil or harmful or wrong. Getting and Protecting Behaviors are therefore morally and spiritually wrong. They interfere, in fact, with our primary purpose for living.
- Getting and Protecting Behaviors are the cause of incalculable destruction and unhappiness in this life and are among the primary tools used by Satan and all those who support the cause of evil.

Putting all the above characteristics together, it should by now be obvious that the Getting and Protecting Behaviors can all be described in a single word: ***sin***. Only a moment's reflection will reveal that all the many activities that God has designated as sins are nothing but Getting and Protecting Behaviors, single or in combination.

Once we recognize that all Getting and Protecting Behaviors are sins and that all sins are Getting and Protecting Behaviors, we gain a clarity of understanding we didn't have before, and with that understanding we find additional power to make more positive choices in our lives. For example:

- We now have a new comprehension of *why* God has given us the many commandments He has. We'll discuss this important concept in the next sub-section.
- We can take a giant step toward eliminating the anger we feel when other people sin and behave in other ways that affect us negatively. We'll discuss this on pages 171-8.
- We can eliminate the sting of our own sins, which we'll discuss on pages 178-81.

- We add another entire perspective—a delightful one, at that—to the process of repentance. For more on this, see pages 182-5.

Understanding *Why* God Has Given Us Commandments

Many people are overwhelmed and even irritated by what they perceive as the endless list of demanding and restrictive thou-shalts and thou-shalt-nots found in God's commandments, and that attitude is one of the major factors that contributes to their distant or difficult relationships with Him. To such people, God can often seem like an egotistical dictator, meddling in far too many of their affairs and bent on taking all the fun out of life.

An understanding of Real Love can give us a very helpful insight into the nature of God, and into the motivations behind His commandments, that will contribute to a closer relationship with Him. Let us first remember that God often refers to Himself as our Father, and that title alone reveals a great deal about His intended relationship with us.

If you are a parent—please consider this a mental exercise if you have no children—what goals do you have for your children? Is your ultimate dream that they will become your slaves, who will contentedly serve you all their lives? Or do you have hopes that they will be more than slaves but only to the point of being half what you are? Or is it possible that you wish much more for them? As a loving parent, do you not wish for them every good thing in life—to know and to have all that you know and have, and hopefully much more? And do you not wish for them the greatest imaginable happiness? Of course you do. And would you not teach them everything you know to make all that possible? Every loving parent would.

Addressing this point, Jesus said, "If a son asks his father for bread or a fish, is there any father who would give his son a stone or a poisonous snake instead? So if you, being wicked and flawed human beings, know how to give good gifts to your children, how much more will your heavenly Father give good things to His children who ask Him?" (Matthew 7:9-11)

And thus we have confirmation of His motivation for everything He says and does. It is His primary goal to give us the best of all possible gifts, which of course is the genuine happiness that we achieve as we:

- feel loved unconditionally by one another.
- feel loved by Him.
- love one another unconditionally.
- love Him.

In all of His instructions to us, therefore, the goal is not to satisfy some egotistical urge to control us or to keep us from having fun. His primary goal is to teach us how to accomplish the four bulleted goals above—along with the happiness that always accompanies them—and how to avoid all the behaviors that would detract from these goals and that perfect happiness.

Although at times God's commandments might seem endless and complicated, they become simple, unified, and delightful in their purpose when we remember that they exist only to help us achieve the joy our Father desires for us. Let's apply what we've just learned to some of the individual commandments we've been given:

- Thou shalt not steal. Why? So other people will never be inconvenienced by the loss of their property? To preserve social order? So God won't be irritated? No. God wants us to avoid stealing because with each act of forcefully taking from another human being, we become a little more selfish, we care a little less about the happiness of others, and then, finally, *we* become less happy—and *that* is what God wants us to avoid.
- Thou shalt not bear false witness against your neighbor. Why? Because it's bad manners? Because someone's reputation might be sullied? No. Because each time you lie about your neighbor, you become just a little more accustomed to behaving with disregard for others. You become a little less loving and travel another degree off the path that leads to genuine happiness.

- Thou shalt not commit adultery. Why? Because your neighbor might resent your sleeping with his wife? Or because it might hurt *your* wife's feelings? Not primarily. Adultery's primary evil is that it is so opposed to the principles of Real Love and genuine happiness. How can we be loving and happy while we're ignoring the spiritual well-being of so many people?

All of God's commandments are intended as a road map that will take us back—literally and figuratively—into His presence and enable us to become like Him, which is what will bring us the greatest happiness. This map points out the behaviors—the sins, the Getting and Protecting Behaviors—that will make *us* miserable. How kind, how generous, and how loving He is to provide us with all that guidance and warning. And how grateful we should be for every word of counsel we receive.

Without the commandments it might seem that we would have a freedom of sorts, but actually we'd be lost. We'd be left to our own devices, to learn by trial and error what works and doesn't work, and that is a slow and painful way to learn.

EIGHT, 34:55 - 36:51   We Can't Change What We Can't See
CD Track Eight, 4:51 - 6:48

As I talk about the many negative behaviors we use when we don't feel loved, it can sometimes sound a bit depressing. I am not being critical or judgmental here. I'm not trying to find fault with us, our parents, our partners, or the world in general. No, my goal is to contribute to our knowledge—and thereby the tools we possess—that will enable us to change the direction of our lives and fully grasp the happiness that is available to us.

With knowledge comes power. The more you understand your behavior—and the behavior of those around you—the more you can do something about it. Let me illustrate that with a story:

Several years ago water began leaking into one side of my basement. In order to expose that outside wall, I dug a trench forty feet long, ten feet deep, and five feet wide—by hand. For weeks my children and I moved all that sticky Georgia clay one bucket at a time out to a cart and then another four hundred feet up a hill for dumping. We tore all the tar paper off the wall, applied new tar, created a new drainage system in the trench, installed a drainage pump, and filled the entire trench with gravel.

But it was worth it, because the wall stopped leaking. I cleaned carpets, repainted the cupboards, and put everything back to its original condition. But then, six months later, the leak returned, so I exposed the wall again—more tar, bigger ditch, bigger pump. As I was finishing the job, I looked around the corner of the house and saw that for all those years there had been a defective connection between the water drain from the roof and the drain that continued underground. That defect had slowly caused all our problems.

I bought a replacement part for less than two dollars and never had another leak. In the end, I had moved almost a *million* pounds of material and performed a great number of other labors, and all that effort was absolutely worthless until I identified the real problem.

Similarly, in our lives and in our relationships we desperately attempt to address what appear to be so many different problems, but until we identify the central cause of all of them, our efforts can only be a tragic waste.

As we identify the flaws in our lives, we don't need to condemn them. We don't need to feel excessively guilty about them either, but we do need to identify them, or we can't do anything about them. We also need to clearly understand the behaviors of other people, not to criticize them but to give us the ability to respond to them ore productively.

CHAPTER NINE
The Drowning Metaphor

NINE, 36:51 - 44:40 Emptiness and Fear are Like Drowning
CD Track Nine, 0:00 - 7:48

I strongly recommend that you commit to memory the basic outline of the drowning metaphor, because it can be a powerful aid in eliminating the anger in your life. People all over the world are using this to great advantage.

When you saw that the man in the pool splashing you was drowning:

How long did it take for your anger to go away?	It happened in an instant.
How much effort was required on your part to eliminate your anger?	None. With a single moment of understanding your anger simply disappeared.
What else happened within you, in addition to losing your anger?	You developed an immediate desire to help him.
Did you require anything from him before you were willing to help him?	No, you were willing to help him freely, unconditionally.

How does all this help you eliminate the anger in your own life? When you can see that the people around you who are behaving badly are just drowning, it will completely change the way you see them, the way you feel about them, and the way you respond to them. So let's compare the drowning man to the people in your life:

The Drowning Man	The People in Your Life
He was splashing you.	They often inconvenience you, hurt you, and fail to give you what you want.
He was splashing you *not* from a primary desire to affect *you* but in an effort to keep his own head above water.	They are not trying primarily to hurt or inconvenience you, but are trying only to keep their own heads above water, emotionally speaking.
He was using his arms and legs to keep his head above water.	They are using Getting and Protecting Behaviors to keep their heads above water.
He behaved crazily only because he suffered from a serious lack of air.	They behave badly only because they are empty and afraid due to a lack of Real Love, which is every bit as important to their happiness as air is to the physical health of a drowning person.
He was doing everything he could to survive.	They are doing everything they can to survive.
His behavior had nothing to do with you.	Their behavior has nothing to do with you.
Once you saw that he was drowning, your anger vanished immediately and without effort. How could you be angry at someone for drowning?	When you see people as drowning, how can you continue to be angry at them? You lose your anger immediately.
Not only did you lose your anger, but you immediately reached out to help him.	No only do you lose your anger at people who are using Getting and Protecting Behaviors, but you immediately want to give them the Real Love they need.
You were angry only because you didn't know that the man was drowning.	You respond poorly to people who are behaving badly only because you don't understand or remember that they're just drowning.

The Drowning Man	The People in Your Life
Telling a drowning man to "stop it" would be very foolish.	When we demand that the people around us stop doing anything to inconvenience us, very often we are telling a drowning man to stop moving his arms and legs. Absurd.

In the space below and on the next page describe someone in your life who is irritating—someone who is hurting or inconveniencing you with his or her lies, anger, or withdrawal. Now, in the terms I suggested in the seminar, "just add water." Explain that person's behavior in terms of Getting and Protecting Behaviors. Some possible examples:

- For years I've been irritated at my wife for being critical and short-tempered. It makes a huge difference to see that she's just been drowning and using attacking to keep her head above water.
- Every time our relationship became intimate, my boyfriend would withdraw from me. It was making me crazy. I wondered how he could keep pulling away. But he was just drowning— empty and afraid—and he was using running as a Protecting Behavior.
- I've been so afraid of my boss, who is an angry and critical man. With a single word, he could bury me. But he's just drowning! His behavior isn't about me, and that changes everything. I'm not afraid of him anymore, and now I think I can actually help him better.

When you see someone as drowning, does that not completely change the way you feel about him or her? And that makes it possible for you to respond to him or her differently. Instead of protecting yourself, you can now be understanding and even give him or her the Real Love he or she needs.

There is so much power in seeing clearly, and Paul recognized that most of us in this lifetime simply would not:

> For now we are seeing unclearly through a mirror, just as now I know things incompletely. (1 Corinthians 13:12)

But he extends a hope that someday we might transcend our condition of darkness:

> But the day will come when we will see clearly, and then I will know fully, just as I have been fully known. (1 Corinthians 13:12)

Then in the next verse Paul provides the means by which we might accomplish this miracle of illumination:

> And now these three remain: faith, hope, and love. But the greatest of these is love. (1 Corinthians 13:13)

Without Real Love—and without an understanding of it—we are blinded by confusion and by emptiness and fear. As we gain an understanding of Real Love, and as we feel its power, we gain the ability to see ourselves and others, and with that ability we can love other people as well. We'll talk much more about that in the rest of the workbook.

Jesus told a story that contributes to our understanding of the metaphor of the drowning man. He said:

Whoever hears and does what I say is like a wise man who built his house on a rock, and then when the rain fell, and the floods came, and the winds blew and beat upon that house, it didn't fall, because it was built upon a rock. But whoever hears me and doesn't do what I say is like a foolish man who built his house on the sand, and when the rain fell, and the floods came, and the winds blew and beat upon the house, it fell, and the fall was great. (Matthew 7:24-7; Luke 6:47-49)

There will always be rain. You can't stop the rain, and it would be foolish to resent it. All you can do is build your house on a foundation of rock so that when the rain does come, your house will still stand. As Paul wrote to Timothy:

Instruct those who are wealthy not to be proud or trust in the uncertainty of their wealth, but instead to trust in the living God, who gives us abundantly all things to enjoy. Instruct them to do good, to be rich in good works, ready to be generous, willing to communicate, thereby building up for themselves *a good foundation* for the times to come, so they may gain eternal life. (1 Timothy 6:17)

Just as there will always be rain, you will always be surrounded by people in various stages of drowning. You can't insulate yourself from the effects of drowning people, and it would be foolish to resent them for drowning. But you can *understand* their drowning, and you can take the steps to find Real Love for yourself, so that you are standing on a foundation of rock. In that condition, you won't be drowning in the water with them, and then you won't be threatened by the splashing and other negative behaviors of the drowning people around you.

Now, an important word here. So far what I've described is mostly a way to *understand* people differently—an *intellectual* way to change your feelings and behavior. Although this intellectual approach is powerful, it alone may not be enough if *you're* drowning also. If you're drowning too, you'll need more than a simple *understanding* of Real Love; you'll need the power that comes from actually *possessing* Real Love—only in that power is the foundation of rock complete—and we'll talk about how you can find that in Module Three.

In the space below and on the next page describe some occasions when you have been irritated at a drowning person. How did that work out for you? A couple of examples:

- My husband was angry when he was talking to me, and I said, "I'm not going to continue this conversation if you're going to use that tone with me." Instead of seeing him as drowning, essentially I walked away from him and hurled insults at him to boot. Then he didn't want to talk to me for days.
- My daughter was crying and being a real brat. It was annoying, so instead of seeing why she was drowning, I said, "Stop that right now." That didn't work very well.

I said on page 160 that when we understand that sins are just Getting and Protecting Behaviors, we can gain power in responding to the sins and mistakes of others that affect us. On these pages (171-8) we'll talk more about that subject. After reading the above section, it should be clear that when we see the negative behaviors of other people—their Getting and Protecting Behaviors and their sins—as just responses to their emptiness and fear, it's difficult to be irritated at them. None of us would be angry at someone for drowning, and drowning is exactly what people are doing emotionally and spiritually when they are treating us badly.

Paul described drowning people, and how we should respond to them:

If someone has caused pain, the punishment inflicted on him by many is already enough. So forgive and comfort him, so that he isn't overwhelmed by despair. I urge you to reaffirm your love toward him. (2 Corinthians 2:5-8)

When people treat us poorly, we tend to get on our moral high horse and justify our hurt and anger, especially if what they have done is classified as a sin, officially condemned by God. We reason that if God himself condemns them for their behavior, what a great opportunity for us to get on the stoning committee and throw a few rocks of our own. Achieving freedom from that temptation is illustrated by the following experience I had with a lady named Julia.

Julia had recently learned that her husband, Nick, had been having an affair, and she was variously enjoying the states of rage, profound victimhood, and righteous indignation. "How could he do this to me?" she cried. "What he did was so wrong." And of course she had enlisted the sympathy of everyone she knew. I have known many people who have stayed mired in that particular combination of anger and victimhood for a lifetime.

"Why did Nick have an affair?" I asked.

"Because he's a selfish pig who thinks nothing of our marriage vows," she said. "He hurt me, he hurt the children, and he broke the laws of God."

I chuckled. "That's certainly one way to describe it. But you've read the Real Love book, so I can ask you to search more deeply in your mind and in your heart. What did he get out of the affair?"

We talked until she realized that he had found another woman because she gave him a fresh supply of Imitation Love. The Imitation Love that had originally brought him and Julia together had worn off, and he was feeling empty and alone. "So *before* he had this affair," I said, "Nick couldn't possibly have felt enough Real Love in his life, could he? Otherwise he wouldn't have gone looking for a new source of Imitation Love."

"I guess that's right," said Julia. "But are you saying this affair is *my* fault, that he had an affair because *I* wasn't loving him enough?"

"Only partly," I said. "He actually came to your marriage already feeling unloved. He hadn't felt Real Love from his parents for his whole life to that point, and then you just made a *contribution* to his not feeling unconditionally loved. So yes, you did have a *part* in causing his affair, but only a small part. True, if you had given him enough Real Love, he probably *wouldn't* have had the affair, but that's like saying if you had wings, you could fly. You didn't love him unconditionally—and you still don't—only because you've never had it to give. Your parents, teachers, and others never sufficiently loved *you* unconditionally either. Neither you nor Nick was in a position to love the other unconditionally. You were both drowning, and there was nobody around to help either of you. Pretty sad, don't you think?"

Now Julia was crying. "It's like our marriage was doomed from the beginning."

"Yes, that's right. Most relationships are doomed from the word *hello*. Now, I want to point something out to you. How angry are you right this minute?"

She paused as she thought about it. "I guess I'm not angry at all. I'm just sad."

"Right. Without realizing it, you lost your anger at Nick when you realized that he was just drowning, that you were both thrown out into the world without enough of the one thing—Real Love—that you both needed most to be happy and to have a healthy relationship. What Nick did was certainly wrong, but it wasn't designed to hurt you. He was just drowning and doing his best to keep from going under."

From that moment, Julia began a process of complete forgiveness and learning how to love her husband unconditionally. She freed herself from the prison of anger and victimhood and instead began to nurture a healthy relationship with Nick. It was a joy to watch.

Now, in the space below and on the next page, do what Julia did. Begin with describing how someone offended you or sinned against you. Then see that person as drowning, and now describe how you see them differently? What does this do to your anger? Do you feel closer to them? Do you feel free of those old negative feelings, the feelings that have been keeping you from feeling loved and loving?

Forgiveness in Real Love and the Bible

We're all familiar with the scriptural instructions we have received about forgiveness.

- If you forgive people when they offend you, your heavenly Father will also forgive you. But if you don't forgive people when they offend you, He will not forgive you. (Matthew 6:14-15)

- When you pray, forgive anything you hold against anyone. If you don't forgive, neither will your Father in Heaven forgive you. (Mark 11:25-26)

- The Jews brought to Jesus a woman who had been caught in the act of adultery. And they said, The law prescribes that she be stoned, but what do you say? Jesus stooped down and wrote in the dirt as though he had not heard them. When they continued to ask him, he raised up and said, He that is without sin among you, let him be the first to throw a stone at her. And again he stooped down and wrote in the dirt. And when they heard it, convicted by their own conscience, they went away, leaving only Jesus and the woman. Jesus said to her, Woman, is there no one left to condemn you? She said, No, Lord, and Jesus said, Neither do I condemn you. Go and sin no more. (John 8:3-11)

- Don't judge others, and you won't be judged yourself; don't condemn others, and you won't be condemned; forgive, and you will be forgiven. Give, and it will be given unto you abundantly, for with the same measure that you give it will be measured to you again. (Luke 6:37-38)

- Don't say that you will repay evil for evil, but wait on the Lord, and he will save you. (Proverbs 20:22)

We hear one especially poignant story about forgiveness when Peter asks Jesus,

How many times shall I forgive someone who does something wrong to me? Seven times? And Jesus said, no, seventy times seven. Imagine that there was a king whose servant who owed him a million dollars, and when the servant couldn't pay the debt, the king ordered all the man's possessions sold, as well as the man and his entire family to be sold as slaves. But when the servant begged the king for patience, the king lovingly freed him from slavery and forgave the debt. But then the same servant confronted another man who owed him twenty dollars, grabbing him by the throat and demanding immediate payment. When the other man begged for patience, the king's servant had the man put in prison. When the king heard about this, he had the servant brought before him and said, I forgave you an enormous debt. Should you not have done the same for the man who owed you a small amount? And then the king punished the servant severely. Jesus said, my Father will do the same to you if you don't forgive everyone the wrongs they commit against you. (Matthew 18:21-35)

God offers us forgiveness for so much—the sins of a lifetime— and He asks only that we forgive the few sins of others that affect us. It seems a small thing to ask, especially when it is *we* who benefit most from the forgiving.

According to scholars, the ancient Aramaic word that translates into *forgive* in English also translates into the word *untie*. So the line from the Lord's Prayer, "And forgive us our debts, as we forgive our debtors" actually translates from the Aramaic as "Loose the cords of the mistakes binding us, in the same way that we release the strands we hold of the guilt of others." Or "Untangle the knots within us so that we can let go of the ties binding our hearts in the old ways to others."

Again, in later modules I'll be talking about how we can respond even more productively to drowning people.

The Disregard of Anger for the Atonement of Christ

We've established the selfishness and destructiveness of anger on so many levels already. Before we leave the subject, allow me to explore one more facet of the selfishness of anger.

Although I did promise in the introduction to avoid a detailed study of the atonement of Christ, I will briefly describe here what most Christians accept as the characteristics of the atonement:

- The Son of man came to give his life as a ransom for many. (Matthew 20:28)

- I am the living bread that came down from heaven, and if any man eat of this bread, he shall live for ever. (John 6:51)

- Jesus said, I am the resurrection and the life. Whoever believes in me, even if he has died, he will live. And whoever lives and believes in me will never die. (John 11:25-26)

- God proves his love toward us by the fact that while we were still sinners, Christ died for us. He proves his love even more by making us righteous through the shedding of his blood and saving us from the punishment to come. We have been reconciled to God by the death of His Son and saved by His life. We also have joy in God through our Lord Jesus Christ, by whom we have received the atonement. (Romans 5:8-12)

- By the grace of God Jesus tasted death for every man. Through His sufferings He became the captain of salvation for many men. (Hebrews 2:9-11)

- If we walk in the light, as He is in the light, we have fellowship one with another, and the blood of Jesus Christ his Son cleans us from all sin. (1 John 1:7)

- John saw Jesus and said, Behold the Lamb of God, who takes away the sins of the world. (John 1:29)

- Jesus learned obedience from the things He suffered, and after He was made perfect, He became the author of eternal salvation unto all those who obey Him. (Hebrews 5:8-9)

The sum of all these verses is that Jesus Christ has taken upon Himself the sins of the world, and through Him all men and women can be forgiven. Through His suffering and His death, Christ alone has earned the right and power to bestow on mankind the condition of grace called forgiveness. Without being aware of it, it is remarkable how often we as human beings attempt to take from Him that right to be the sole dispenser of forgiveness.

Although we don't think about the following process consciously, when we are angry at someone, this is what we're saying to him or her with our anger (assuming we have a belief in the atonement of Christ at all):

- I believe in the atonement of Christ and that through Him all mankind may be forgiven of their sins.

- I even believe the atonement applies to you personally. Even *your* sins can be forgiven.

- If you do something that personally inconveniences *me*, however, the atonement of Christ isn't quite enough to take away your sins. When you mess with My Royal Highness, Jesus' atonement is not enough to give you forgiveness.

- In order to satisfy the demands of *my* justice—in order to appease and eliminate *my* anger—you have to suffer a little extra, just for *me*. In some cases, a lot extra. When it comes to sins that inconvenience me, you have to work through a special Supplemental Atonement of your own, and then maybe I'll be satisfied. Maybe.

Anger is more selfish and arrogant than most of us have ever imagined, and that awareness alone can become another useful tool that will help us cast our anger aside. Let me illustrate with a metaphor from everyday life. Sometimes we pick out an article of clothing that seems suitable at the time—a hat, a blouse, whatever— but then when we finally see it in the mirror, and we realize just how ridiculous it looks, we just can't keep it on. Similarly, just one clear glimpse of how ridiculously selfish we're being when we're angry is sometimes enough to give us the strength to let it go.

CHAPTER TEN
More About the Power of
Understanding Getting and Protecting Behaviors

TEN, 44:40 - 47:12   Eliminating Anger and Guilt
CD Track Ten, 0:00 - 2:35

Do you know how to run a nuclear reactor? If not, are you ashamed of your inability to do so? *Should* you feel ashamed of that shortcoming? Ridiculous. Why should you be ashamed of not knowing how to do something you were never *taught*. This need for acceptance and tolerance seems obvious when we're talking about an ignorance of nuclear reactors, but somehow we think everything should be different when we're talking about a knowledge of relationships, like dating, marriage, and parenting. Somehow we're all just magically *supposed to know* how to have fulfilling relationships, find loving partners, create and maintain happy marriages, and raise happy and responsible children.

But learning about relationships—and love and anger—*is not different* than learning about anything else. The metaphor holds. Most of us have never seen any consistent examples of Real Love, so how could we possibly know how to give it to others? And that's why we have problems in our relationships. We just *don't know how to love*, and it's a complete waste of time to feel guilt and shame about it. I'm not suggesting that we use our ignorance as an *excuse* to continue being unloving. I'm saying only that rather than feeling guilty, it's far more productive for us to focus on the steps that will help us find Real Love, which we'll discuss in Module Three.

Most of us have learned from early childhood that when people make mistakes, somebody must *pay*. If other people make mistakes that affect us, we must see to it that they suffer in some way so they won't make the same mistake again. We have forgotten what the Lord has said on the subject, in this case as spoken by Paul:

Repay no one evil for evil, but consider what is good before all people. As much as possible, live in peace with everyone. Do not avenge yourselves, but allow God to do that, for the Lord has said, Vengeance is mine and I will repay. (Romans 12:17-19)

We also feel a need to punish ourselves for our own mistakes. Certainly the people around us made it clear that they hated our mistakes, so we feel ashamed of them. We carry our shame around like hot coals, never to be cooled.

Guilt is a feeling of regret about a *thing* we've done. Shame is a feeling of regret about who we *are*. We feel guilty about a *mistake*. We feel ashamed about *ourselves*. A "teaspoon" of guilt is good—it motivates us to learn from our mistakes and avoid them—but shame and excessive guilt are needlessly painful and deadly.

We don't begin life ashamed of ourselves. Shame is learned. It's a judgment that who we are with our warts is unacceptable, even disgusting, to other people, and then we suffer the deadly fear that we'll be unloved and alone forever.

Shame is crippling. When people feel ashamed, they can't feel loved. They can't see clearly. They can't learn or grow. How can all that possibly lead to the peace promised by the Lord? We must stop the excessive guilt and shame we feel over our sins. As I said on page 160, we need only to see our sins as reactions to a lack of Real Love, and then we realize that needless suffering can only interfere with our growth and our joy, which is not the will of God. We need to see that sins are *Getting and Protecting Behaviors* that are born out of emptiness and fear, and with that perspective we know that the wise solution to sins is to find the Real Love that will eliminate them. We'll be talking shortly about eliminating sins.

The apostle Paul talked about the productive role of guilt when he wrote to the Corinthians and said,

> Godly sorrow (or guilt) produces repentance that leads to salvation, but the sorrow (or guilt) of the world produces death. Look at the results of this godly sorrow in your own lives, how it produced in you a caution, a desire to be cleared of wrong, an anger at wrongdoing, a fear, an earnest desire, a zeal, an eagerness for justice. (2 Corinthians 7:10-11)

The only kind of guilt that is useful and therefore "godly" is that guilt which prompts us to change (repent) and take the steps that lead to Real Love and genuine happiness.

When we indulge in excessive guilt, we're going through a process similar to that which we discussed on pages 177-8 (this is what we're saying to him or her with our anger) about our anger. When we wallow in guilt, we're saying this:

- I believe in the atonement of Christ, and that through Him all mankind may be forgiven of their sins.

- I even believe there's a possibility that the atonement might apply to me personally. Perhaps even *my* sins can be forgiven.

- If I do something really bad or embarrassing, though, the atonement of Christ isn't quite enough to take away my sins. When I'm really bad, Jesus' atonement is not enough for me to be forgiven.

- In order to satisfy the demands of *my* justice—in order to eliminate *my* guilt and shame—I have to suffer more, a lot more. My sins are extra bad, so I have to work through a special Supplemental Atonement of my own, and then maybe I'll be all right. Maybe.

In our shame, we demonstrate a strange kind of arrogance, denying the power of Christ's atonement and insisting on our own.

In the space below write the following:

- Christ died for the sins of all mankind.
- He died for my sins too—all of them.
- When I keep feeling guilty or ashamed, I deny Christ's atonement.
- I will accept the atonement and the wholeness I have been offered.

We need to begin to see our mistakes as inevitable in the process of learning and growing. I'm not advocating that we intentionally work at making mistakes, only that we not obsess over them.

TEN, 47:12 - 48:04   The Loss of Getting and Protecting Behaviors, and Repentance
CD Track Ten 2:33 - 3:25

As we understand Real Love—and the Getting and Protecting Behaviors that inevitably result from the lack of it—we finally gain the first shreds of power with which to eliminate the unproductive behaviors that have held us captive and caused us so much misery for a lifetime. What remains is a profound and lasting happiness. There is no greater accomplishment or way to live.

Understanding Getting and Protecting Behaviors also gives us an added perspective on the act of repentance, as I suggested on page 161. We have long known that repentance is an important part of our spiritual growth:

- The Lord says, I will judge each of you according to his ways, so repent and turn from all your transgressions, so wickedness will not be your ruin. (Ezekiel 18:30)

- Jesus said, The time is fulfilled, and the kingdom of God is at hand, so repent and believe the gospel. (Mark 1:15)

- So repent and be converted, that your sins may be erased. (Acts 3:19)

Unfortunately, repentance has often been associated with some very negative connotations. What does one repent of? Of evil, wickedness, sloth, sin, filth, and the like, so if we're considering the possibility that we might repent, we also pretty much have to admit that we're evil, wicked, slothful, sinful, and filthy, and most of us aren't eager to have those words tattooed on our foreheads. Little wonder that we'd rather schedule a colonoscopy without anesthesia than begin the process of repentance. And with that negative attitude, we usually take one of two approaches to repentance:

- We find it so daunting, so discouraging, that we don't even begin. If we're doomed to fail, why invest the wasted effort and experience the inevitable pain?
- We begin with a less-than-optimistic attitude, so when we hit our first several speed bumps, we interpret our stumblings as confirmation that we couldn't possibly succeed. Then we quit.

But what if we can completely change our perspective of repentance? What if we remember what we learned on page 160, that sins are just Getting and Protecting Behaviors? *Those* don't look quite as bad. Getting and Protecting Behaviors are just responses to emptiness and fear. Shoot, we can stomach the idea of doing something about *those*.

Now that we remember that sins *are* only Getting and Protecting Behaviors, we can completely exchange all the following words (and their associated stigmata):

- Evil
- Wickedness
- Sloth
- Sin
- Filth
- Guilt
- Shame

for concepts far more *productive*, such as:

- Seeing our emptiness and fear, conditions largely imposed upon us since childhood
- Understanding that our sins (our Getting and Protecting Behaviors) are largely a response to our emptiness and fear
- Learning how to fill our emptiness with Real Love, from one another and from God
- Accepting responsibility for change (or repentance)

That latter group doesn't seem nearly so scary, does it? Let me emphasize several things about this exchange:

- This is an *exchange in perspectives only*, or an *offer* of a different perspective of sin and repentance.
- *Both perspectives are true.* As an illustration of this particular point, I offer you two perspectives of an apple, which we'll refer to shortly:
  1. A high-pectin content, penti-carpeled, seed delivery system, containing anti-oxidants, various ferrous molecules, polyphenol oxidase, 25% air, ethylene, and amygdalin (which with hydrolysis is capable of producing hydrogen cyanide, the "gas" used in the "gas chamber" for human execution).
  2. A sweet, crisp, juicy fruit whose intoxicating taste, scent, and texture are capable of briefly making you forget the world around you, not to mention its ability to sustain life and—at the rate of one a day—keep the doctor away.

- Another perspective of sin and repentance is offered because we as human beings are generally frail, weak in faith, and susceptible to terminal discouragement when a task appears to be too difficult. If we can see something potentially discouraging in a different light, we will often tackle it with enthusiasm. As long as that "different light" (or perspective) is *still true*, then it is also quite useful isn't it? If it turns out, for example, that apples are good for your health, would it be better for me to offer them to you using the first or second description offered above? The same is true with sin and repentance. We need a way to see them in a way that encourages us to approach repentance, rather than feel discouraged and defeated.
- There is no denial here of anything God has ever said about our acts being evil, wicked, slothful, sinful, and filthy. All these terms are still true.

We have now demonstrated in just one way how an understanding of Getting and Protecting Behaviors—especially how they are related to sins—is an enormous asset in the process of repentance, primarily because this understanding makes repentance far more palatable and possible.

And it keeps getting better. An understanding of Getting and Protecting Behaviors also gives us an immediate understanding of *how* to repent. What a blessing that is, because for most of us the *how* has always been a source of great frustration in repentance. We've known that we *should* repent, but how is that done? We've know that we should give up our greed, lust, hatred, and so on, but how do you do that? Make a New Year's resolution? Make a promise that we *really* mean? We all know how well those work. Do we simply promise not to do bad things and have bad thoughts ever again? Who hasn't tried that and failed?

But look at what happens with an understanding of Real Love and Getting and Protecting Behaviors. We can flow through a sequence of thoughts like the following:

- Getting and Protecting Behaviors are sins.
- Getting and Protecting Behaviors (and therefore sins) are a response to emptiness and fear.
- Emptiness and fear result from a lack of Real Love in our lives.
- It is painfully obvious, then, that with enough Real Love we can eliminate emptiness and fear.
- As emptiness and fear are eliminated we simply lose our *need* for Getting and Protecting Behaviors, as well as for sins.
- Real Love therefore eliminates Getting and Protecting Behaviors.
- Real Love is the greatest power for eliminating sin.
- In the process of repentance, Real Love—from one another and from God—is our greatest tool.
- In repentance, self-control is also very important (more about this shortly).

With the perspective of sins being Getting and Protecting Behaviors, therefore, we can have both a freedom of mind *and* the actual means for repentance. What a gift. Whereas repentance has often been a great drudgery for many of us, we can now see it as a great potential joy. As Paul said to the Galatians,

> The deeds of the flesh are obvious: adultery, sexual sins, uncleanness, indecency, idolatry, witchcraft, hatred, contention, jealousy, anger, conspiracies, heresies, envyings, murders, drunkenness, partyings, and so on. And those who do such things shall not inherit the kingdom of God. But the fruit of the Spirit is love, joy, peace, patience, gentleness, goodness, faith, kindness, and self control. There is no law against those qualities. (Galatians 5:19-23)

Paul is encouraging us to lay aside the burden of our anger, jealousy, and other Getting and Protecting Behaviors, and to take upon ourselves instead the lightness of love and joy. Not a bad exchange, and we can facilitate that exchange in part as we trade the concept of sin for the concept of Getting and Protecting Behaviors.

The Interacting Effects of Real Love and Self-Control

Earlier in the seminar on pages 137-8, I made the point that having sufficient Real Love is like having twenty million dollars with you all the time. And then, when people are inconsiderate, when they fail to do what we want, and even when they attack us, they're only taking two dollars, which we can easily afford to lose. When we feel unconditionally loved, every inconvenience becomes relatively insignificant. We lose our *need* to respond with Getting and Protecting Behaviors. We relatively lose our need to sin.

How we react to other people is largely determined by how unconditionally loved *we* feel and not by *their* behavior. Without Real Love, we're starving to death and down to our last two dollars. In that condition, we're limited in our ability to remain happy and loving—and sinless—when a thief steals our money. Children who are raised without unconditional love can only be *severely* affected as they attempt to find happiness in the absence of the most essential ingredient for emotional and spiritual health. If that lack of Real Love is not corrected, a child will then become an adult who feels empty and afraid, and who will respond to others with Getting and Protecting Behaviors—and sin.

But is there more to us than our past experience? If you've received no Real Love as a child, does that mean you are absolutely doomed to use nothing but Getting and Protecting Behaviors as you interact with other people all your life? No. We're not sticks and stones, which can only be acted upon. We always have a measure of self-control we can choose to exercise. Even when we don't feel sufficiently loved, *to some extent* we can still choose to withhold our Getting and Protecting Behaviors and make efforts to be loving. I re-emphasize, however, that our ability to choose is greatly affected by the Real Love we have. Most people raised without Real Love simply cannot choose to be as loving as those who *have* been loved unconditionally, anymore than a starving man can choose to run as fast as a healthy one.

As I say in Chapter Two of the book *Real Love*, for years I found it very difficult to split oak logs with an ax. And then I discovered a maul, a tool that enabled me to split oak quite easily. I initially made a *choice* to split logs with an ax—no one *made* me use it. It was the best choice *I could see* at the time—better than a shovel or my bare hands. A maul would have worked much better, but I didn't know it existed. After learning about it, I was able to make a better choice.

In a similar way, we always have choices about how we feel and behave, but if we don't have experience with Real Love, Getting and Protecting Behaviors—sins—may be the only choices *we can see* in a given situation. And even after Real Love—or repentance—has been described to us, we may *see* it as a choice but still be incapable of *making* the loving choice, because we don't actually have the love to give. As we find Real Love and feel it, we're better able to make new choices—loving, happy choices. We're better able to repent.

Although I stress that a lack of Real Love causes the emptiness and fear that lead to our Getting and Protecting Behaviors, I intend that to be an *explanation* for our behaviors, not an *excuse* for continuing them. Even when we feel unloved and unhappy, it is always *our* responsibility to learn what we can do to change our choices, and as we make wiser choices we will find the love and happiness we seek.

I share with you here a story of unknown origin that illustrates the role of self-control in the elimination of Getting and Protecting Behaviors as we take the path toward Real Love:

One evening an old Cherokee told his grandson about a battle that goes on inside people. He said, "My son, the battle is between two wolves inside us all. One is Evil. It is anger, envy, jealousy, sorrow, regret, greed, arrogance, self-pity, guilt, resentment, inferiority, lies, false pride, superiority, and ego. The other is Good. It is joy, peace, love, hope, serenity, humility, kindness, benevolence, empathy, generosity, truth, compassion and faith".

The grandson thought about it for a minute and then asked his grandfather, "Which wolf wins?"

The old Cherokee simply replied, "The one you feed."

At this point, many people ask, With each decision we make, what is the relative influence of self-control compared with the amount of Real Love we feel? Exactly how strong is our ability to simply *choose* a loving behavior even when we've experienced relatively little Real Love? To what degree can our will power overcome the obviously crippling effects of insufficient Real Love?

I don't know anyone who can answer these questions with any certainty, and even if they could, the answer wouldn't change the fact that we can—and must—do all we can to increase *both* our self-control and the Real Love we have. Both factors operate in a synergistic way—they support and nourish one another and create an effect much greater than either could do alone. We can exercise self-control and make a conscious choice to tell the truth about ourselves instead of using our familiar Getting and Protecting Behaviors. That choice creates the opportunity for us to feel more unconditionally loved. With Real Love, in turn, we have less *need* to use Getting and Protecting Behaviors and can more easily make conscious decisions to be more loving instead. As we make decisions (self-control) to love other people even when we don't feel completely loved, we experience the miracle of feeling more Real Love ourselves (to be explained later in the seminar).

Other than Real Love and self-control, there are other factors that contribute to our behavior. Certainly genetics plays a role, but how much? And what is the effect of other inborn qualities we don't fully understand—in the spiritual realm, for example? I haven't addressed these issues simply because they make no practical difference to us. Although the questions are fascinating and provide stimulating conversation, the answers wouldn't change the fact that at this point we can't alter our genetic structure, nor can we control what other characteristics we'll be born with. So regardless of the answers to all these interesting questions, our approach to altering our feelings and behavior remains the same: tell the truth about ourselves (more about this later in the seminar), find Real Love, share it with others, and exercise self-control as we make decisions to be loving instead of using Getting and Protecting Behaviors.

Giving Up Getting and Protecting Behaviors: Being Reborn

Despite the enormous advantages we've described thus far for abandoning our Getting and Protecting Behaviors, many of us are still quite attached to them. We've been using them for so long that they've become like old friends. We're comfortable with them. We can hardly imagine life without them. We're certain that if we didn't diligently protect ourselves on a continuous basis, we'd feel naked and intolerably vulnerable.

One day I was talking to a woman who had been angry and controlling and "right" all her life. As I described what it would be like to give up Getting and Protecting Behaviors, she finally screamed—literally—"But you're suggesting that I give up who I am!!"

"What a shame that would be," I responded. "Right now you're angry, alone, and miserable. Almost everyone in your life hates being around you, and you're in constant conflict with them. What a shame it would be to give all that up."

Her life was a wreck, but it was a familiar wreck, and the thought of changing it to something unknown—something she might have even less control over—was understandably terrifying to her.

In truth, when we give up our Getting and Protecting Behaviors, we don't give up who we are. We actually *find out* who we are. Getting and Protecting Behaviors are just *reactions* to emptiness and fear. They're not who we *are*. To illustrate this, imagine that when I first meet you I immediately begin slapping you in the face, and you respond by running away. Would it be fair for me to summarize who you are solely on the basis of your running? Of course not. It's not until we eliminate your fear and protecting behavior that I could learn who you really are.

Most of us have been responding to emptiness and fear our whole lives, and for that reason we really don't know who we are. I have received hundreds of communications similar to this e-mail:

When I watched *The Essentials of Real Love* video, I realized that I've been empty and afraid my whole life, and I've used Getting and Protecting Behaviors almost constantly. It's been an endless round of trying to protect myself, control other people, and find enough Imitation Love, and I was exhausted. Now that I'm understanding myself and other people, and now that I'm finding Real Love, I don't need Getting and Protecting Behaviors as much, and as those are going away I'm discovering who I really am. I like what I'm seeing.

As our lives are changed through the power of love and the Spirit, not only do we discover who we really are, but we are reborn. The Bible describes the sequence nicely:

- It is through love that we are reborn unto God. "Let us love one another, because love is of God, and every one who loves is born of God, and knows God. Whoever doesn't love God can't know God, because God is love." (1 John 4:7-8) Of course, this is entirely compatible with other verses on the subject of rebirth. In John 3:5 we read of the necessity of being born of the Spirit, and in Galatians 5:19-23 we read that love is a fruit of the Spirit.

- When we are sufficiently changed by love and the Spirit— when we are reborn—we lose our need to use Getting and Protecting Behaviors (to sin). "Whoever is born of God doesn't commit sin; for the nature of God stays in him: and he cannot sin, because he is born of God." (1 John 3:9) Also, "Whoever is born of God overcomes the world." (1 John 5:4)

As we lose our Getting and Protecting Behaviors—as we lose our desires to sin and are reborn—we experience profound changes in our lives. As Paul taught:

- If any man lives in Christ, he becomes a new creature. In Christ old things die and everything becomes new. (2 Corinthians 5:17)

- Now put aside all these: anger, rage, ill will, evil speaking, and filthy talk. Don't lie to one another, seeing that ye have gotten rid of your old self with his old actions and *have become a new person,* who is made new in knowledge after the image of him that created him. (Colossians 3:8-10)

Describe below what your life and your relationships would be like without emptiness and fear, without Getting and Protecting Behaviors. Can you even imagine it? What are you willing to do to achieve that condition?

CHAPTER ELEVEN
Event → Judgment → Feeling → Reaction

ELEVEN, 48:04 - 49:08 "You Make Me So Angry"
CD Track Eleven, 0:00 - 1:05

What an incredible irony it is that we hate being controlled by other people, and yet the instant we claim that someone "makes us angry," that person *owns* us—and *we* gave him or her the title to our soul.

Paul wrote, "The servant of the Lord must not be quarrelsome, but be kind to everyone, skillful as a teacher, willing to suffer offenses, kind in teaching those who oppose him, because God may give them a change of heart to a full knowledge of the truth, that they may wake up and escape the trap of the devil, having been taken captive by him to do his will." (2 Timothy 2:24-26) So many of us are captive to the devil and his ways, but it's always a captivity that we have agreed to. Notice that Paul says we may escape our chains simply by "waking up," which is accomplished by coming to a "full knowledge of the truth." One of those truths is an understanding that other people never make us angry, a subject we discussed on pages 137-8.

In the space below and on the next page describe a relationship where you have felt that someone made you angry. Can you see that:

- by *believing* that he made you angry, you actually did give him the power to make you angry? It was your choice.
- you *made* him a very influential person in your life? Again your choice.
- you were then a slave to the choices made by him?

Do you like being a slave? Wouldn't you prefer to make your own decisions about how you feel and behave?

ELEVEN, 49:08 - 52:17   It's All about the Judgment
CD Track Eleven 1:05 - 4:14

Event

↓

Judgment

↓

Feeling

↓

Reaction

Let's be clear on definitions before we discuss each of the elements in this progression.

Event: This is what happens to us and around us. Events include what people do and the physical events that occur around us (weather, traffic, and so on).

Judgment: The meaning we apply to an event—how we *judge* that the event will affect us.

Feeling: The emotions we experience after judging the
                    meaning of an event. Our feelings can have many
                    names, but they usually boil down to emptiness,
                    fear, or happiness.

Reaction: How we respond to an event, usually a choice
                    between loving or a combination of the Getting and
                    Protecting Behaviors.

From the story of the spider and the pretty red box with the
letter "S," we can see that our behavior is not caused by events but
is determined by our judgments of events. When we understand how
these elements interact (Event → Judgment → Feeling → Reaction),
we can change the way we feel about everything, because then we
realize that we can *choose* the way we respond to events.

ELEVEN, 52:17 - 54:17 The Folly of Changing Feelings and Behavior
CD Track Eleven 4:14 - 6:12

We've always known that ideally we should be loving all the time.
We've known that returning anger for anger is wrong, and that when
we have ugly feelings, we should repent of them. For example:

> Blessed are those who are persecuted for doing the right thing,
> for the kingdom of heaven is theirs. You are blessed when people
> speak abusively to you, and persecute you, and speak badly about
> you falsely, for my sake. Be exceedingly happy, for your reward
> in the kingdom of heaven is great. They persecuted the prophets
> before you in the same way. (Matthew 5:10-12)

In this passage it's plain that when people treat us abusively, it
is preferred that we feel blessed and happy, not angry and vengeful.
But how do we do that? When someone has just spit on you—
figuratively or literally—how do you decide to be "exceedingly
happy?" We've all experienced the frustration of trying to change
the way we feel and behave in situations like that.

In the space below describe some situations or relationships where you have tried to change your feelings or behavior without changing your judgments. Possible examples:

- I know I shouldn't hate my mother-in-law—hate just isn't an admirable quality—but no matter what I try, I still hate the woman. She's been nothing but trouble to me and to my family.
- When I was a child, sometimes my parents would say, "Stop crying." I remember that those were very difficult occasions. I couldn't just stop feeling the way I did.
- I'm afraid of my boss. I've tried meditations. I've tried communication techniques. I've tried affirmations like, "I will not be afraid of him. I am a strong person who isn't afraid of anybody." But I'm still afraid of him.
- I made a New Year's resolution to control my temper, but that didn't last a whole day.
- My wife has nagged me to be more loving. I've tried doing some loving things—even read a book about random loving acts to do—but it just doesn't last.
- I've tried to quit smoking for years, but I've failed every time.

It can be very frustrating to put our best efforts into changing how we feel and how we behave, only to fail again and again. What a relief it can be to realize that there's another way—a way that's easier and more effective.

ELEVEN, 54:17 - 55:39   The Judgments We Make
CD Track Eleven 6:12 - 7:40

The judgments that affect our feelings and behavior most strongly are those we make about how any given event will affect *us* personally. If we judge that an event will hurt us, fear follows immediately and involuntarily, and from that feeling there follows a cascade of Protecting Behaviors.

In the space below and on the next page, describe a couple of interactions that went badly for you. Then describe how your judgment played a pivotal role in them. Following are a couple of examples to give you an idea about how your answers might look:

Event:	My boyfriend was irritated at me.
Judgment:	He didn't love me.
Feeling:	Fear
Reaction:	At first I yelled at him (attack), which made me feel stronger and less helpless, but then I withdrew and sulked (ran).

Event:	My wife was making us late for a party we were going to.
Judgment:	She didn't care enough about me (love me) to get ready on time, which she knew was important to me.
Feeling:	Emptiness and fear
Reaction:	Anger, criticism (attack).

Event:

Judgment:

Feeling:

Reaction:

Event:

Judgment:

Feeling:

Reaction:

ELEVEN, 55:39 - 56:46   Controlling Events
CD Track Eleven, 7:40 - 8:46

Controlling events and people is very tempting, as we discussed on pages 139-40. But controlling events is very difficult and quite unproductive, so why keep trying to do that?

In the space below, describe some situations or relationships where you tried to control events.

- How did it work out?
- With all you've learned so far, now do you see *why* it didn't work to control people or events?
- What would you do differently in the future?

To help you understand the above exercise—and the attendant principle—even better, let me discuss one example of someone doing the exercise (a woman talking about trying to control events, in this case her husband):

- For years I've tried to get my husband to spend more time with me and to be more tender toward me.
- I did not understand the process of Event → Judgment → Feeling → Reaction.
- Now I can see what has been really happening:

  Event: My husband has been spending less time with me than I'd like.

  Judgment: He doesn't love me. He refuses to spend time with me. He'll never love me.

  Feeling: Emptiness and fear

  Reaction: Clinging, attacking, acting like a victim

- I've tried changing the event—by manipulating him with anger, guilt, and so on to spend more time with me—but that has never worked, because when I try to control him he just feels more empty and afraid. Then he wants to spend even *less* time with me.
- I've tried changing my feelings, by just being more positive about the whole situation. Failure.
- I've tried changing my reaction—being nice to him instead of being angry and clinging—but as long as I felt empty and afraid I could only react badly toward him.
- But I can change my judgments. How? By examining whether each of them is true. So let's look at them:
    1. He doesn't love me: True. While he's withdrawing from me, he's protecting *himself* and is not unconditionally loving *me*.
    2. He refuses to spend time with me and care about me. False. It's not that he *refuses* to care about me. He just *can't*. He's empty and afraid—just as I am—and in that condition he simply has nothing to give me.
    3. He'll never love me:

       (A) Not necessarily true. As I learn more about Real Love, and as I bring that back to our marriage, he may feel loved enough that he can let go of his Getting and Protecting Behaviors and participate in a mutually loving relationship with me.

(B) Irrelevant. Even if he doesn't learn how to love me, my real fear is that I'll never feel loved at all, by anyone. But I *can* learn how to find Real Love. If he isn't capable of unconditionally loving me right now, that's not a problem. I'll get loved by other people. (More about that in Module Three)

- As I begin to see that my judgments were mostly false, everything else changes. He's not intentionally withdrawing from me, so how can I be angry at him when he's doing the best he can do? And I see that his withdrawing doesn't mean I'll never feel loved, so I don't feel as desperate. When my judgments change, I don't feel nearly as afraid, and now I lose my need to be angry at him or cling to him.

**ELEVEN, 56:46 - 58:09   Controlling Feelings and
    Reactions
    CD Track Eleven, 8:46 - 10:05**

With a judgment that we won't feel loved—accompanied by emptiness and fear—fear is inevitable, and then Getting and Protecting Behaviors are automatic. If we want to change our feelings and reactions, we must change the judgments. Fortunately, we *can* learn to do that.

CHAPTER TWELVE
Changing Our Judgments

**TWELVE, 58:09 - 59:18   Where We Learn Our Judgments
    CD Track Twelve, 0:00 - 1:12**

A judgment is an *assessment* we make about a situation. When we make a judgment, we apply a *meaning* to events. We don't make up our judgments out of thin air. We acquire them from past experience—we are taught them—a process that usually began very long ago.

In Diane's case—the story from the seminar of the woman whose husband had said something unkind, starting at 55:00 in the video recording of this module and at 6:56 of Track Eleven of the audio recording—she had seen from the time she was a small child that when she made mistakes, the people around her frowned, sighed with exasperation, spoke harsh words, and so on. She learned that if she made mistakes, people would become angry and not love her— which was very painful. She saw that pattern confirmed many times in adulthood too, so whenever she made mistakes, or whenever people became irritated, she immediately made the judgment that she would be hurt, which was followed by fear and her use of Protecting Behaviors.

In the space below and on the next page describe some judgments that you acquired as a child, judgments that have continued to affect you as an adult. Examples:

- I learned that in order for other people to like me, I had to do what they wanted.
- If I don't do what other people want, they will *withdraw* their approval from me.
- When people withdraw their approval, I feel empty and afraid, and that is painful.
- When people are angry, they hurt me.
- When people cling to me, they want something for themselves, and then I don't feel loved.
- When people act like victims, they're manipulating me for something, so I feel pressured to take care of them, not loved.

We learned these judgments from thousands of experiences, and in most cases our judgments were *accurate*. Again, we didn't make them up. We distilled them from many events. When Diane concluded that if she made mistakes, people would be angry at her and not love her, she was *right*.

Regrettably, she generalized from this accurate judgment to another judgment that was *not* correct, and we'll discuss that in the next section.

TWELVE, 59:18 - 1:00:14   The Two Judgments We Fear
CD Track Twelve, 1:12 - 2:06

Most of us—including Diane, above—have had many unloving experiences. We have seen that when we make mistakes and when we don't do what other people want, they withdraw their love from us, and then we feel empty and afraid.

When we have had enough experiences with people loving us conditionally, eventually it's natural that we would make the judgment that *no one* will *ever* love us unconditionally. It's this second judgment that is especially frightening. Let me illustrate this with a story:

As a child I lived in a neighborhood where it seemed that all the dogs were vicious. From consistent experience, I learned that when I heard a dog bark, I was about to be chased or bitten. I learned the judgment that all the dogs in my neighborhood would bite me and that barking meant danger. Were those accurate judgments? Yes, and they enabled me on many occasions to run, climb a tree, or grab a stick before I was bitten. Many times my judgments saved me.

Years later, as a young adult long removed from my old neighborhood, I still became afraid when I heard a dog bark. Why? Because the dogs were dangerous in the present? No, I had no evidence to support my belief that the dogs around me would bite. I was afraid because I had generalized my judgment from "All the dogs in my neighborhood will bite" to "All dogs bite." Where did that judgment come from? From past experience.

Almost all of us are carrying the burden of judgments that (1) may have been accurate at the time they were made from past experiences but (2) are now inappropriate and harmful. Diane, for example, correctly judged that the people in her life as a child would not love her if she were flawed. And her husband confirmed that judgment with *his* behavior. But then she went a step further and judged that she would never feel loved—by *anyone*. That's a natural conclusion for someone who has never seen Real Love, but it's a false and harmful judgment.

It's a false judgment because there *are* loving people out there, and Diane simply needed to be taught how to find them. It's a harmful judgment because it kept Diane feeling empty and afraid. These feelings in turn led her to protect herself all the time and to push people away who might try to love her. Feeling afraid and defensive, she was unable to really enjoy her association with anyone, much as I in young adulthood was unable to enjoy the association of dogs, even though there were many that were delightful.

In the space below discuss a couple of occasions or relationships where you have become anxious or angry. As you know, our emptiness and fear are a result of a lifetime of unloving experiences, not just the behavior of any single person in a given moment. Can you now recognize that when you have become anxious or angry, you were reacting to a belief that a lifetime pattern of conditional love would continue, and that you would never get the Real Love you want?

In fact, *any time we become upset, we are declaring that the only love in the world is that piece that is being withheld from us in that moment.* We show no faith in the love that is available.

So how could we change the kind of false and harmful judgment that Diane was making, a judgment that nearly all of us have made at times? That's the subject of the next several sections.

TWELVE, 1:00:14 - 1:01:17 Recognizing Our Judgments
CD Track Twelve, 2:06 - 3:09

As Diane talked to me about her interaction with her husband, Ken, we explored her judgments. Her first judgment was that Ken didn't love her. Was that true? *Yes*, at least while he was angry, he was *not* loving her. But what was really upsetting her was the judgment that if she couldn't get loved by Ken, she would *never* be loved. That judgment was false.

I explained to Diane that there were many people in the world capable of loving her, and that her happiness was not dependent on being loved by any *one person*, including Ken. Real Love from any source is healing, and Diane needed to know that it was available to her, even though Ken may not have been able to love her as she wished.

Identifying these judgments is important, because it frees us from old prisons. Diane, for example, had always been captive to the unconscious notion—her judgment—that she had to be loved by Ken, or she couldn't be happy. Once she identified that judgment, she could see that it wasn't true and could begin to focus on getting love from other sources, in addition to her husband. It gave her a tremendous freedom.

Discuss below and on the next page some past situations or relationships where you felt especially hurt when you weren't being loved by a particular person. Now can you identify that you were making a judgment that if you couldn't be loved by that person, you would never feel loved? When you see that this judgment is false, do you feel a sense of freedom from your chains to that person?

TWELVE, 1:01:17 - 1:01:53   We Always Have a Choice
**   CD Track Twelve, 3:09 - 3:44**

Discuss some occasions when you have said—to yourself or out loud—"I just don't have a choice" or "I feel so trapped."

We always have a choice. No matter what is going on around us, we can always choose to learn more about Real Love and be more loving, instead of reacting blindly with Getting and Protecting Behaviors.

In our defense, when we know nothing about Real Love, we don't even *see* that being loving is a choice. Getting Imitation Love and protecting ourselves are often the only choices we can see, and that's why it's so important to become immersed in an education about Real Love. The more we learn, the more choices become available to us and the more clearly we are able to see them.

On one occasion Jesus said, "O you people of Jerusalem, who kill the prophets I have sent to you, how often I have tried to gather you together as a hen gathers her children under her wings, but ye would not come." (Luke 13:34) We might ask ourselves, how could a young chick resist the warmth and safety waiting under his mother's wing? Similarly, how could the people of Jerusalem not have responded to the call of the Savior of the world to enjoy the blessings He offered? Because they didn't *recognize* the choice they were being offered. In their emptiness and fear, they could see only Imitation Love and Getting and Protecting Behaviors as their choices.

And we fail to choose to be loving for the same reason. Emptiness and fear—as well as plain ignorance—blind us to the wiser choices. It should be our goal then to increase our knowledge of Real Love and to fill our lives with it, thereby removing both causes of our blindness and greatly increasing our chances of making the choices that will lead to the happiness we seek.

TWELVE, 1:01:53 - 1:02:42 Learning to See Others Clearly
CD Track Twelve, 3:44 - 4:34

As I shared the story of the drowning man with Diane, she finally lit up and said, "Oh my, he's just drowning, isn't he?" (She was referring to her husband.)

The moment she realized that, her judgment that he could hurt her with his anger disappeared. How can we feel hurt or offended by a drowning man? He's not drowning *to us*. He just needs help.

Discuss some situations and relationships where you have felt hurt or offended or angered by the behavior of a partner. Can you now see that person as drowning? And when you do, does that change your feelings toward him or her?

You can see, then, that there is great power in making correct judgments. Regrettably, on the subject of making judgments, we commonly hear the following verse quoted:

> Don't judge others, so you won't be judged yourself. Because you will be judged in the same way you judge others. (Matthew 7:1-2)

We tend to interpret this verse as saying that we should make no judgments at all, but it should be obvious that that makes no sense, because *wise* judgment is necessary to wise living. We *must* judge the behavior of others, or we can't wisely respond to them. We can look to other verses to give us guidance about judgment:

- Don't be unrighteous in your judgment, but judge your neighbor in righteousness. (Leviticus 19:15)

- Don't judge according to superficial appearances, but judge righteous judgment. (John 7:24)

TWELVE, 1:02:42 - 1:03:39   Changing Judgments with Real Love
CD Track Twelve, 4:34 - 5:31

So far we've talked a lot about *intellectual* ways of changing our judgments. As we learn to see ourselves and others clearly—through the lens of the truth and Real Love instead of the distorting lens of emptiness and fear—our feelings change, as do our behaviors.

If we're sufficiently empty and afraid, however, an intellectual tool alone is often not enough. We need to eliminate our emptiness and fear with Real Love, after which we can see everything more clearly and respond more productively. To use a familiar metaphor, when we have twenty million dollars, the loss of two dollars seems insignificant and we can then choose from a number of responses.

Let me continue with the story I began on page 203 about the barking dogs:

> As a young adult I knew intellectually that it was unlikely that all dogs would bite, but my past experiences with dogs had been so memorable that I was still unable to shake my old judgment that they would. I began to spend time with a friend, Bill, however, who had several dogs that were absolutely delightful.
>
> As I spent time with Bill's dogs, my judgment that all dogs would bite was changed. Just as past experience had created the old judgment, so had new experiences in the present changed that judgment.

Our judgments really can change with new and consistent experience. Diane demonstrated this as she took the steps to find Real Love—discussed in Module Three—and as she felt loved by a number of people in her life. She realized that there *are* people who can love, and as a result she became far less demanding toward Ken. She also began to trust people more. When we have twenty million dollars, we're not nearly as afraid of losing two dollars, and then we're far less protective of what we have.

TWELVE, 1:03:39 - 1:05:52   Changing Everything with Real Love
CD Track Twelve, 5:31 - 7:44

People behave badly only because they don't feel loved. So, what if you gave them what they needed? What if you loved them? What if you reached your hand out to them while they were drowning? Would that change their behavior?

I can tell you that Real Love doesn't always have an immediate effect, but it is *the* most powerful force in human relationships. You can't really know what a relationship can be until you've tried it.

I have seen thousands of relationships change in dramatic ways, and those changes did not always require the participation of both partners. If *one* person in a relationship is willing to introduce the effects of Real Love, the changes can be miraculous. Look on pages 153-4 at just the first six steps of a vicious cycle that continued for days. Now let's suppose we can go back in time and see how Real Love could have changed that pattern:

The first step is the same: Cynthia says, "The kids have a ton of homework to do tonight, and I'm not getting any help from you." This is an attack. She is clearly saying, "I don't love you," because she is angry and focusing only on *herself*. But she is empty and afraid, and she's also saying, "I need some help. Please help me and love me."

In this new scenario, John is a different person. He has previously engaged in the process of finding Real Love, so that when Cynthia attacks him, he isn't already empty and afraid, which is the second step in the destructive process on page 153. In this new sequence, he sees that Cynthia's attacking is just the thrashing of a drowning woman, and he responds by reaching his hand out to help her out of the water. He says, "What can I do?"

The conflict is over. John continues to love Cynthia with more and more Real Love, and as he does so, he helps her out of the water. She's not drowning anymore. Without emptiness and fear, her *need* for Getting and Protecting Behaviors simply disappears, and she quits attacking him.

When people are no longer drowning, they have no *reason* to thrash around. They change the way they behave toward us. When people experience enough Real Love, the changes in them can be rather dramatic. It is of such people that Jesus spoke when he said, "Whoever drinks of the water that I give him shall never thirst, but the water that I give him shall become a well of water in him springing up into everlasting life." (John 4:7-14)

Describe below a recent conflict you had with someone. Imagine how the interaction *would* have happened if either of you had reached out to the other in a compassionate, loving way. How could the conflict possibly have continued? In most cases, it doesn't. In the following modules, we'll talk about how to find and share Real Love.

CHAPTER THIRTEEN
Loving, Happiness, and Old Wounds

THIRTEEN, 1:05:52 - 1:06:47   The Power of Loving
CD Track Thirteen, 0:00 - 0:55

As you learn to unconditionally love the people around you, you'll be giving them what they've needed and wanted all their lives, so the effect on them is often powerful. In some cases, however, people have been so damaged that they just can't feel Real Love. Whether they can or not, however, *you* will always be happier as a result of being loving, because you will be filled with "the peace of God, which is beyond all understanding, which will keep your hearts and minds through Christ Jesus." (Philippians 4:7)

THIRTEEN, 1:06:47 - 1:08:27   The Primary Wound
CD Track Thirteen, 0:55 - 2:34

In our society, we tend to classify people—and they identify themselves—according to the wounds they've received. We organize support groups, marches, benefit dinners, and national political organizations devoted to the causes of people who have been injured because they are:

- gay.
- black.
- poor.
- short.
- survivors of incest.
- children of alcoholic parents.
- native Americans.
- women.

As we focus on these differences, however, we're losing track of the worst wound any of us could suffer, which is not feeling unconditionally loved. After interviewing thousands of people, I have seen that it doesn't matter *why* other people don't love us or *how* they delivered the message. What matters is the central wound: not feeling loved.

God has made it plain that love should be absolutely central in our lives:

- There are three things that last: faith, hope, and love, but the greatest of these is love. (1 Corinthians 13:13)

- Let everything you do be done with love. (1 Corinthians 16:14)

- Above all else be loving, which ties everything together perfectly. (Colossians 3:14)

And yet most of us have been deprived of this essential element. How could we suppose that the effects would not be far-reaching?

In the space below and on the next page describe some of the painful moments in your life:

- Abandonment
- Betrayal by a partner
- Harsh criticism
- Mockery
- Failure
- Infidelity
- Sexual abuse or injury
- Physical abuse
- Death
- Divorce
- Lawsuits

And be as specific as you can about these experiences.

Can you see how at the heart of all of these injuries is the message that you were not or are not loved? Now imagine that on each of these occasions, you had been surrounded by people who loved you unconditionally, as you experienced in the meditation of Module One. Would the pain of the events have been diminished?

We also must see that we are not what was done *to* us. What was done to us is a description of *other people*, not *us*.

CHAPTER FOURTEEN
Example of Changing Getting and Protecting Behaviors

FOURTEEN, 1:08:27 - 1:14:52 Changing Our Lives
CD Track Fourteen, 0:00 - 5:19

Notice that in the two examples discussed—a boss and a spouse—loving was very simple. There was no clinical analysis, little to no talking, just direct and gentle compassion. In the case of my boss, I just asked what I could do to help. The example of the spouse involved just a simple touch.

A drowning man often doesn't need a kiss or hug or verbal expression of "I love you." He just needs a hand to help him out of the water, as I did with my boss. We can all learn to love like that, and miracles will routinely follow our efforts. Love really does melt away Getting and Protecting Behaviors. Love melts monsters.

There are so many ways we can love, and we need to practice as many of them as possible, so they become natural to us. The Bible discusses many of them:

- Do all things without complaining and quarreling, that you may be blameless and harmless, the sons of God, without blame, in the middle of a twisted and foolish world, among whom you shine as lights. (Philippians 2:14-15)

- Be kind to one another in brotherly love, showing honor to one another over yourselves. Don't be lazy in your work but on fire with the spirit, serving the Lord, rejoicing in hope, patient in affliction, continuing steadfastly in prayer, giving what you have for the needs of the saints, showing hospitality. Bless those who persecute you rather than curse. Rejoice with those who rejoice and weep with those who weep. Treat one another as equals. Don't be ambitious, but associate with those who are humble. Don't be self-important. Don't return evil for evil. Be honest with all men. As much as you can, live peacefully with all men. Dearly beloved, don't seek revenge, but leave anger alone, for it is written that God has said, Vengeance is mine, and I will repay. So if your enemy is hungry, feed him; if he is thirsty, give him a drink; because when you do that, he will feel the fire of shame on his head. Don't let evil overcome you, but overcome evil with goodness. (Romans 12:10-21)

- So let us pursue whatever contributes to peace and things that will build one another up. (Romans 14:19)

- Those of us who are strong should bear the failings of those who are weak and not just try to have our own way. Let all of us please his neighbor for the sake of his good and to build him up. (Romans 15:1-2)

- Do not allow foul speech to come from your mouth, but speak what is good for the purpose of building up, that it may bless those who hear. And don't offend the holy Spirit of God, which seals you unto the day of redemption. Let all bitterness, and rage, and anger, and fighting, and evil speaking, and evil intent be banished from you. And be kind to one another, tenderhearted, forgiving one another, even as God has forgiven you for Christ's sake. (Ephesians 4:29-32)

- As the chosen of God, holy and beloved, clothe yourselves with tenderness of heart, kindness, humility, gentleness, patience, and forgiving one another. If any of you have a quarrel with another, forgive him, even as Christ forgave you. (Colossians 3:12-13)

- Comfort one another and build one another up, as you are doing. (1 Thessalonians 5:11)

- We urge you, brethren, warn those who are disorderly, comfort the fainthearted, support the weak, be patient toward all *men.* See that no one pays back wrong for wrong to anyone, but always follows that which is good, both among yourselves, and to all men. (1 Thessalonians 5:14-15)

- Lift up the weary hands and the weak knees, and walk rightly, so that those who are crippled will not be turned away. But instead administer healing and live peacefully and in holiness with all men, without which no man shall see the Lord: Looking carefully so that no man fails to partake of the grace of God, so that no root of bitterness will spring up to trouble you and thereby poison many. (Hebrews 12:12-15)

Perhaps getting hints from the verses above, or getting clues from the list below, in the space below and on the next page write down some loving things you could do for several people in your life with whom you have experienced some contention or cause for offense. These might include (but certainly would not be limited to):

- Send a card for birthday, Easter, anniversary, or other special occasion.
- Inquire about recuperation from an illness.
- Ask about the welfare of that person's family.
- Call for no reason to ask about his or her day, or what's been going on lately.
- Take over a small vase of wildflowers.
- Take a plate of simple desserts you have made yourself.
- Ask him or her over for coffee or other brief occasion.
- Apologize for past mistakes.
- Call to express gratitude for something he or she has done, even if it's been some time since the event took place.
- Next time you see this person, look him directly in the eye and express pleasure at seeing him.
- Send an e-mail that contains a piece of the Internet humor that often floats around.
- E-mail a digital picture of you and an accompanying heading, "Thinking of you."

CHAPTER FIFTEEN
Module Summary

FIFTEEN, 1:14:52 - 1:16:30   Module Summary

MODULE THREE

CHAPTER ONE

Eliminating Getting and Protecting Behaviors
Truth → Seen → Accepted→ Loved

ONE, 0:00 - 1:47   The Intellectual Approach
  CD Track One, 0:00 - 0:47

Many of us have been trapped in the same old patterns of behavior for a lifetime. How can we change those patterns? One way involves a simple change in understanding, which we discussed in Module Two. When we *see* things differently, we immediately have the ability to *behave* differently. Remember on pages 165-7 what happened when you saw the man in the pool differently—when you saw that he was drowning versus intentionally trying to irritate you. That single moment of insight completely changed how you felt and behaved toward him.

ONE, 1:47 - 2:36   Getting out of the Pool with Real Love
  CD Track One, 1:47 - 2:36

On many occasions, however, understanding alone may not be enough. You may realize, for example, that people are behaving badly toward you only because they're empty and afraid—because they're drowning—but if you're empty and afraid too—if you are also drowning—you may need much more than an intellectual understanding. You may also need some help actually getting out of the water. That's why this module is so important: It will teach you how you can consistently get out of the pool and stay out.

To use the metaphor that Jesus chose, each of us builds the house where we'll live emotionally and spiritually in this life and in the life to come. The rains will come down upon all of us, and the winds will blow against us, and the floods will rise, and when those calamities arrive it will not be enough just to have the intellectual insight that our houses need a firm foundation. No, when the rains come and the winds blow, if we haven't already built our house upon the rock, our houses will fall, and great will be the fall thereof (Matthew 7:24-7; Luke 6:47-49).

ONE, 2:36 - 3:34   Truth → Seen → Accepted→ Loved
CD Track One, 2:36 - 3:34

In Chapter Two of Module Two, I introduced the above sequence. As I tell you the truth about myself, you can now see who I really am. This creates the *opportunity* for you to accept me for who I really am—unconditionally—and to love me.

So what? Why is this so important? Because our emptiness and fear and our Getting and Protecting Behaviors—together the cause of virtually all our unhappiness—are reactions to a *lack* of Real Love. As we tell the truth about ourselves, we create the opportunities to *find* the Real Love that can eliminate all those causes of unhappiness. Finding Real Love and happiness all begins with telling the truth about who we are.

To continue with the drowning metaphor from Module Two, imagine again that you've discovered a drowning man in a pool. How is he behaving? He's thrashing with his arms, kicking with his legs, sputtering with his mouth, and using an array of facial expressions that are terrifying. You reach out and help him out of the water. Now that he stands on dry land, what is the likelihood that he will continue to thrash, kick, and sputter? Zero. Once out of the pool, he simply loses his *need* for those behaviors, so they will stop instantly and completely.

It is the same with Getting and Protecting Behaviors. When people have enough Real Love—when they are pulled from the water—they lose all their need to use these behaviors, so the behaviors simply disappear. As you find more Real Love in your life, you will be astonished at how effortlessly and consistently this occurs.

The Fields of Life and Death

The role of Getting and Protecting Behaviors—and the need to give them up—is so important that I want to illustrate it with another metaphor.

Imagine that life is one great game. Everyone who uses Getting and Protecting Behaviors is playing with rules and tools that can lead only to Imitation Love, disappointment, and misery. Because these conditions are in direction opposition to our highest purpose in *life*—to be loving and happy—it is appropriate that we regard them as the opposite of life. In short, everyone using Getting and Protecting Behaviors is playing on the Field of Death, and no matter how cleverly and effectively they use these behaviors, everyone on that field dies—emotionally, spiritually, and often physically. If you choose to play on that field, you might acquire more points—toys, praise, power, and so on—than the other players through the use of more effective trading and manipulating. You might inflict more wounds on others than are inflicted upon you. But in the end you still die.

There's only one way to find genuine happiness: Get completely off the Field of Death and play on the Field of Life, where Getting and Protecting Behaviors are not the preferred rules and tools. On the Field of Life, the game is played by the guidelines of truth and Real Love. There are still ups and downs, to be sure, and it's still a struggle at times, but on the Field of Life the end product is happiness. Everyone lives.

As you tell the truth about yourself, you move from the Field of Death to the Field of Life. When we get enough Real Love, a fruit of the spirit (Galatians 5:19-23), we become reborn of the Spirit into the family of Jesus Christ. The apostle John makes it especially clear that we can in this lifetime move from the Field of Death to the Field of Life, and that transformation occurs by the power of love:

We know that we have passed from death unto life, because we love our brothers. He who doesn't love his brother remains in death. (1 John 3:14)

CHAPTER TWO
The Story of the Wart King

TWO, 3:34 - 6:17   The Story of the Wart King
CD Track Two, 0:00 - 2:41

In the space on the next page describe some of what you regard to be your warts. These might include:

- Lack of success in your career
- Lack of money
- Physical appearance
- Lack of social skills
- Socio-economic status
- Family problems
- Your sins and unworthiness before God
- Disability
- Race

- Lack of education
- Alcohol or drug use
- Cultural background
- Sexual orientation
- Age

In the space below and on the next page describe how people have not accepted you because of your warts, which might include (but would not be limited to):

- Laughed at you
- Criticized you
- Excluded you from their group
- Talked about you behind your back
- Avoided you
- Ignored you

In the space below describe some of the ways you "stay in your room"—as the Wart King did—to avoid occasions where your warts might be seen. Some of your answers might be similar to these given by others:

- I avoid social situations: parties, family reunions, anyplace where there will be a lot of people.
- When I'm in a group, I hardly ever speak. I try to remain invisible.
- I never talk about my family.
- I avoid discussions where I don't feel competent.
- I've stopped dating.
- I work out of my home, because office politics terrifies me.
- I've avoided promotion at work so I can stay with people who already know me.

In the space below describe some of the ways you have "put out a decree that if anyone talked about your warts they'd be killed"— as the Wart King did. For example:

- I've let people know with my past reactions that talking about my weight is absolutely not permitted.
- I become so agitated on the subject of race that nobody dares to bring it up around me.
- When people dare to mention a mistake I've made or a flaw I have, I become so angry that they don't dare do it again.
- I'm such a militant gay activist that everybody knows to tiptoe around the subject when I'm around.

In the space below discuss how you wear a cloth bag over your head. Following are some of the answers given by others:

- Nobody knows I'm gay.
- I lie about my age.
- I've had plastic surgery.
- I drive a car that's probably a step or two above my means.
- I go to great lengths with my hair, clothing, and makeup to look younger than I am.
- I wear much more expensive clothing than I can afford.
- I never share how I really feel about things.
- I say what people want to hear.
- I don't tell people where or how I was raised.
- I lie about how much money I make.
- I've never told anybody how empty and alone I often feel.
- I always insist on being right.

Notice how the Wise Man helped the Wart King in the process of telling the truth about himself. The Wise Man:

- didn't avoid the truth about the king's warts. He said directly, "You have warts on your face."
- was kind. There was no tone of criticism as he told the truth.
- didn't become defensive when the king attacked him. He simply persisted in telling the truth.
- followed the king when he ran away.
- helped the king when he began to drown.
- reassured him that he wasn't laughing at him.
- made suggestions about the king's telling the truth to others.
- loved and taught the king.

As you tell the truth about yourself, you will find wise men and women (page 17) who will accept and love you as the Wise Man did with the Wart King.

CHAPTER THREE
Telling the Truth about Ourselves

THREE, 6:17 - 8:15   Why We Keep Bags on our Heads
CD Track Three, 0:00 - 2:00

Putting bags on our heads seems to make so much sense in the short term. When we hide, people do tend to laugh at us and criticize us less. But they also have no opportunity to love us, and then we feel alone and miserable. The price of protecting ourselves is very high.

Although telling the truth about ourselves is the key to finding the Real Love we need, being truthful is a new and frightening activity—mostly because of our past experiences. Let me illustrate:

Imagine that as you're walking on the sidewalk you see a man on the opposite side of the street who is wearing a red baseball cap. The instant he sees you, he runs across the street and slaps you in the face. The next day another man wearing a red cap does the same thing. This happens nine days in a row. On the tenth day, you see a man wearing a red baseball cap. Will you immediately run in the opposite direction, or will you wait until he sees you, to learn what his response will be?

Similarly, many of us have had thousands of experiences—often in a row—with people treating us unfavorably when they saw the truth about our mistakes and flaws. After being "slapped" a thousand times in a row—even a few times in a row—it's understandable that we're less than enthusiastic about allowing anyone the slightest opportunity of slapping us again. So we hide the truth about who we really are—we hide our warts—in order to avoid the disapproval that has been so painful in the past.

The Ultimate Cost of Not Telling the Truth

As we hide the truth about ourselves, we tend to do a thorough job of it. Our lies to other people are usually fairly apparent. Less obvious is how we lie to ourselves, but it's virtually inevitable that we would do that as well.

Imagine, for example, that we receive a whispering from the Spirit that in a given interaction, our anger was selfish and unloving—certainly not Christ-like. In most cases, we can see only two choices before us at this point:

A. We could embrace the truth and face our selfishness. This would require that we humbly acknowledge our error, to ourselves and to the person we wronged. Of course, this also requires that we consider how many other times we have been selfish and unloving with our anger, and that could involve quite an extensive process of self-examination and change.

   OR

B. We could hide the truth in some way, or twist it beyond any ability to prick our conscience. We could, for example:

1. simply deny the whispering and deny that anger is selfish.
2. claim that our anger in this particular case was justified because of the behavior of the other person.
3. claim that some positive result came from our anger— we successfully defended a position that was *right*, we stopped someone from doing something wrong, and so on—so how could it be wrong.

Choice A requires honesty, humility, and the possibility of years of continued self-examination and self-discipline. Choice B, on the other hand, requires the exercise of no virtue and can be accomplished in a brief moment of mental and moral sleight of hand. Is it any wonder that we so often make Choice B?

Choice B involves lying to *ourselves*, and without intending to, as we lie to ourselves we lie also to God. One reason, in fact, that we excuse our behavior and hide our flaws is precisely so He will find us acceptable and worthy of His love. But now we've started down that slippery slope that we have discussed above. The moment we lie to God in any way, we cannot feel His acceptance of who we really are. We can feel His love only as a reward for our manipulations. *When we lie, however unintentionally, we cannot feel loved by God.*

God's love is a fruit of the Spirit. It is conveyed by the Spirit into our hearts, and if we are engaged in Getting and Protecting Behaviors, we cannot feel the Spirit nor the love that is spiritually felt. Paul talked about this when he said, "The natural man doesn't receive the things of the Spirit of God, for they are foolishness to him: neither can he know them, because they are spiritually understood. (1 Corinthians 2:14)

Paul further said to the same group of Saints,

Brethren, I could not speak to you in a spiritual way, but only in a worldly way, as though you were infants in Christ. I have fed you with milk and not with meat, because then you were not able to bear it, nor can you bear it now, because you are still worldly. For while there is jealousy and contention among you, are you not worldly and walking as men?" (1 Corinthians 3:1-3)

Paul could not speak to them by the Spirit, because they were engaged in the behaviors of the world—Getting and Protecting Behaviors—and God is often unable to convey His love to us by the Spirit for the same reason.

To the Ephesians, Paul said,

I testify in the Lord, that from now on you should not walk as others in the world walk, in the pride of their minds, with their understanding darkened, being separated from the life of God through their ignorance, because of the blindness of their heart. They are past feeling because they have given themselves to lusts and to greedily act in unclean ways. (Ephesians 4:17-19)

When we are engaged in sin—in Getting and Protecting Behaviors—where we walk as most of the world does, we are "past feeling." We simply can't *feel* the things of the Spirit, including God's love.

John further confirms this when he says,

Don't love the world or the things in the world. If a man loves the world, the love of the Father is not in him. Because everything in the world—the lust of the flesh, and the lust of the eyes, and the pride of life—is not of the Father, but is of the world. And the world will disappear, with all its lusts, but whoever obeys the will of God will live forever. (1 John 2:15-17)

Man's Way Versus God's Way

On countless occasions, people have said to me, "I don't think I can do this truth telling thing. It's just too difficult. But God has promised us that His way is easier than the way of sin and Getting and Protecting Behaviors:

Come to me, all you who work and are heavily burdened, and I will give you rest. Do my work instead, and learn from me. For I am gentle and humble, and I will give your souls rest. (Matthew 11:28-30)

It's sin that's hard work. Lying, attacking, acting like victims, clinging, and running all require a great of effort. By comparison, telling the truth about ourselves and finding Real Love are relatively easy. That burden is light.

THREE, 8:15 - 8:35   Take Your Time
CD Track Three, 2:00 - 2:10

When I talk about telling the truth about ourselves, many people immediately think of disclosing the most intimate and frightening secrets of their lives. I do *not* recommend that you even think about sharing these in the beginning, for at least two reasons:

- Your fear of sharing the most frightening truths will prevent you from sharing *anything*, and then you'll keep the bag on your head.
- Sharing too deeply or quickly makes most people quite uncomfortable, and that actually interferes with their ability to give you moments of unconditional acceptance.

I'll talk more in Chapter Twelve about how it looks to tell the truth about yourself gradually.

THREE, 8:35 - 9:11   Tell the Truth about You, Not
Everyone Else
CD Track Three, 2:10 - 2:46

In the process of presenting hundreds of seminars and speaking individually to thousands of people, I have given many people the opportunity to tell the truth about themselves. Even with considerable guidance and numerous examples, many people seem to be absolutely stuck in the pattern of describing the mistakes and flaws of *other people*. On some occasions, in fact, I have asked people to tell the truth about themselves without making any reference whatever to anyone else, and they are usually struck dumb by that request. They simply cannot describe a difficult interaction without pointing the finger of blame at someone else in some way.

The reason we must avoid talking about other people is not because it violates some arbitrary rule, like "It's not nice to talk about other people." Talking about other people is harmful because it prevents us from realizing our primary purpose in life. We're here to feel unconditionally loved, to be loving toward others, and to be genuinely happy. We find Real Love in the process we discussed earlier: Truth → Seen → Accepted → Loved. Feeling loved can happen only as we tell the truth about ourselves, not others.

On several occasions in the New Testament, people came to Jesus with a story to tell about *someone else*. On each occasion, however, what did Jesus say? He said, why not look at the truth about *yourself*. Let's look at a few of those incidents:

- One man said to Jesus, tell my brother to divide the inheritance of my father with me. And Jesus said, (you) be careful of greed, for a man's life is not what he owns. (Luke 12:13-15)

- Some people told Jesus of some Jews who had been killed in a humiliating way by members of the Roman occupation army, implying that those people had sinned in some way. And Jesus said, do you suppose that those men were sinners because they suffered? No, but unless *you* repent, you will all be destroyed. Or how about those eighteen who died when the building in Siloam fell on them? Do you think that happened because they sinned? No, but unless *you* change your hearts, you will all be destroyed. (Luke 13:1-5)

- The Jews brought to Jesus a woman who had been caught in the act of adultery. And they said, the law prescribes that she be stoned, but what do you say? Jesus stooped down and wrote in the dirt as though he had not heard them. When they continued to ask him, he raised up and said, he that is without sin among you, let him be the first to throw a stone at her. And again he stooped down and wrote in the dirt. And when they heard it, convicted by their own conscience, they went away, leaving only Jesus and the woman. And Jesus said to her, Woman, is there no one left to condemn you? She said, No, Lord. And Jesus said, Neither do I condemn you. Go and sin no more. (John 8:3-11)

On another occasion, Jesus summarized His attitude toward all these varied situations, when he said,

And why do you look at the speck of dust in your brother's eye, but you don't look at the log in your own eye? Or how can you say to your brother, Let me pull the speck from your eye, when there is a log in your own eye? You hypocrite, first take the log out of your own eye; and then you will see clearly to take the speck out of your brother's eye. (Matthew 7:3-5)

THREE, 9:11 - 12:52   Tell the Truth about Your Mistakes
CD Track Three, 2:46 - 6:37

Let's discuss some examples of telling the truth about your mistakes, in most cases preceded in parentheses by the usual lie we tell:

- (I couldn't help it.) I planned poorly, and because of that I made several mistakes that could have been avoided.
- (It's not fair.) I just didn't get what *I* wanted. I really didn't put enough work into the project to get out of it what I expected, but I still had hopes that I'd get more.
- (I forgot.) I wasn't really excited about doing what you asked, so I put it off, and eventually I did forget about it. But the forgetting was mostly my choice.
- (The traffic was bad.) I stayed at home till the last possible moment, doing some things I thought were more important than being on time. So I didn't allow for bad traffic or anything else that might delay me.
- (I didn't know what you meant.) I should have asked you exactly what you meant when you gave me that assignment,

but frankly, I chose the interpretation that would mean the least work for me.

- (I didn't have time.) I was irresponsible. I could have started the assignment long before I did, but I put it off, and when the deadline came near, I really didn't have time. But that was my fault.
- (How could she talk to me like that?) I knew she wouldn't like what I did, but I chose to do it anyway. I shouldn't be surprised at her reaction.
- That was my fault. (That can be especially difficult to say when somebody else was wrong too, but you only gain by talking about the part that was *your* responsibility.)

Telling the truth about our mistakes isn't intended to be some kind of ritualized confession. No, we tell the truth about ourselves because it creates the opportunities that we need so badly to feel loved. Notice in the video segment that the man who admitted the truth about his being late discovered that several people accepted him unconditionally. He would not have found those people if he had lied. We *attract* wise men and women—people who can love us unconditionally—by sharing the truth about who we are. Let me illustrate this concept further with a comparison:

> I have a friend who hunts wild turkeys. I asked him how he finds them, since I've been in the woods many times and have rarely seen wild turkeys. He said he makes the sounds of a turkey, and they come to him.

Similarly, we attract wise men by speaking the truth. They're naturally attracted to it and respond by accepting and loving those who speak it. If, on the other hand, we don't tell the truth about ourselves, it's much less likely that we'll ever find wise men and women.

Truth Telling in the Bible

Let's take a brief look at what the Bible says about our telling the truth about ourselves, including our mistakes.

James said, "Confess your faults to one another, and pray one for another, that ye may be healed." (James 5:16) Healing of our spirits can come only by the Spirit and by the power of love, and a pre-requisite step is that we tell the truth about ourselves ("confess our faults to one another").

John wrote, "This is basis of the condemnation God makes, that light came into the world, and men loved darkness rather than light, because their deeds were evil. Because everyone who does evil works hates the light and doesn't come to the light, for fear that his deeds would be condemned. But whoever lives by the truth comes to the light, so his deeds may be known, that they are done through God." (John 3:19-21) Those who do evil hide their deeds from the light, while those who live by the truth bring their deeds to the light. In the process of changing our deeds from evil to good, it is necessary for us to bring our deeds to the light, which includes telling the truth about them.

Paul suggested, "Look at yourselves, to see if you are truly faithful. Test yourselves." (2 Corinthians 13:5) And how could we possibly look at ourselves without telling the truth about ourselves?

And finally, again from John: "If we say we have no sin, we deceive ourselves, and the truth is not in us. *If we confess our sins*, God can be depended upon to forgive our sins, and to cleanse us from all unrighteousness. If we say that we have not sinned, we make him a liar, and we don't believe what he has said." (1 John 1:8-10)

Jesus as a Bold Wise Man

Many of us have been protecting ourselves by hiding the truth about our mistakes—particularly about our Getting and Protecting Behaviors—for so long that we hardly know when we're lying anymore. It's become an unconscious reflex. We often need the guidance of wise men—and women—who can lovingly help us see the truth about our feelings and behavior. On some occasions, seeing the truth is frightening to us, and we resist these revelations. In these moments, considerable courage—and sometimes directness—is required from a wise man.

In His lifetime Jesus provided some examples of telling other people the truth about themselves in a rather direct way. He didn't do this to be harsh but to help them change the direction of their lives, so they might find the living waters He promised them. Following are a few examples of His telling the truth to other people:

- You're like poisonous snakes, so how can you possibly say anything good? (Matthew 12:34)
- You are hypocrites and will be cursed, because although you are leaders of the people, you actually make it more difficult for people to enter into the kingdom of heaven, nor do you go there yourselves. You take widows' homes from them but make a show of long prayers, so you will receive the greater damnation. (Matthew 23:13-4)
- You leaders are blind, because you make a big deal of little things and miss the point on the things that are very important and could destroy you. (Matthew 23:24)
- Woe unto you, hypocrites, because you are like white-washed tombs, which appear beautiful on the outside but inside are full of dead men's bones and filthiness. In the same way, you appear good to men on the outside, but on the inside you are full of hypocrisy and wickedness. (Matthew 23:27-28)

In our search for genuine happiness we need the pure, unvarnished truth as spoken by the Savior and by other wise men and women in our lives. It is these truths that create the opportunities for us to feel the Real Love that will change our lives. To learn more about the role of wise men, read the book, *Real Love for Wise Men and Women*.

Courage to Tell the Truth

As you tell the truth about your mistakes, some people will *not* like you. We'll talk more about this in Chapter Six of this module, but for now just know that even though some people won't like you, telling the truth is still the only way to find the people who *will* love you. You can't lose by telling the truth, especially as you follow the guidelines described in Chapter Twelve of this module.

In the space below draw a circle that represents the size of your fear of telling other people the truth about your mistakes.

Now, in the space above, and next to or below the first circle, draw another circle that represents how much you want to have a life filled with Real Love, a life:

- without emptiness and fear.
- without Getting and Protecting Behaviors.
- where you feel as you did during the meditation in Module One, where you were among the loving people in the village.

When your second circle is larger than your first, you'll begin to tell the truth about your mistakes.

CHAPTER FOUR
Would You Rather Be Happy or Right?

FOUR, 12:52 - 13:56   The Price of Being Right
CD Track Four, 0:00 - 1:04

In the absence of sufficient Real Love, insisting that we're right provides us great quantities of praise, power, and safety. When we're right, we:

- feel superior to the people who are wrong, and that's quite a powerful feeling.
- feel more worthwhile and deserving of praise.
- believe we wear a moral armor that protects us from the attacks of those who are wrong.
- feel justified in attacking those who don't share our opinion.

All these feelings give us temporary doses of Imitation Love, but they also separate us from everyone around us, which uniformly makes us feel less loved and more alone.

When I talk about the enormous disadvantages of "being right," I'm not referring to being *in the right*, or doing the *right thing*. I'm talking about our insistence on *claiming* that we're right and our need to shove our "rightness" down everyone's throat with a disregard for what they say, do, and believe. That kind of *being right* is not compatible with Real Love.

Some of us are quite reluctant to admit that we have a strong need to be right, and that's because unconsciously we recognize the selfishness of being right, and we don't want others to identify that quality in us. If you wonder whether you might have a need to be right, ask yourself the following questions:

- In conversation, do you often find yourself stating the same opinion several times? If you restate your opinion over and over, you have a serious need to be right.
- When people ignore your point of view, do you become irritated? People without a need to be right do not become irritated when they're ignored.

- Do you become argumentative when people tell you that you're just plain wrong? We argue only when we have to be right.
- When people are talking, do you ask questions to learn all you can about what the speaker is saying, or do you tend to punctuate the conversation with the word *but* and statements of what *you* think? When we have a need to be right, we just can't resist interrupting people and telling them what we know.

When you have to be right, the people around you hear these messages from you:

- I am smarter than you, wiser than you, and better than you.
- You are a moron. It's a good thing I'm here to show you the only true way.
- Being right is more important to me than working together with you.
- *I* am more important than you.

In the space below and on the next page discuss some occasions or relationships where you have felt a strong need to be right. On those occasions:

- Did you feel closer to the people you were talking to?
- Did you feel loved?
- Did you feel loving?
- Were you genuinely happier?
- Did the people you were talking to feel more loved, or did you even notice?

The rewards of being right are superficial and temporary, while the negative effects are devastating.

In the process of seeing the effects of being right, and as you learn to overcome this destructive pattern, you may find the following exercise valuable. I will describe it as a written exercise to be completed on the following page, but with a little creative adaptation you could also do it orally with a friend or a group of people:

- Briefly describe a recent conflict you had.
- Describe all the ways that the other person involved in the conflict was selfish, stupid, misguided, and otherwise wrong. Write this on a separate piece of paper.
- Fold up this piece of paper and put it in an envelope. Seal it. You can open it up and talk about it all you want in one week.
- Between now and then, you cannot refer in any way—written, verbal, hinting, nothing—to the contents of that envelope. You cannot mention the mistakes or foolishness of the other person. Period.
- Describe all the ways that you were brilliant, clever, wise, responsible, far-seeing, all-knowing, articulate, analytical, and otherwise *right* in that conflict. Write this on a separate piece of paper, not on one of the blank pages in this book.
- Fold up this piece of paper and put it in an envelope. Seal it. You can open it up and talk about it all you want in one week.
- Between now and then, you cannot refer in any way—written, verbal, hinting, nothing—to the contents of that envelope. You cannot mention how you were right. Period.

- Now, in the space below, describe all the ways *you* were *wrong* in the conflict. Yes, I know the other person was wrong in many ways, and you were right in many ways, but we've already talked about those—that discussion is over. The subject now is how *you* were *wrong*.

It is a simple fact that when you talk about how you were right and how other people were wrong, you will almost never foster the Real Love that is absolutely essential to any healthy relationship or interaction. That approach just doesn't *work*.

In the next few sections, we'll discuss *why* talking about how you are wrong makes such an enormous contribution to any interaction. For now, just make your list in the space above.

Most of us have been defending ourselves and insisting that we're right for so long that we really don't know *how* to talk about being wrong. The very thought of such an admission is paralyzing. To help get the process started, let me suggest some examples of what a "being wrong" list might look like. I will phrase it as though you were speaking to the person you had the conflict with.

You might say, "In our last conversation,

- I did a lousy job of listening to you. I kept interrupting and telling you how I was right instead of really listening to what you had to say."
- I was irritated, which is a terrible way to communicate with anybody. I apologize and would like to try again to really listen to you."
- I kept hitting you over the head with what *I* thought. I'm sure you got my opinion the first time I said it, but I thought if I kept saying it I could somehow persuade you to take my point of view. I was being selfish."
- I was much more interested in being right than I was in working together with you toward a solution that would benefit everyone. I'd be grateful if you'd give me another chance to try to discuss the issue again, but maybe I could actually listen this time."
- I described the *advantages* of my position, but I left out the *drawbacks*, because I wanted to be right. Not a selfless approach on my part."
- I did not acknowledge the positive aspects of your point of view at all. That was a huge mistake on my part."
- I was thinking only of myself. You tried to tell me several times—with your words and your behavior—that you weren't ready to talk, but I kept pushing because I wanted you to listen. Next time I will wait until you are ready."

Notice that these admissions of error have little to do with the *content* of the discussion. Suppose, for example, that you and a professional colleague are talking about routing electricity through enormous power lines all over the country. You believe a particular line should carry 55 jillion watts per minute, and he believes the figure should be 62. If you really believe that 55 would be a better figure—based on your analysis of the data available to you—you would be foolish to say you were wrong about the *number 55*. But you can always admit being wrong about your selfish *approach* to the conversation. You can admit to being selfish, to not listening, to being angry, and to being inconsiderate.

And *that* is what your partner needs to hear. The source of conflict in an argument is *not* a difference of opinion. It's emptiness and fear. It's a lack of Real Love. When you insist on being right, you only add to the emptiness and fear, and then the conflict is certain to worsen.

FOUR, 13:56 - 14:52   The Miracles of Truth Telling: First, Eliminating Conflict
CD Track Four, 1:04 - 2:00

I know it's very tempting to talk about the mistakes of others, but if you'll make a commitment to tell the truth only about your mistakes, four miracles will happen with amazing consistency.

- The conflict will be over.
- You will create opportunities to feel unconditionally accepted.
- You will create a safe environment for your partner.
- You'll be able to put your focus on the things you can actually do something about.

Let's discuss each of these four miracles. First, as you tell the truth about your mistakes, the conflict will be over. Again, conflicts are not about differences of opinion. They're caused by emptiness and fear and the exchange of Getting and Protecting Behaviors. In our world, these behaviors characterize our interactions with alarming frequency. In fact, we compete to use them more cleverly and effectively, so we can "win" the conflicts in which we engage.

Few of us realize that the use of Getting and Protecting Behaviors *never* leads to genuine happiness, which is our primary goal in life. These behaviors quite literally destroy our lives.

When we tell the truth about ourselves, as we discussed on pages 221-2, we move from the Field of Death to the Field of Life, the only place where meaningful progress can be made and relationships enriched. As you move from the Field of Death to the

Field of Life, it's very difficult for your partner—spouse, boyfriend, friend, co-worker, child—to continue a conflict with you, because he or she is now *alone* on the Field of Death. There cannot be a conflict unless you move back to the Field of Death. On occasion you'll be tempted to do that, but it's never worth the price.

In the space below describe a recent conflict where you now recognize you were playing on the Field of Death. No matter how hard you tried to fix things or protect yourself or win the conflict, it only got worse for you. Can you see how no amount of adjustment or compromise or cleverness ever makes any real difference as long as you're on that Field—as long as you're using Getting and Protecting Behaviors?

Can you imagine now what it would be like to simply tell the truth about yourself and be removed entirely from the conflict?

FOUR, 14:52 - 15:03   Second, Creating Opportunities to Feel Loved
   CD Track Two, 2:00 - 2:11

Telling the truth about ourselves is the first step toward feeling unconditionally loved. Until we do that, we will remain empty, afraid, and alone, the conditions we hate more than any others.

Are you willing to begin that process? Are you willing to move from the Field of Death to the Field of Life? Are you willing to replace the frustration, anguish, and despair of Getting and Protecting Behaviors with the peace and confidence that always accompany finding Real Love?

What often stops us from sharing who we are with others is the risk involved. We're afraid that if we're truthful, some people won't like us. *So what!?* If I tell you the truth about myself and you don't like me a bit, what have I really lost? Nothing, except perhaps the *illusion* that you did like me. What I've really learned is that you're simply incapable of being unconditionally loving. It's not really about *me*.

Allow me to borrow a parable taught by Jesus. As you read it, consider the seeds to be the truth about yourself.

And Jesus said, A farmer went out to sow, and some of the seeds fell on the footpath, and the birds came and ate them. Some fell on rocky places, where there was little soil, and they sprouted quickly, because the soil was shallow. And when the sun rose, they were burned, and because they had no root, they withered away. And some fell among thorns; and the thorns sprung up, and choked them. But other fell into good ground, and brought forth fruit, some a hundredfold, some sixtyfold, some thirtyfold. (Matthew 13:3-8)

As you tell the truth about yourself, it's true that some people will *not* like you, just as some seeds sown in a field will fall on the road or on rocky places or among thorns, where they won't sprout, or they'll sprout but not long survive. Should a farmer then plant *no* seeds, for fear that some of them might not grow? Ridiculous. He will plant anyway, knowing that only by planting can he create the opportunity for some seeds to grow and produce an abundant harvest. And he knows that one price for a rich harvest is that some seeds will fail. It's the price of doing business.

In the book of John we have an example of someone experiencing the results of truth telling. Jesus was speaking to a woman at a well, and after a conversation with her, He said,

Go and bring your husband here. The woman said, I have no husband, and Jesus said, You have spoken the truth, because you have had five husbands, but the man you live with now is not your husband. She said, I see now that you are a prophet, and she went into the city and told the people there, Come and see a man who has told me everything I ever did. Is this not the Christ? (John 4:16-18, 28-29)

Jesus didn't just exchange social pleasantries with this woman. He told her the truth about her immoral behavior—which by most people would be considered an attack—and she didn't deny it. In the process of allowing herself to be seen by Him, she felt His love so strongly that she rushed into the city and encouraged people to come out and meet this extraordinary man. Had she denied the truth about herself, she would not have had this transformative experience.

You'll take a huge step off the Field of Death as you begin to share with others the list you made on page 241, the list of ways *you* were wrong in that single conflict. That list is just a beginning. If you're really feeling brave, share that list with the person you had the conflict with. We'll talk about how to do that on pages 249-50.

FOUR, 15:03 - 16:13   Third, Creating a Safe Environment
CD Track Four, 2:11 - 3:21

In conflicts, people fight you—they use Protecting Behaviors—only because they're empty and afraid. When you make the choice to tell the truth about your mistakes, you're no longer attacking them. You're no longer screaming "I don't love you" on the Field of Death, and at that point everything has the potential of changing.

When you tell the truth about yourself, you're issuing an invitation for your partner to participate in a moment of connection with the real *you*, and most people are eager for these moments. We *want* a sense of genuine connection with others. It's the beginning of the Real Love we've all desperately sought for a lifetime.

In the majority of cases—probably 70-80%—your partner will then feel safe enough that he or she will begin telling the truth about his or her mistakes. He or she will do that just for the privilege of participating in a moment of genuine connection, for the privilege of stepping onto the Field of Life. When that happens, there is virtually nothing you can't work out. It's a bit miraculous to observe, actually. I've seen people go from full-blooded, sword-wielding conflict to mutual cooperation in minutes when one person is willing to tell the truth about his or her mistakes.

It should be noted that some people carry around such an enormous burden of emptiness and fear from a *lifetime* of insufficient Real Love that even if you tell the truth about your mistakes, they will still not be able to tell the truth about themselves. No matter. You will still see an enormous decrease in the intensity of the conflict, and *you* will feel much happier as a result of choosing to move off the Field of Death.

Fourth, Focusing on What We Can Actually Do Something About

Another benefit of telling the truth about our own mistakes is that then we're not distracted from attending to the only problems we can really do anything about: *ours*. I can't change you. Collectively, as a human family, we've all proven billions of times that changing other people is foolish, and yet we keep trying. As I focus on *your* mistakes, I can't fully pay attention to how I can correct my own, and that's a real waste.

One ounce of effort that I spend working on myself will be far more productive than a ton of effort I might spend working on you.

The benefits of focusing on my own problems are enormous. Paul said, " If we only judged our own lives honestly, we would not need to be judged. But when we are judged, we are corrected by the Lord so that we will not be condemned along with the world." (1 Corinthians 11:31-32) If we pay closer attention to the log in our own eye (Matthew 7:3-5), we will find that great miracles will become possible. We will literally become a new person, as Paul said to the Ephesians:

The truth found in Jesus is that you should put away your old behavior and old self, which is corrupted by deceptive lusts, and be renewed in the spirit of your mind and put on a new self, which by God is created in righteousness and true holiness. (Ephesians 4:21-24)

FOUR, 16:13 - 16:38   Happy or Right
CD Track Four, 3:31 - 3:46

On countless occasions, as I have recommended to people that they tell the truth about their mistakes to their partners, they have made responses like the following:

- "But *he . . .*"
- "But *she . . .*"
- "But if I say *I'm wrong,* he'll think *he's right!*"
- "But then they might not do what I want, and this is *important.*"

Most of us are very afraid to let other people be right, and that's understandable. In the absence of sufficient Real Love, praise and power become important commodities, and then we're quite reluctant to give up the sense of power we get from being right. We're afraid that other people will gain a position of power over us by being right while we're wrong. But remember, all that commerce takes place on the Field of Death, where everybody dies and *nobody* wins the prize that matters.

How much better it is that we listen to these words of wisdom:

- Fools insist on being right, while wise men listen to the advice of others. (Proverbs 12:15)
- Rebuke a wise man, and he will love you. (Proverbs 9:8)
- Whoever loves being instructed loves knowledge, but whoever hates correction is crude. (Proverbs 12:1)

If we haven't known many moments of Real Love, letting go of Imitation Love can seem unthinkable, but letting go is the only way we'll ever know what it feels like to be on the Field of Life. There is no other way. You can't play on both fields at the same time. Do you want to be happy, or do you want to be right? Again, you can't have both. Exercise a little faith—more about that in Chapter Six of this module—and let go of being right. Tell the truth about how *you* were wrong, without the slightest mention of how your partner was wrong. As you do that, miracles will follow.

Go back to the recent conflict you described on pages 240-1. Would you be willing to actually tell that partner how you were wrong, as you described on page 241? If you're too uncomfortable discussing this conflict with that particular partner, would you be willing to choose another partner, one with whom you could more comfortably complete this exercise? If so, do it. Tell your partner how you were wrong in your interaction with him or her.

Before you do this, I suggest some preparation:

- Finish viewing the remainder of Module Three and complete the part of the *Workbook* that goes with it.
- Remember that you really can't lose here..You already blew it—you were already unloving and destructive—in the conflict. Telling the truth about yourself couldn't go a whole lot worse.
- Remember that you're creating an opportunity here for miracles. No kidding. Although you might feel some fear, how will you ever find the Field of Life until you do something genuinely different? You'll never find happiness on the Field of Death.
- Practice what you'll say about being wrong with a loving friend—wise man or woman—before you try it with the partner you had the conflict with. It can be much easier to talk to someone who was not involved in the conflict, and it will give you confidence in what you're planning to say. You'll also benefit from the acceptance and love you'll receive from this wise man or woman.
- Make an absolute promise that even though *you* will be telling the truth about *your* mistakes, you will *not* expect your partner to tell the truth about *his* or *hers*. That expectation would ruin the entire conversation.

- Practice telling the truth about your mistakes without the slightest excuse. Just be *wrong*.
- Practice telling the truth about your mistakes without the slightest reference to your partner being wrong.

Now, after you've shared with your partner how you were wrong, in the space below describe how your interaction went:

- Were you afraid? That's entirely natural.
- Was your partner surprised at your admission of error?
- Was there a change in the tension that had existed between you?
- Did you experience a sense of relief?
- Did your partner respond with any truthfulness of his or her own? If so, what a nice bonus, but do not expect it.

Realize that your interaction may not go well. Occasionally, your partner may be so empty and afraid that he or she will use this occasion as an opportunity to attack you even more, saying things like:

- You sure *were* wrong!
- It's about time you saw this.
- That's not all. Let me tell you some more things you've been stupid about.

This negative response does not usually occur, but if it does, it happens for one or both of two reasons:

- Although you told the truth about yourself, you were still afraid—understandably—and therefore at some point in the conversation you used some Getting and Protecting Behaviors. You may, for example, have made excuses about your mistakes. The instant you use a Getting and Protecting Behavior, the person you're with generally feels less loved and will react to protect himself or herself.
- Your partner was so empty and afraid that he or she just could not leave the Field of Death, despite your gracious invitation to do so.

If you get a negative response from admitting you were wrong, remember that you still did the right thing, and in the long term *you* will be happier for doing it.

As we tell the truth about ourselves, we can't avoid the occasional negative experience. Those experiences are part of the price to be paid for changing a lifelong pattern of destructive behaviors. If you want a life filled with Real Love and genuine happiness, you *must* be willing to pay that price.

I was a surgeon for twenty years. On many occasions I told people that the only way to help them—to improve their health or even save their life—was to operate on them. I told them I'd have to *hurt* them in order to help them. Understandably, they often experienced some fear, but almost without exception they were willing to experience the short-term pain to avoid the long-term disability or worse.

How about you? Are you willing to experience the occasional moments of discomfort in order to find a life of indescribable peace? I certainly can't make the decision for you, but I can tell you personally that it's worth it, and I can tell you that hundreds of thousands of others have confirmed what I'm saying. If you have a bad experience with telling the truth, don't give up. It's the only way to learn.

Now discuss below another conflict and make another list of how you were wrong, as you did on page 241. Again, share it with others. As you do this, you'll begin to notice that you feel more accepted, more peaceful, less anxious, and certainly happier.

CHAPTER FIVE
Telling the Truth about Getting and Protecting

FIVE, 16:38 - 17:36   Telling the Truth About Getting and
      Protecting
      CD Track Five, 0:00 - 0:58

Our Getting and Protecting Behaviors are often a big part of what we do, so we need to share the truth about our use of these behaviors with others if we want to feel unconditionally accepted. You do not need to share the truth all at once. More about that—and other guidelines for telling the truth—in Chapter Twelve of this module.

Paul told the Galatians to "bear one another's burdens, and so fulfil the law of Christ." (Galatians 6:2) And what are the greatest burdens we carry? Our fears, lies, anger, resentments, offenses, and shame, which are all Getting and Protecting Behaviors and their precursors. As we share these burdens—as we tell the truth about our Getting and Protecting Behaviors—we fulfill the law of Christ, which is summed up in the word *love*.

Additionally, we know that our Getting and Protecting Behaviors are our sins, and in Proverbs we read, "He that covereth his sins shall not prosper: but whoso confesseth and forsaketh them shall have mercy." (Proverbs 28:13)

In the space on the next two pages discuss some examples of your Getting and Protecting Behaviors. You did some of this on pages 122-8, 140-5. You might also share these with a friend. Following are some additional examples that might help you get into the spirit of the exercise:

- Yesterday my wife asked me why the garbage in the kitchen wasn't emptied, which is my job. I made some lame excuse about not having time (lying), instead of admitting that I just hate doing it and always put it off until the trash overflows and inconveniences everybody. I didn't want her to be mad at me.
- When my girlfriend was late getting ready for us to go out, I was really impatient and irritated (attacking). It ruined our entire evening.
- Today my son wasn't being careful and dropped a glass and broke it. He already knew he'd made a mistake and felt bad about it. All I needed to do was encourage him to get the broom to clean it up, but I couldn't let it go. I sighed and raised my voice and told him he was clumsy (attacking). He looked devastated.
- At work I often complain about how things aren't fair and how the boss doesn't care about what anybody thinks (victim). It makes me feel good for a minute, but it's not helping me or the business.
- My boss asked me who was responsible for an order being late, and I blamed the shipping department (victim, lying).

Well, the shipping department *was* slow, but *I* was the real problem. I got it to them two days late, so there was no way it could have gotten out on time. I just didn't want to look bad to the boss.

- Sometimes I complain to my boyfriend that he doesn't spend any time with me (victim, clinging).
- The boss asked me what I thought about an issue at work, but instead of telling him what I thought—which I really think would have helped the company—I told him exactly what I thought he wanted to hear (lying, clinging).
- My husband was describing an event to a friend, and even though it was his story to tell, I butted in and corrected the details several times. It was really none of my business, and I was not kind in my corrections (attacking).
- I complained for days that my family hardly did anything for my birthday (victim).
- My friend said something I didn't like, and I avoided her for three weeks (running).
- The other day I really exaggerated my part in a success at work (lying, clinging).
- My wife nagged me about something, and I went right down her throat (attacking). Not exactly loving on my part.
- Just yesterday I talked to a friend about how my girlfriend doesn't appreciate anything I do for her (victim).
- When I know my husband wants to have sex, I just avoid him (running).
- My brother offended me, and we haven't spoken in two years (victim, running).
- I sent my sister a Christmas gift, and I was pretty mad when she didn't send me one in return (victim).
- At parties and family gatherings, I hardly ever talk (running). Those kinds of things just make me nervous.
- I was really irritated with my husband when he didn't want to go out to eat with me this weekend (victim, attacking).
- When my kids don't do what they're told, I get angry at them and raise my voice (attacking).
- Before I go to visit my mother, I almost always have a couple of drinks. It's the only way I can handle it (running).

Now in the space below and on the next page, write down some examples of your own Getting and Protecting Behaviors:

Notice that in these examples of truth telling, there is no weird, uncomfortable, psychological language. These are relatively easy things to say. And you're not dredging up secrets from the past. You're describing your mistakes of today, yesterday, and last week. Truth telling can be relatively easy.

Remember what I said in the Introduction: You can do all these exercises alone, with a friend, in a group, or in a structured class, or using a combination of these approaches. Although there is a measure of safety in doing these exercises alone, you'll experience much more acceptance as you do them with other people.

In the space on the next page, describe the results of your truth telling experiences above:

- Were you initially uncomfortable? That's entirely natural.
- The more you talked, did you notice a sense of acceptance and connection with the person you were talking to? This is

what matters most. Truth telling is not an intellectual exercise but an opportunity to *feel* loved.

- Did you find it easier to tell the truth the more times you did it?
- Did you notice a tendency on the part of your partner to share the truth about himself or herself also?

Being Accepted

What's it like when someone accepts you as you are? It's rarely dramatic. Seldom do people throw their arms around you and say, "I love you." Usually, as you tell the truth about yourself someone who accepts you will:

- gently smile.
- show no impatience nor try to change the subject.
- look at you with genuine interest.
- ask questions to get even more information about you.
- say something like, "Wow, that was really honest."
- say, "I don't think I've heard anyone take responsibility for themselves like that before."

In these moments, you'll begin to feel the quiet acceptance you've been looking for. As Jesus said, "I leave peace with you. I give you my peace, not the kind the world gives. Don't let your heart be troubled or afraid." (John 14:27)

The power of this peace is beyond description, as Paul said: "The peace of God, which is beyond all understanding, will keep your hearts and minds through Christ Jesus." (Philippians 4:7) This peace—this feeling of acceptance—has greater power than armies. Robert E. Lee, the commanding general of the largest army in the Confederacy, was faced with a decision at the end of the war. Should he surrender, or should he encourage his troops to engage in a guerilla warfare that would have prolonged the war for a very long time, and perhaps resulted in a divided nation after all. He chose to surrender, and he said to a colleague on one occasion, "I surrendered more to the basic goodness of Lincoln than to the armies of Grant." We are more affected by quiet, genuine acceptance than we are by force of any magnitude.

FIVE, 17:36 - 19:16   What if You're not Loved?
CD Track Five, 0:58 - 2:36

Again, as you tell the truth about yourself, some people will *not* accept you. So what? When someone doesn't accept you, all it means is that you've found one person who's simply not *capable* of unconditionally accepting you. But people can't *take* love from you; they can only *not give* it to you.

Describe below a few examples of circumstances where you were not accepted and loved as you told the truth about yourself:

What should you do if you share the truth about yourself, and the other person is obviously not capable of loving you? Move on. Don't give up. Keep telling the truth about yourself to others until you find people—and you *will* find them—who will accept and love you, as described above.

After a situation where you didn't have a particularly positive experience with truth telling, describe below how you exercised the courage to keep telling the truth till you found someone who *did* accept or love you.

CHAPTER SIX
Faith

SIX, 19:16 - 20:17   Definition of Faith
CD Track Six, 0:00 - 1:00

In any given moment you cannot know what will happen as you share the truth about yourself with someone. You may be accepted; you may not. That's why it takes *faith* to keep telling the truth. Growth is possible only by faith. Faith is:

- taking a step into the unknown.
- much more than believing.
- the act of consciously choosing to experience what we don't know.
- taking action even though we don't understand the reasons or the consequences.

- acting in the face of fear.
- taking a bite of something you've never tasted.
- often frightening in the beginning but much more powerful than trying to be in control.

SIX, 20:17 - 24:23   The Risk of Telling the Truth about Yourself
CD Track Six, 1:01 - 5:07

Remember the metaphor of the farmer planting seeds. Everywhere you go, share yourself—much like planting a seed. It's true that some seeds won't grow, but some *will*, and you'll find those only by planting them. You'll find the people who are capable of loving you only by exercising the faith to actually share who you are with others. We talked about that earlier in this module with regard to the parable of the sower.

Discuss below how you have protected yourself by hiding who you were or by minimizing your risks.

With that approach certainly you have achieved moments of safety, but have you ever found genuine happiness? Which would you prefer, superficial and temporary safety or genuine and lasting happiness?

SIX, 24:23 - 24:58   The Lightness of Telling the Truth
CD Track Six, 5:07 - 5:42

When I was seven, I walked everywhere I went—to school, to my friends' houses, and so on—at a rate of maybe two to three miles per hour. And then I learned how to ride a bicycle. Initially, that was a strange and frightening experience. There were pedals and brakes and handle bars and that whole balance thing. I fell several times and rode into the neighbor's bushes, but I persisted in my attempts, and eventually I was riding all over town at a speed five to eight times greater than I had ever walked. I felt like a bird.

When I was sixteen, I learned to drive a car. That too was scary. I had to learn how to simultaneously operate a clutch, brake, accelerator, turn signals, and steering wheel, all the while checking mirrors, a speedometer, and surrounding traffic. But again I persisted in learning, and suddenly the whole country was within my reach.

Shortly after learning to drive a car, I took my first flight on a plane, and then I found myself almost magically transported from one coast to another between breakfast and lunch.

During each of these transitions, there were moments of unfamiliarity and even discomfort, but because I continued through these uncomfortable moments, my world expanded exponentially. Had I not endured the unknown, I'd still be walking. That might have been safer in the short term, but it would have been a great deal more work for me and would have severely limited the world in which I lived.

Similarly, although we've become quite familiar with the Getting and Protecting Behaviors, and although they have given us some measure of predictable relief and reward, lying, attacking, acting like victims, clinging, and running require enormous quantities of effort. Most of us, in fact, are utterly exhausted by the process. By comparison, exercising faith and simply telling the truth about ourselves are a bit novel and uncomfortable in the beginning, but they're *much* easier than the unending and futile labor of using Getting and Protecting Behaviors.

Faith may seem uncomfortable in the beginning, but as with my progression from walking to flying at nearly the speed of sound, with faith miracles become possible. In Jesus' words:

- If you have even the smallest amount of faith, you will say unto a mountain, move over there, and it will be done. Nothing will be impossible for you. (Matthew 17:20)

- Jesus said, if you can believe, all things are possible for you. (Mark: 9:23)

By contrast, if we rely only on what we know and what we can do, we are greatly limited in our power. During Jesus' lifetime ministry he performed many miracles: returning sight to the blind, giving strength to limbs long crippled, healing leprosy, casting out evil spirits, and even raising the dead. But Matthew describes that on one occasion when Jesus traveled in the land where he was raised, "He did not do many miracles there because of their unbelief." (Matthew 13:53-58) Although he was the Son of God, he was limited in his ability to help these people because they lacked faith.

SIX, 24:58 - 25:40   Choosing Faith
   CD Track Six, 5:42 - 6:24

It is not with our words that we demonstrate what we have faith in. We demonstrate our faith with our behavior. When you want to know what is important to people, don't listen to what they *say*. Simply observe what they *do*. We invest our time and effort in those things we have faith in. For example:

- The student who puts off doing his homework demonstrates that he has faith in rather spectacular and unfounded miracles. He believes that without preparation, knowledge and recognition will somehow descend upon him like dew from heaven.

- The man who spends unusually long hours at work while ignoring his family obviously believes that money and success in his career will give him the happiness he seeks.
- People who have sex with their partners early in their relationships have faith that the praise, power, and pleasure produced by sex will somehow result in genuinely loving and fulfilling relationships.
- People who get angry at others have faith that anger will produce happiness and satisfactory relationships.

The Bible teaches us this same principle, that faith is demonstrated in our behavior, in the following passages:

- You will recognize the true nature of people by what they do, just as you recognize a grape vine by its production of grapes, not thorns. Not everyone that says my name will be accepted into heaven, only those who **do** as my Father in heaven has instructed. If you hear what I say and **do** it, you will be like a man who has built his house on a rock, which will stand despite the rains, flood, and winds. But if you hear what I say and don't live accordingly, you will be like a foolish man who has built his house on the sand, where it will be destroyed by the rain, floods, and winds. (Matthew 7:15-27)

- Even so faith, if it has no deeds, is dead, being alone. (James 2:17)

- Faith without action is dead. (James 2:20)

- A man had two sons; and he said to the first, go work today in my vineyard. The son said, I will not, but later he thought better of it and went. The man said the same to his second son, who said, I will go, but he did not. Which of the two did his father's will? And they said to Jesus, the first son, and Jesus agreed with them. (Matthew 21:28-32)

In the space below discuss what you have faith in—not what you *say* you have faith in but what an outside observer would say you have faith in, based on your behavior. This will take considerable honesty and courage on your part.

We always have faith in something—productive or not, and whether we realize it or not. In the next section we'll discuss some of the possible objects of our faith that might be more effective in leading to happiness.

CHAPTER SEVEN
Faith in What?

SEVEN, 25:40 - 26:40   Faith in the Truth and in the Power of Love
CD Track Seven, 0:00 - 1:00

Imagine that you are in the middle of the ocean, floating on a small raft. You have no food, no water, and no idea whatever of your location. After you have floated about aimlessly for two days, a ship comes by and offers to help. The ship is bristling with the latest navigation equipment, and the captain says he has made the trip to the nearest port many times. You have a choice. You could have faith in the person who has successfully negotiated his way across the ocean many times—and who also has the best tools to make the trip—or you could have faith in your own ability to get yourself to shore.

You might think no one would be foolish enough to insist on making such a trip on his or her own, and yet we make that kind of choice every day. As we've discussed previously, there are no more powerful forces in the creation of happiness and fulfilling relationships than the truth and Real Love. Nothing else comes close. Every time we hide who we are, however, or act like victims, or become angry, or run, we're demonstrating that we believe that our own feeble power to control the world is more effective than the power of truth and Real Love. We're choosing to send the ship on its way and find the shore on our own.

We demonstrate great faith in the truth and in the power of Real Love simply by the act of telling the truth about ourselves and hoping to find the Real Love that will change our lives. As we do that, we are actively seeking—with all its risks and without protecting ourselves—the joy God has promised us. We have many examples in the Bible of people demonstrating their faith by actively asking for what they want:

- A leper came and worshipped Jesus, saying, Lord, if you choose, you can make me clean. And Jesus touched him and said, be clean. And immediately, his leprosy was healed. (Matthew 8:2-3)

- A woman who has been bleeding for twelve years came behind him and touched the hem of his clothing, saying to herself, if only I can do this, I will be healed. Jesus saw her and said, daughter, be glad; your faith has made you whole. And she was healed from that hour. (Matthew 9:20-22)

- Two blind men followed Jesus, saying, Take pity on us. And Jesus said, Do you believe I can heal you? They said, Yes, Lord. And then he touched their eyes and said, It will be a result of your faith. And immediately they could see. (Matthew 9:27-30)

- A captain in the Roman army said to Jesus, Lord, my servant lies at home paralyzed and suffering greatly. And Jesus said, I will come and heal him, but the captain said, Lord, I am not worthy to have you in my house. Just say the word and my servant will be healed, in the same way that I as a commander of men simply speak a word and men accomplish what I say. When Jesus heard this, he was amazed and said, I have not found faith as great as this in all Israel. It is men like this that shall be in the kingdom of heaven, not those who just claim to be born into the house of Israel. And Jesus said to the captain, go, and it will be done as you have asked. And the servant was healed in that hour. (Matthew 8:5-13)

In the space below describe a relationship where you have used anger—or any other Getting and Protecting Behavior—repeatedly. On each such occasion you were demonstrating faith in that behavior, that it would result in the happiness you seek.

- Did it work?
- Were you happier?
- Was the other person happier?
- Did you feel closer to the person you were angry at?

When something hasn't worked a few hundred times in a row, would it be worth considering the possibility of placing your faith in another approach?

Faith and Love

Faith and love are inextricably intertwined. As we exercise faith, our ability to feel loved grows. As we are more loving, in turn, we tap into the power of God and thereby increase in our faith.

- For in Jesus Christ it isn't custom or law that matters, only faith working through love. (Galatians 5:6)

- I pray that God will bless you that Christ may dwell in your hearts by faith, and that you, having strong roots and a good foundation in love, may be able to fully grasp the breadth and length and depth and height of the love of God, which is beyond our understanding, that you might be filled with all the fullness of God. (Ephesians 3:14-19)

SEVEN, 26:40 - 29:48   Faith in Your Partner
CD Track Seven, 1:00 - 4:08

Have you ever gotten up in the morning and said to yourself, "Today I could be loving and make a contribution to the happiness of everyone around me, but *no*, I think I'll be empty, afraid, and selfish instead. I'll use Getting and Protecting Behaviors and spread my own emptiness and fear as far and wide as possible." The very thought is ridiculous. Why? Because on the whole, we really are doing the best we can. We don't intentionally withhold love from people. We fail to give it only because we don't have it to give.

To continue the drowning metaphor from pages 165-7, people drown only because they don't have the strength or skill to move their arms and legs sufficiently to keep their heads above water. No one chooses to let his or her head slip under the water and drown if he or she has the ability to prevent that.

So if people are doing their *best*, does it make any sense for us to demand that they do *better than their best*, just because it would be more convenient for *us* if they did? For any given person, there just isn't a level of performance above *best*, and for us to insist on more than someone's best is both foolish and selfish.

But we do exactly that almost every day. Every time we become impatient or irritated with someone, we're communicating one of the following two messages to that person:

- "Who you are and what you're giving—the best you have—are simply not enough for me. I require much more from you."
- "You could be doing much more, but you're choosing to be less than you could be. You could be swimming safely to shore, but you're *choosing* to drown."

The effect of either message is terribly destructive to other people. When they hear that we believe their best is not enough, or that they're not giving their best, they feel unloved—little surprise, since with our selfishness we're loudly declaring that we *don't* love them. When people feel unloved, they respond to their emptiness and fear with the very Getting and Protecting Behaviors we dislike. Simply by not having faith in people, therefore, we tend to *cause* the behaviors in others that we dislike most.

In the space below and on the next page discuss some situations or relationships where you demonstrated a lack of faith in your partner (husband, wife, friend, child, co-worker). Among other behaviors, perhaps you:

- became irritated with your husband or wife.
- were far too controlling with your children.
- meddled too much in the daily activities of your employees.
- became annoyed with a friend who failed to meet your expectations.

On these occasions when you showed a lack of faith in these partners, what was the result?

- Did your partner respond with Getting and Protecting Behaviors?
- Did your interaction go smoothly?
- Were you happy?
- Did you feel loving?

Get out a 3 x 5 card or a piece of paper. Write the following on it: "The people around me are doing the best they can. When they behave badly, they're just drowning. For me to insist that they do better than their best is foolish and selfish." Carry this message around in your pocket or purse for a week. Get it out and read it at least ten times a day. Then discuss below what difference reading this message had on your interaction with other people for that week.

SEVEN, 29:48 - 32:18   Faith in God
CD Track Seven, 4:08 - 6:38

Describe below your relationship with God. Some possibilities:

- God is angry when I don't do what He wants.
- God is distant and judgmental.
- God loves me sometimes, but not when I'm "bad."
- God loves me even when I make mistakes.

Our ability to have a loving relationship with God is greatly enhanced when we:

- strive to understand His nature.
- tell the truth about ourselves.
- keep His commandments.
- make a conscious effort to exercise faith in Him.

Let's discuss each of these behaviors in turn:

Strive to Understand His Nature

God is our father. The references to this aspect of our relationship are numerous:

- I have said, You are gods; and all of you are children of the most High. (Psalms 82:6)

- Jesus gave to all those who received him the power to become the sons of God. (John 1:12)

- Since we are God's children, we should not think that the Godhead is in the form of gold or silver or stone, which are made by man's efforts. (Acts 17:29)

- All those who are led by the Spirit of God are the sons of God. You have not received a spirit of slavery to return to a condition of fear, but instead you have received the Spirit of adoption, in which we cry out, My dear Father. The Spirit itself testifies to our spirit that we are the children of God, and if we are children, then we will inherit all that God and Christ have, if we suffer with Him, that we may be glorified together with Him. (Romans 8:14-17)

- The Lord God Almighty said, I will be a Father unto you, and you will be my sons and daughters. (2 Corinthians 6:18)

- Because you are sons, God has sent forth the Spirit of his Son into your hearts, crying, my dear Father. So you are no more a servant but a son and therefore will inherit all that God has through Christ. (Galatians 4:6-7)

- We are the sons of God. (1 John 3:2)

Once we understand that God is our *Father*, a father with perfection of every virtue at that, how can we help but begin to change—at least a little—the way we see Him and feel about Him. Earlier in this book I quoted this verse:

If a son asks his father for bread or a fish, is there any father who would give his son a stone or a poisonous snake? So if you, being wicked and flawed human beings, know how to give good gifts to your children, how much more will your heavenly Father give good things to His children who ask Him? (Matthew 7:9-11)

We human beings are flawed, foolish, and weak as parents, and yet we try very hard to give our children the best. Would God not be at least as motivated to love us and give us the best as His children?

The love He promises us is vast. As Paul told the Ephesians,

I pray that God would bless you that Christ may dwell in your hearts by faith, and that you, having strong roots and a good foundation in love, may be able to fully grasp the breadth and length and depth and height of the love of God, which is beyond our understanding, that you might be filled with all the fulness of God. (Ephesians 3:14-19)

Tell the Truth about Ourselves

We have discussed this at length. The more truthful we are with God and with others, the more we can *feel* His love.

Keep His Commandments

As we have discussed elsewhere (pages 161-3), God's command-ments are intended by Him as a way for us to become more loving. They help us to avoid the Getting and Protecting Behaviors (sins) that keep us from feeling all the workings of the Spirit, including His love.

Make a Conscious Effort to Exercise Faith in Him

Faith is a decision. If we make a conscious choice to have faith in God and in His love, we have nothing to lose. If we trust Him, and as a result we feel His love, the reward is infinite. Until we make that choice, however, we will view everything with an air of skepticism that will prevent us from ever feeling His love. Ironically, choosing *not* to have faith in Him is also a kind of faith—a faith that God is *not* what He claims to be. Why make such a choice when it can only lead to emptiness and despair? Why not at least experiment in faith with His promises?

In the following months, diligently apply yourself to the process of telling the truth about yourself and finding Real Love. As you do that, you will be exercising the faith we have spoken of. After you have had considerable experience with feeling unconditionally loved, perhaps months from now, come back to the space below and repeat the exercise you completed above on page 268—where you described your relationship with God. How has exercising faith, telling the truth, and feeling love changed your relationship with God?

As we experience more of the Real Love other people have to offer, we can begin to recognize that Real Love from a Divine source has been more available to us all along than we had realized. That realization changes our understanding of God.

Jesus has actually encouraged us to experiment with His words, to put Him to the test, as it were.

Jesus said, My doctrine is not mine, but His that sent me. If any man will do His will, he shall know of the doctrine, whether it be of God, or whether I speak of myself. (John 7:16-17)

Jesus is saying that if you really want to know whether something is true, you must actually *live* according to that principle. And if we will, the promised rewards are great:

He that believes on the Son has everlasting life. (John 18:36)

CHAPTER EIGHT
Truth Telling with Holly

EIGHT, 32:18 - 33:56   The Prison of Anger
CD Track Eight, 0:00 - 1:38

- Imagine that someone who didn't like you invited you to enter a prison cell and give him or her the key to your cell. Would you accept the invitation?
- Would you be willing to put a ring through your nose, fasten it to a chain, and hand the chain to someone who had clearly indicated that he or she had malignant feelings about you?
- Would you give the keys to your car and the passwords to your computer and bank accounts to just anybody walking on the street?

Obviously, you wouldn't make any of these choices that would lead to your being controlled or imprisoned by people who'd be likely to hurt you, and yet we make choices just this foolish every time we claim that someone has "made us angry." In the moment you claim that I've made you angry:

- you've turned your happiness over to my control.
- I can probably make you angry any time I'd like.
- you've become powerless.
- I own you.
- you're in a prison created by *you*, but a prison you falsely believe I control.

Discuss below and on the next page some situations or relationships where you have been angry at someone:

- Did your anger fill you with peace, contentment, and joy?
- Did you feel like anger made you freer, or did you feel trapped by your anger?
- Did you notice that this person you were angry at became the absolute center of your thoughts? Was that enjoyable?

Anger is a self-created prison, whose key we turn over to others. Not a real bright choice on our part.

EIGHT, 33:56 - 35:37   The Real Reason for Anger
CD Track Eight, 1:38 - 3:19

Even after she had attended a seminar on Real Love, notice what Holly said when she was asked why she was angry. The next word she spoke was *He*. In our society, it is absolutely accepted that other people make us angry. She wasn't fabricating her blame. She really believed that her husband caused her anger.

We've discussed on several occasions, however, the real cause for anger. Anger is a Getting and Protecting Behavior. It's a response to emptiness and fear, which are caused by a lack of Real Love, a condition which has usually existed for a very long time before the individual event we believe has "made" us angry. When we finally get enough Real Love, therefore, our anger disappears.

EIGHT, 35:37 - 36:00   Anger and "I don't love you"
CD Track Eight, 3:19 - 3:41

Holly demonstrates nicely in real life what we discussed in Modules One and Two: When we're angry, other people really do hear us say, "I don't love you." Then they tend to become more empty and afraid, after which they respond with more Getting and Protecting Behaviors, all of which communicate "I don't love you" to us. The cycle is quite destructive.

EIGHT, 36:00 - 39:17   The Power of Real Love
CD Track Eight, 3:41 - 6:58

Imagine that you're dying of thirst in the middle of the desert. I drive up in a Humvee and offer you a large bottle of water. Assuming that the water is clean, would you ask me *where* the water came from? Would it matter to you which company bottled the water? Water from *anywhere* will eliminate your thirst and save your life, so it doesn't really matter where it comes from, does it?

Similarly, Real Love from any source will fill us up, heal our wounds, and make us happy. We make a huge mistake when we insist in any given moment that our love come from a particular person. Holly did that with her husband. She became angry at him only because she had an expectation that in that moment *he* had to supply the love she wanted. Then when he was not accepting and compassionate, she became empty and afraid, and she reacted with Getting and Protecting Behaviors.

When we're angry, we need to get Real Love from anywhere, from anyone who has it, and the first step is to tell the truth about ourselves.

Notice how useless it was for Holly to go into all the details of what her husband did. The more we talk about the details of other people's behavior:

- the more we're trying to be right. As we discussed on pages 238-43, insisting on being right is incompatible with genuine happiness.
- the more distracted we become from what's important. We tend to get lost in the tangle of endless details, which keeps us from focusing on the more important issues of telling the truth and finding Real Love.

In the space below discuss some occasions when you've described an unpleasant interaction with another person.

- Did you enumerate in great detail the mistakes made by the other person?
- Were you trying to be right?
- Did that approach make you genuinely happy?

EIGHT, 39:17 - 40:10   Becoming Loved and Loving
CD Track Eight, 658 - 7:52

Interactions and relationships begin to change dramatically for the better when we change our goals. If we stick with the following two goals, miracles begin to happen:

- Find Real Love for ourselves
- Become more loving toward others

Let's break the entire process of changing our lives and relationships into three simple, concrete goals, and we'll see if it all makes more sense.

1. Find Real Love for ourselves. We accomplish this goal by telling the truth about ourselves, which naturally creates opportunities for other people to see, accept, and love us.

Becoming more loving (the second bulleted goal above) is a natural result of accomplishing two other goals that we have previously discussed, so we'll list them separately here:

2. See other people more clearly. We talked a lot about this mostly intellectual step in Module Two. As we understand that when other people behave badly they are only using Getting and Protecting Behaviors in response to emptiness and fear—they are only drowning—we usually find it much easier to accept them and care about their happiness.

3. Find more Real Love for ourselves. The more Real Love have, the easier it is to give to others.

I'm sure you've noticed that the first and third goals are the same, so we really have only two goals:

Goal	**Method of Attaining the Goal**
Find Real Love for ourselves	Tell the truth about ourselves
See other people more clearly	Tell the truth about others—not about their mistakes but about their emptiness and fear, the true cause of their unproductive behaviors

Although finding more love and being more loving are certainly worthy goals, they can also seem impossibly idealistic. From the time we were small children, we've heard commands to "Be nice" or "Be more kind." We've sat in church and heard that we should be more loving. But most of us simply didn't know *how* to do that. We need simple, clearly identifiable, attainable steps that will enable us to reach those goals, or they won't do us any good at all.

Fortunately, in the above chart you can see that finding and sharing love both begin with telling the truth—about ourselves and others. Telling the truth is a simple action that we can consistently identify and work to accomplish, and it really does "make us free." (John 8:32)

CHAPTER NINE
Holly and What-What-Why-What-What

NINE, 40:10 - 41:06   Keeping it Simple: What Did They Do?
CD Track Nine, 0:00 - 0:56

Let's make the process of truth telling as simple and reproducible as possible. We can do that by remembering five words:

- What
- What
- Why
- What
- What

Let's take these one at a time. First:

- *What* did *they* (or he or she) do?
- What
- Why
- What
- What

Let me clarify again what I mean when I use the word *partner*. A partner is anyone with whom you're interacting—spouse, boyfriend, girlfriend, parent, child, co-worker, or complete stranger—even if it's just for a moment.

When we describe the behavior of a partner, we tend to provide meticulous details about his or her mistakes, mostly for the purpose of making us look right. But all those details tend to distract us from the issues that really matter—finding and sharing Real Love, for example. We need to distill all the details into what they really *mean*, into what really matters.

Notice that I did that here with Holly. She said that her husband:

- was upset at her.
- was unfair in deciding that she was driving too much.
- was unfair and unkind in keeping her children from attending the best school.
- had no understanding about what she was trying to do.
- irritated her.
- was a butt.
- was angry at her.
- argued with her.
- spoke condescendingly to her.

I could have spent all day listening to these details, and if I had done that she might well have been encouraged to provide a hundred more. But we didn't dwell on the details. We boiled the facts down to their meaning. Holly's husband was:

- attacking her.
- not loving.

Throughout their interaction, Holly's husband communicated the message that he was not unconditionally loving her, and that brought an end to any possibility of a loving and productive conversation with her. Feeling unloved, she couldn't possibly have responded in a loving way to his attack. It's his "I don't love you" we need to identify—that's *what* he did—not all the *evidences* of it.

In the space below describe a conflict you've had with someone. Write down a list of his or her individual behaviors. They might include:

- He raised his voice.
- She didn't let me finish what I was saying.
- He said I was stupid.
- She hit me.
- He walked out of the room before the conversation was over.
- She accused me of something I didn't do.
- He was sarcastic.
- She found something wrong with everything I did.
- He didn't appreciate a thing I did.
- She said I never do anything for her.
- He accused me of never wanting to have sex.

You could make this list a hundred pages long, and it would all boil down to this:

- My partner used Getting and Protecting Behaviors.
- My partner was unloving because he or she was empty and afraid and simply *incapable* of loving me. My partner was drowning.

No matter how many offenses or details you list, they'll only confirm the two simple truths above, so why bother to list them? Stick with what matters: *My partner was drowning.*

Now describe another conflict and boil it down to what matters. When you see what all the details really mean, do you see how much more accepting you can be toward your partner? Do you lose your anger?

NINE, 41:06 - 42:28   What Did You Do?
CD Track Nine, 0:56 - 2:18

- What
- *What* did *you* do?
- Why
- What
- What

Holly began to talk about the details of what she did wrong—maybe she drove the car too much—but again, these details just don't matter much. It's not the details that cause conflicts. It's emptiness and fear and Getting and Protecting Behaviors that cause conflict.

We tend to offer buckets of details about our behavior, mostly to justify ourselves. But in the process, we do not help the situation or relationship. As with the details of your partner's behavior, boil the details of your own behavior down to what matters:

- I used Getting and Protecting Behaviors (name them if you'd like).
- I wasn't loving.

It's important to note that when I talked to Holly about being attacking and unloving—and her husband behaving in a similar way—there was no judgment, no criticism, no condemnation. I was simply helping her to *identify* what had happened. If she had felt criticized, the process of Truth → Seen → Accepted → Loved would have come to a crashing halt.

Every good thing becomes possible when we're dealing with the *truth*. We can't make positive progress with lies. So our goal is simply to *identify* the truth. Nobody needs to be beaten for their mistakes. They just need to *see* them. We can't make any progress in a situation or relationship until we have the *truth* to deal with. If we're critical as we identify the truth, people are much less likely to be willing to tell it.

In the space below describe a conflict between you and another person, perhaps one you've already described from before.

Regarding the above conflict, I'm quite certain of two things:

- Your partner was wrong.
- You can justify your behavior in a hundred ways.

Set aside both of those "facts" for a moment, and just answer this question: In the interaction you're describing, were *you* accepting and loving? The answer to this question can be only *yes* or *no*. In fact, circle one of those two words below. You can't answer:

- "No, but . . ."
- "But he . . ."
- "But she . . ."

YES   NO

Some of us have a difficult time answering this question, because we're not entirely certain what it even looks like to be unconditionally loving. To give you some guidelines, if you are unconditionally loving in a given conflict, you:

- show no sign of disappointment or disapproval or irritation.
- are just as interested in hearing what your partner has to say as you are in saying what you want to get across.
- are not hurt by anything your partner says.
- feel no compulsion to correct the mistakes your partner makes during the conversation.
- take complete responsibility for the mistakes you make.

Using those criteria, were you loving in the conflict you described above? If not, simply tell the truth about it. As you do that, you'll create opportunities to feel unconditionally loved, and you'll make much wiser choices in the future.

NINE, 42:28 - 43:52   Why Did You Both Behave As You Did?
CD Track Nine, 2:18 - 3:42

- What
- What
- *Why* did you (and he/she/they) behave as you did?
- What
- What

Discuss the conflict you've been using as an example in the previous sections. On that occasion—or on other occasions when you've had difficult interactions with people—did you feel loved? When we feel loved, we don't behave selfishly.

Now consider the possibility that it's the same with other people in your life. When they behave badly, *they* don't feel loved either. People behave badly because they have a deficiency of Real Love in their lives, *not* because their goal in life is to inconvenience or hurt you. Nobody drowns *to you*. When you understand that, it's much harder to remain irritated at people.

Notice that Holly took responsibility for the fact that her husband wasn't feeling loved. Certainly her emptiness and fear, and her Getting and Protecting Behaviors, *contributed* to his not feeling loved, but it's a virtual certainty that he'd felt unloved long before he even met her. Most people carry around the burden of a lifetime of not feeling loved. We may contribute in some small way to their emptiness or fear, but *we do not cause it.*

NINE, 43:52 - 46:30 What Would You Do Differently Next Time?
CD Track Nine, 3:42 - 6:20

- What
- What
- Why
- *What* would you do differently the next time?
- What

Knowing what you know now about Real Love, how would you handle a similar situation if it were to occur again? Notice that Holly's first inclination was to admit that she had driven the car too much. Actually, whether or not she'd driven the car too much isn't that important, because again, conflict isn't caused by differences of opinion.

So the real question is what would you do differently the next time to address the need for Real Love? In the space on the next page discuss *your* answer to that question as it relates to the conflict you've been examining in the above segments. You might, for example, say, "With the understanding I have now of Real Love, next time I would:

- really listen instead of arguing."
- see the other person as drowning instead of trying to hurt me."
- recognize whether I felt loved enough to continue the interaction."
- say, 'I'm not listening very well. Could you repeat that so I can really understand what you're saying?'"

- apologize."
- not insist on being right."

The examples of how you could behave differently with an understanding of Real Love are endless. As a member of the Real Love Institute—found at www.RealLove.com—you can view the Video Coaching Sessions with Greg to see many examples of how you will be able to respond differently to situations as your understanding of Real Love grows.

Do not admit to being wrong about something if you weren't. You will discover, however, that in any given interaction, you were probably wrong about *something*—you weren't loving enough, didn't listen well enough, and so on.

NINE, 46:30 - 48:07   What Can You Do Now?
CD Track Nine, 6:20 - 7:57

- What
- What
- Why
- What
- *What* can you do now?

What can you do now to address the past event? To be sure, you can't make an unpleasant interaction go away—you can't change the past—but you *can* do something about the emptiness and fear that were generated by the unpleasant interaction.

In the story of Holly, for example, we identified that she could say something to her husband like:

- When we last talked I didn't listen to you.
- I was more interested in being right than in listening to what you were saying.
- I wasn't being loving.
- Would you be willing to talk to me again and give me a chance to really listen?

Notice that I didn't suggest she say anything different about the *position* she took regarding the driving. She didn't have to *agree* with *his* position, because again, the conflict wasn't about differences of opinion. The conflict was about an absence of Real Love.

And what can we do about the lack of Real Love? We've talked about that. We find Real Love for ourselves and share it with others, both of which are accomplished by telling the truth. *That* is what I was recommending to Holly. She responded by telling the truth about her own selfishness and seeing the truth about his emptiness and fear.

As I described to Holly what she could say to her husband in the present about that past conversation—as outlined above—did you notice the change in the expression on her face? She became relaxed. There was no more tension. She could see that such a conversation would actually be delightful.

You'll have a similarly freeing experience as you think of how you could bring more Real Love into *your* relationships. Referring again to the conflict we've been addressing all along, in the space on the next page discuss what you can do now that would change the feelings that were generated by that event. That might include saying things like the following to your partner:

- When I talked to you yesterday, I did a lousy job of listening to you. Would you be willing to talk to me again so I can have another chance to listen to you better?
- You tried to tell me what you thought, and all I did was defend myself. That must have been pretty frustrating for you.

- You've been trying to tell me the same thing many times, haven't you? But every time you try, I get angry, and then it's impossible to tell me anything. I'm sorry I've been so difficult to talk to.
- I need some help with this. The next time I interrupt you when you're talking, would you help me see what I'm doing? Just raise your hand like you were stopping traffic, and I'll try to remember that I asked you to do that so I'd realize I was interrupting you again.
- Thanks for staying with me, even though I can be pretty difficult at times.

NINE, 48:07 - 48:50   The Effect of Real Love
CD Track Nine, 7:57 - 8:40

I'm about to make what is probably the most important point of this entire module. Holly shared a number of quite unflattering characteristics about herself during our discussion—that she had been selfish, hurtful, insensitive, unloving, attacking—and yet did you notice how all these admissions made her feel? After she shared all that, she actually became *relaxed*. She was laughing and obviously happy.

Why? Because she felt *loved*—not *despite* her flaws or *because* of them but *with* them. We simply cannot feel unconditionally loved until we are seen, accepted, and loved for all of who we are, flaws and all, and in this conversation Holly allowed me to see a lot of her.

The lesson here for all of us is very important. As we share who we are with people, we create these opportunities to feel loved, just as Holly did. I cannot encourage you too strongly to do this. As much as possible, share your answers to the questions and exercises in this workbook with others. Although this may feel unfamiliar to you at first, the rewards are enormous.

Practice sharing yourself with others and in the space below discuss how it felt to do that. Some possible examples:

- At first, I felt nervous telling the truth about myself.
- I realized how much of my life I've been hiding from people.
- I was so relieved to finally let people see who I really am.
- It was fun to see that people really like to hear the truth.
- I felt closer to some people almost immediately.
- People are disarmed and charmed by the truth.
- Some people didn't want to hear what I had to say, but it was no big deal. I just changed the subject.
- I got closer to some people in an hour than I've been to other people after years of superficial conversations.

As we have discussed previously, the power of feeling loved is indescribable. We inherit the peace and love of God. We become His children, and then anything is possible.

NINE, 48:50 - 49:50   The Simplicity of Truth Telling
   CD Track Nine, 8:40 - 9:40

When I talk about telling the truth about ourselves, many people envision the following:

- Therapy
- Lying on a couch
- Telling the most embarrassing secrets of their lives
- Exposing themselves in a frightening way

Telling the truth about ourselves is much simpler and less threatening than all that. Just share the mistakes you made today, yesterday, and last week. You'll find plenty to talk about without dredging up the distant past.

In previous sections, we discussed many ways you could tell the truth about yourself. Review those opportunities to share who you are with others. Practice them over and over.

CHAPTER TEN
Truth-telling with Eric

TEN, 49:50 - 51:51   Eric and His Daughter
   CD Track Ten, 0:00 - 2:01

Eric describes his twelve-year-old daughter who doesn't put away the CDs and DVDs she uses. (Imagine a twelve-year-old behaving irresponsibly!) He has a difficult time using the word "angry" to describe his reaction to his daughter, but that is the correct word. We tend to cover up our anger with more socially correct words— some of which are listed on page 50 of the *Workbook*—but until we tell the truth about our anger, we can't begin to take steps to change it.

This next exercise may be difficult for you to remember and to do, but give it a shot. The next time you're angry at someone, detach yourself from the situation for a moment, and observe the reaction of the person you're angry at:

- Does she look happy?
- Does she seem to feel loved?
- Does she look frightened?
- Do you feel closer to her?

TEN, 51:51 - 52:39 What Did She Do?
CD Track Ten, 2:01 - 2:21

- *What* did *they* (or he or she) do?
- What
- Why
- What
- What

It made an enormous difference for Eric to get to the answers that mattered here with his daughter. Sifting away all the details of her behavior—separating the wheat from the chaff, so to speak—he saw that:

- she was selfish.
- she tuned him out.
- she ran.

All of these behaviors are evidences of her not feeling loved, and that's what we need to identify. She was not feeling loved by her father. Until we realize that, we can't come up with a meaningful solution to the conflict.

TEN, 52:39 - 54:26   What Did You Do?
CD Track Ten, 2:21 - 4:10

- What
- *What* did *you* do?
- Why
- What
- What

I told Eric that he had *attacked* his daughter—with his anger—and initially he didn't like hearing that. He preferred to use the word *lectured*. We like to use gentle words to describe our unloving behaviors, because we hope that then we won't look quite so unloving. But until we can describe our behaviors directly and accurately, we will not be able to change them. Eric was angry, and that was an attack.

I persisted in helping Eric see the truth about his behavior not to make him feel guilty but to give him the ability to change his behavior and better love his daughter. The truth—naked, unadorned, and often difficult—really does give us great power and freedom. If we refuse to see the truth, we are forever captive to our ignorance.

So what is the truth about Eric's behavior? With his impatience and anger, he told her, "I don't love you." That was the central message. It was all that mattered. Nothing else he said was of any consequence compared with that message.

In the video segment 50:20 - 52:21 of this module (CD Track Ten, 0:30 - 2:31), Eric talked about his daughter's behavior. He said:

- When she uses the computer, the case is "right there" on top of the computer, and still she doesn't put the CD away.
- I get frustrated when it happens "several times in a short period."
- I get frustrated when it's a "borrowed DVD."

These details all serve to make her look more irresponsible and more wrong, which would justify his anger even better. Most of us have a tendency to look for such justifications. In the space below, describe a conflict where you talked in detail about the mistakes and flaws of the other person. What did you say about him or her to justify your irritation?

TEN, 54:26 - 55:42 Why Did You Both Behave As You Did?
CD Track Ten, 4:36 - 5:59

- What
- What
- *Why* did you (and he/she/they) behave as you did?
- What
- What

As we've discussed before, why do people behave badly? Why do they sin? Because they don't feel loved. Because they're drowning. Regrettably, drowning people do great damage to one another.

TEN, 55:42 - 56:01 What would you do differently next time?
CD Track Ten, 5:59 - 6:11

- What
- What

- Why
- *What* would you do differently the next time?
- What

Eric had a difficult time answering this question. Until we have considerable experience with Real Love, and until we feel more loved ourselves, we often *can't* answer this question. Most of us have been living in a world of Imitation Love and Getting and Protecting Behaviors for so long that we simply cannot imagine behaving differently.

For that reason, be patient with yourself as you begin to take the steps necessary to change your life. Real, lasting changes take time and persistence. Relax. Recognize that you'll make lots of mistakes. You don't have to feel guilty about them. Just tell the truth about them, learn from them, and move on.

CHAPTER ELEVEN
Loving and Teaching Children

ELEVEN, 56:01 - 57:43   Children Need to be Loved and Taught
CD Track Eleven, 0:00 - 1:14

We've established beyond doubt that what children need more than anything else is Real Love. Until they feel loved, they can't hear anything else we want to communicate to them. For that reason, we must always be simultaneously loving and teaching them. As soon as we separate loving from teaching, the learning stops.

As parents we are very attached to the notion that we love our children. We know we're *supposed* to love them, so we're quite fond of the belief that we *do* love them, even on the occasions when that's not true. How can we know, then, if we're loving them? I suggest that one of the more reliable signs is the absence of evidence that we're *not* loving them.

As we've discussed thoroughly in Modules One and Two, during the times we're using Getting and Protecting Behaviors, our primary concern is for *ourselves*. As we interact with our children we therefore need to ask whether we are:

- disappointed with them.
- angry.
- frustrated.
- impatient.
- hurt by their lack of respect or cooperation.
- withdrawing from them.
- avoiding them.
- seeking their approval.
- afraid to offend them.

During the times that the answers to any of these questions is *yes*, we cannot be unconditionally loving our children.

If I could distill the important elements of parenting into a single sentence, it would be this: Never express disappointment or irritation at a child. Why? Because in those moments children can't feel loved, and then it doesn't matter what else you're trying to teach.

Does that mean you can't correct a child? Heavens no. Children need lots of teaching, guidance, and correction. As we are taught in scripture,

- "Children, obey your parents in the Lord, because this is right," (Ephesians 6:1) which of course implies that parents must be instructing their children.

- Correct your son while there is hope, and don't weaken when he cries. (Proverbs 19:18)

- Train a child in the way he should go, and when he is old, he will not leave that path. (Proverbs 22:6)

- Correct your son, and he shall give you peace. Yes, he will give joy to your soul. (Proverbs 29:17)

Immediately after the verse above, however, which states, "Children, obey your parents in the Lord, because this is right," (Ephesians 6:1) Paul adds this:

And you fathers, don't irritate your children, but bring them up in the nurture and counsel of the Lord." (Ephesians 6:4)

Paul adds to this counsel when he speaks to the Ephesians, saying,

Fathers, don't irritate your children, for fear that they will become discouraged. (Colossians 3:21)

Our children certainly do need our guidance, but not with disappointment or anger. No child—or any adult, for that matter—learns better in the presence of anger. We all learn better while we're feeling unconditionally loved.

When your children make mistakes, inconvenience you, fail to do what you've asked, and make you look bad in public, what do you do? Do you:

- sigh with exasperation?
- raise your voice?
- speak in a tone that says, "I mean business"?
- move toward them in an aggressive posture?
- use words that make them feel bad?
- frown?
- roll your eyes?
- raise your hand?

If you're like virtually all parents, your answer to many of these questions is *yes*. Your children do need correction, but they need it in the form of information, guidance, and sometimes consequences to *teach* them the best way to behave. When we're disappointed and angry at them, we're saying they have inconvenienced *us* and that our primary concern in that moment is *ourselves*, not them. We're telling them we do not love them unconditionally, and that message cuts a child to the bone. There is nothing worse we could do, and when we communicate that message, they are wounded every time.

Feeling our disappointment and anger is so painful that they hear virtually nothing else we say.

For the next week, closely watch yourself in each interaction with your children. Do you show any of the signs above? Do you demonstrate disappointment and anger in any way? Nearly all of us do that as parents.

From what you've read here, and from your observations of your children, in the space below on the next page discuss what you've learned about being a parent. You might write, for example:

- What my children need from me more than anything else is Real Love. They need to feel that I care about their happiness no matter what mistakes they make.
- When I'm disappointed and angry, I'm thinking of myself, not the love and happiness my children need.
- I have hurt my children on *many* occasions as I have failed to unconditionally love them. (List a few of those times.)
- I have always fooled myself into believing that I'm a great parent. I've always believed that I love my children.
- I hate to admit it, but with my disappointment and anger, I can see that I'm communicating that my love is conditional.
- I *am* loving my children the best I can—certainly as well as I was ever loved, or as well as I was ever taught by others—but it's not enough. Rather than defend how I've taught them, I need to get enough Real Love in my own life that I can more easily love my children as they really need to be loved, and I need to make conscious decisions to be more loving.
- Every time I begin to feel disappointed or angry at my children, I will think about how I'm being unloving.
- I will still have occasions when I'm not loving, but at least I will recognize them and admit them.

Now talk to a friend about the occasions when you've been an unloving parent, and make a commitment to report to someone each time you're disappointed and angry at your kids. If you have this kind of accountability and truth telling, you'll soon see just how selfish you've been, and you'll feel loved by people who accept you while you're selfish.

When you really get brave, sit down with your children and tell them how you've been selfish and angry, and how you're committed to learning how to be a better parent.

If you'd like to learn a great deal more about becoming a great parent:

- read the book, *Real Love in Parenting*, available at www.RealLove.com.
- go to www.RealLove.com where you can:
  - watch Video Coaching sessions with Greg.
  - watch the Live Video Chats with Greg.
  - participate in the Real Love Forums.
  - watch for other materials on parenting.

ELEVEN, 57:43 - 1:01:36   Consequences
CD Track Eleven, 1:14 - 4:50

Sometimes simply loving and teaching aren't quite enough in getting through to a child. This is when you can move on to the use of consequences, but before you do that you must understand the difference between a consequence and a punishment. The difference is not a matter of technique or the words that are spoken—the difference is *motivation*. The same action that is a consequence when imposed by a loving parent becomes a punishment when it comes from an angry and unloving parent.

Consequences are imposed:

- to teach a principle.
- with genuine concern for the happiness and growth of the child.
- with no desire from the parents for a reward of Imitation Love.
- with no impatience.
- with no anger whatever.

Punishments are given:

- to make a child "pay" for what he's done.
- to teach a child the "lesson" that he must not inconvenience his parents.
- for the sake of "justice."
- with impatience.
- to make a parent feel powerful and "in control."
- with some pleasure that the child is uncomfortable.
- with anger.
- with shaming.

In short, the difference between a consequence and a punishment is anger—or the presence of any of the Getting and Protecting Behaviors. The instant you're angry, you're not teaching with a consequence; you're punishing your child, and the only thing he or she will hear from you is, "I don't love you." Any time we feel irritated with a child, we can only punish him and teach him that he's unacceptable to us. He learns that his safety and happiness are far less important to us than our own convenience. He learns that he's an object to be manipulated and controlled, and then he feels empty and afraid, and he responds with his own special recipe of Getting and Protecting Behaviors. Punishment might temporarily change a child's behavior, but the overall effect is disastrous.

As parents we also must understand the *purpose* of consequences, which is to make the wrong choices sufficiently *inconvenient* to our children that they will *want* to make the right choices. The correct role of consequences is only to guide children toward long term, genuine happiness. Eventually, a child who is sufficiently loved and taught will make right choices simply because he wants to—because it makes him happier—and then he no longer needs the imposition of consequences. We can't impose consequences on a child all his life.

Remember that we as adults learn from consequences—as in the case of getting a speeding ticket from a highway patrolman—so we might consider allowing our children to learn the same way.

God has long used consequences as a teaching tool:

- Whoever strikes a man and kills him will surely be put to death. (Exodus 21:12)

- All souls are mine, and the soul who sins, he will die. (Ezekiel 18:4)

- Jesus said, all those who use the sword will die by the sword. (Matthew 26:52)

- If you will not listen to the voice of the Lord thy God and follow all His commandments, all these curses will come upon you. You will be cursed in the city and in the field, in your basket and your bowl. Your children, harvests, flocks, and herds will be cursed. Because of your wickedness and because you have turned away from me, you will be cursed in everything you do, until you are destroyed. The Lord will plague you with deadly disease until He has completely removed you from the land. He will smite you with weakness, fear, a severe burning, the sword, and diseases of your crops, until you are destroyed. The Lord will strike you with madness and blindness and confusion. And you will be blind at noonday and will not prosper. He will strike you with painful and incurable boils all over your body. You will plant many seeds but harvest little because the locusts will eat them. You will plant vineyard but not drink the wine because worms will eat the grapes. You will have sons and daughters but not enjoy them, because they will be taken into slavery. All these curses will come upon you and follow you until you are destroyed, because you didn't listen to the voice of the Lord. And they will be upon you and your descendants for a sign and a wonder forever, because you did not serve the Lord with joy and gladness. (Deuteronomy 28:15-47, excerpts)

Notice in this last, rather lengthy, list of consequences that some of the consequences are *externally imposed* by God, including diseases, boils, and the like. But in most cases, God is simply describing what naturally happens to us when we don't listen to Him. God's laws exist for our happiness. He describes the behaviors that will lead to our misery, and He tells us to avoid those. And then He describes what will naturally happen when we *don't* avoid those behaviors. For example:

- Weakness. When we ignore the laws that lead to happiness—when we immerse ourselves in Getting and Protecting Behaviors—how could we be anything but weak when it comes to the things of the Spirit? That's a natural consequence of our own choices, not a punishment imposed upon us from without by God.
- Death by sword. God is not talking here only about the material object made of steel. The "sword" refers to a way of life and a condition of the soul—one of anger and contention. And "death" refers not only to what happens when our hearts stop beating. God is far more concerned about the spiritual death that occurs when we are separated from the fruits of the Spirit. When we engage in attacking (just one of the Getting and Protecting Behaviors) with those around us, they only naturally respond with their own Protecting Behaviors, one of which is attacking. And thus we tend to die "by the sword"—spiritually and physically—that we have drawn ourselves.
- Madness and confusion. Getting and Protecting Behaviors—our sins, which is what God is telling us here to avoid—naturally lead to even more emptiness and fear, and many of

us can attest that enough emptiness and fear certainly qualify as madness and confusion.

- Destruction. A life of Getting and Protecting Behaviors— sins—*is* destruction, a living hell.

It's important that we notice the *reason* for God's "cursings"— or consequences—here. He didn't say that the cursing was a consequence of His personal irritation. He said that the curses "will be upon you and your descendents for a *sign* and a wonder." Consequences are a teaching tool, a way of reminding us of the way God has described for our happiness. We should impose consequences upon our children for the same reason.

ELEVEN, 1:01:36 - 1:03:18   What will you do now?
CD Track, 4:50 - 7:17

What better way to show children how to be truthful and willing to admit their mistakes than to be an example of those traits ourselves? As we tell our children the truth about our mistakes, they will actually feel closer to us.

Don't miss this opportunity. Choose a mistake you have made with your children recently and describe it below and on the next page. You don't have to describe all your failures, just an occasion when you responded to them in less than a loving way.

Now admit your mistake to them (or to one of them). You can learn a lot more about how to do this in the book, *Real Love in Parenting*.

CHAPTER TWELVE
Guidelines for Telling the Truth about Ourselves

TWELVE, 1:03:18 - 1:04:34   Tell the Truth Gradually and Persistently
CD Track Twelve, 0:00 - 0:43

Holly and Eric demonstrate that telling the truth about ourselves need not be difficult. We can all learn to do this, and in the process we will find the Real Love we seek.

As you begin the process of sharing who you are with people, don't be in a hurry. Tell just a little of the truth to one or two people, and then assess the result. Gradually, share more of yourself with those who are accepting of you. If you try to share too much too soon, you'll become uncomfortable, and then the process will actually be slowed. As Paul says,

God is not the author of confusion but of peace. Do everything in a decent and orderly way. (1 Corinthians 14:33, 40)

TWELVE, 1:04:34 - 1:06:02   So Many Opportunities to Tell the Truth
CD Track Twelve, 0:43 - 2:21

When I was a young child, I was told that four-leafed clovers were quite rare, and my own experience in looking for them confirmed that. Then one day my aunt came to visit, and for most of that day she had the responsibility of watching over me, my siblings, and her own children. One of her attempts to keep us busy was to pay ten cents for every four-leafed clover we found. With a much greater motivation than I'd had before, I began looking, and I began to find them everywhere—in lawns, vacant lots, sidewalk cracks, and so on. My aunt finally called a halt to the search, because she was running out of money to pay me.

When we really want something—including Real Love—we *will* find a way to get it. But we really have to want it. Many people have said to me that they don't have time to:

- read a book.
- listen to a tape.
- watch a DVD.
- make a phone call to practice telling the truth to a friend.
- attend a Real Love group.
- watch the Live Video Chats and Video Coaching sessions with Greg on the website at www.RealLove.com.

But Real Love isn't something we add to our already busy lives. Real Love *is* life. It's what we do everything else *for*. We're here for the primary purpose of being genuinely happy, and that is simply not possible without Real Love. Don't wallow in excuses about why you *can't* take the steps that lead to a happier life and more fulfilling relationships. Just act. Make the phone calls. Talk to people in person. Attend a group. Tell the truth about yourself and experience the rewards that always follow:

It is written, Eye has not seen, nor has ear heard, neither has entered into the heart of man, the things which God has prepared for those who love Him. (1 Corinthians 2:9)

And the more we immerse ourselves in the effort, the greater shall be our reward:

He who sows sparingly shall also reap sparingly, and he who sows generously shall also reap generously. (2 Corinthians 9:6)

Make a commitment to begin the process of changing the rest of your life. In earlier sections, you discussed examples of truth telling. Now make a list of some of the people you'll share yourself with. Refer to this list daily to remind you of your commitment.

TWELVE, 1:06:02 - 1:07:15   Real Love Groups
CD Track Twelve, 2:21 - 3:28

Real Love isn't just a principle. It's a power that will transform our lives if we'll do what it takes to experience it. The people who participate in Real Love groups tend to learn more and grow faster than everyone else.

If you know of a group already functioning, join it. If you don't know of a group, form one. Starting a group can be relatively easy. The book *Real Love for Wise Men and Women* will tell you all about how to start a group. As you tell the truth about yourself, as you share the book *Real Love* with people, as you share *The Essentials of Real Love* DVDs with friends, you will naturally find people interested in Real Love. Once you've found a few, start meeting together, where you can:

- read the book, *Real Love*, together.
- read the book, *Real Love for Wise Men and Women.*
- watch *The Essentials of Real Love* DVD set, and work on the *Workbook* together.

Real Love groups are nothing more than an opportunity for people to practice being truthful and to practice loving one another. What could be more natural and important than that?

Those interested in pursuing the truth and love have always met with one another, to strengthen each other:

- The members of the church were diligent in meeting with the apostles and studying their doctrine, and in breaking of bread, and in prayers. (Acts 2:42)

- But if we walk in the light, as He is in the light, we have fellowship one with another, and the blood of Jesus Christ His Son cleanses us from all sin. (1 John 1:7)

TWELVE, 1:07:15 - 1:08:15   Real Love for Wise Men and Women
CD Track Twelve, 3:28 - 4:28

Most people are uncomfortable in the beginning of the process of telling the truth about themselves, because it's a new experience for them and because they've rarely seen other people do it. With trial and error, we can figure out this process, but it's much faster if we use the principles found in the book, *Real Love for Wise Men and Women.*

TWELVE, 1:08:15 - 1:09:12   The book, Real Love
CD Track Twelve, 4:28 - 5:55

As you share the book, *Real Love*, with friends, you'll quickly find out which of your friends is interested in learning more about Real Love. It's a non-threatening way of sharing the principles of Real Love with people.

TWELVE, 1:09:12 - 1:10:24   Get Loved Every Day
CD Track Twelve, 5:55 - 7:05

Fires can be very difficult to put out, while preventing them is often a matter of the smallest effort, like flipping a match into a trash can. The healing of our bodies after an automobile accident can sometimes take months or even years, while preventing an accident may take only a fraction of a second. Fixing things can be a lot of work, while prevention is usually much easier.

Similarly, every day I receive phone calls and e-mails from people all over the world, and most of them are in varying degrees of emotional crisis: Their husbands have left them, their wives are screaming at them, their children are in trouble, and so on. Recovering from such crises often requires considerable time and energy, while preventing them can be much easier.

Referring to the metaphor found in segment on pages 137-8, it's easier to steadily build up a supply of twenty million dollars than it is to constantly fuss at people over the loss of two dollars here and there. We need to get doses of Real Love at least every day, because then we'll build up a supply large enough that no single event—or even series of events—can take our happiness from us.

When Joseph, son of Jacob, was in captivity in Egypt, he was called upon to interpret two of Pharaoh's dreams. Joseph told Pharaoh that there would be seven years of abundance in the land, followed by seven years of famine. And Joseph suggested that during the seven years of plenty, Pharaoh should store up excess grain to carry them through the seven years of famine. (Genesis 41:29-36) Pharaoh did as Joseph suggested, and Egypt survived the famine.

We need to do the same in spiritual matters. Spiritual crises are inevitable. There will always be times when we'll be sick, tired, alone, afraid, criticized, lied to, betrayed, and otherwise stressed. When these times come, if we haven't stored up sufficient spiritual reserves, we'll be sorely tried. If, however, we have taken the steps to fill our stores daily, we will not be overwhelmed when the days of difficulty arrive.

We also need to increase our stores of Real Love daily so we'll always be prepared to *give* Real Love. Until we are filled ourselves, we cannot give, and, delightfully, as we give love to others, we miraculously experience a refreshing of the love we have ourselves.

To illustrate this principle, consider that the River Jordan first flows *into* the Sea of Galilee and then *out* to the Dead Sea. The Sea of Galilee of course is where Christ walked on water and where he instructed the fishermen to cast their nets. It's abundant with life. The water stays fresh because there is a flow into the Sea and out of it. The Dead Sea, however, is just that—dead. Why? Because although the River Jordan flows *into* it, nothing flows *out* of it. It's stagnant.

Similarly, we are surrounded by sources of love pouring into us—from our brothers and sisters and from the Lord—and if we allow it not only to flow into us but also to pass through us in our sharing with others, we we will be like the Sea of Galilee, fresh and alive. If we treat love only as something we take, however, we'll become as the Dead Sea, stagnant and dead. Love must circulate to stay alive.

CHAPTER THIRTEEN
The Power of Real Love

THIRTEEN, 1:10:24 - 1:11:39   The Peace and Power of Real Love
   CD Track Thirteen, 0:00 - 1:14

Remember in Module One that you imagined what it would be like to be in a village where everyone loved you. Surrounded by that love, your fear, anger, and other Getting and Protecting Behaviors just disappeared.

We really can live like that all the time. We can find enough Real Love that Getting and Protecting Behaviors are virtually banished from our lives. It's a much more fulfilling way to live, and it's actually *easier* than the exhausting efforts of all that getting and protecting. No sacrifice could be too great in our process of finding that kind of life. As Matthew writes,

> Blessed are those who hunger and thirst after righteousness, for they will be filled. (Matthew 5:6)

The same author also writes that

> Every one that has given up houses, or friends, or family, or wealth, in my name, shall receive a hundred times more and will have eternal life. (Matthew 19:29)

If those are our rewards for giving up houses and wealth, imagine our reward for giving up Getting and Protecting Behaviors.

CHAPTER FOURTEEN
Module Summary

FOURTEEN, 1:11:38 - 1:13:20   Summary of Module Three CD Track, 0:00 - 1:58

MODULE FOUR

CHAPTER ONE
Introduction

ONE, 0:00 - 2:24   Introduction
   CD Track One, 0:00 - 2:24

I once poured a foundation for an addition to my home. The completed foundation didn't look like much of an accomplishment—it rose only a couple of inches above the surrounding ground—but without it all the rest of the building would have been impossible. After completion of the foundation, however, we were able to proceed with construction of the walls, windows, doors, and roof. Without that humble beginning, the rest of the building would have been impossible.

Similarly, Real Love is the foundation for our individual happiness and healthy relationships. Without Real Love, emptiness and fear predominate, and then no productive and loving interactions are possible. With sufficient Real Love, however, emptiness and fear are reduced so much that people can achieve levels of cooperation that in most cases they have never known before. Differences must still be resolved, but that becomes infinitely easier when one or both of two parties care about the other. We have to establish a foundation of Real Love first, after which everything else becomes possible. Remember:

Whoever hears and does what I say is like a wise man who built his house on a rock, and then when the rain fell, and the floods came, and the winds blew and beat upon that house, it didn't fall, because it was built upon a rock. But whoever hears me and doesn't do what I say is like a foolish man who built his house on the sand, and when the rain fell, and the floods came, and the winds blew and beat upon the house, it fell, and the fall was great. (Matthew 7:24-7; Luke 6:47-49)

In the space below, discuss a conflict you recently had with someone. Now imagine that instead of behaving as you did—defending yourself and being right, for example—you had felt completely and unconditionally loved, as you did in the meditation in Module One. Feeling loved and peaceful, can you imagine—even a little—how your interaction with that person would have played out differently? Would you have:

- had a need to be right?
- defended yourself?
- been angry?
- been selfish?

CHAPTER TWO
Keys to Success in Relationships

TWO, 2:24 - 3:25 The Two Keys to Success in Relationships
CD Track Two, 0:00 - 1:01

- Tell the truth about yourself.
- Never try to get any one person—or group of people—to like you.

Most of us spend our entire lives trying in various ways—with what we say, what we do, how we look—to get other people to like us. In the absence of sufficient Real Love, it's only natural that we would do that. The instant we attempt to *get* people to like us, however, we cannot feel loved unconditionally. Even if people were actually to give us Real Love, we couldn't feel it. We could assume only that we were being rewarded for our manipulations.

In the space below discuss some relationships where you really wanted the affection of a particular person. For most of us, that describes every close relationship we have. When you succeeded in winning the attention or affection you wanted, did you notice any of the following?

- The initial rush you felt from the attention didn't last long.
- Although the affection felt great, you felt anxious about the possibility of losing it.
- You felt like you had to be continuously doing something to *keep* it.

These are certain signs that you were *buying* Imitation Love, which never produces happiness. Regrettably, buying Imitation Love is so common in relationships that it's become the standard.

TWO, 3:25 - 4:43   Stop Getting Love and Start Finding It
CD Track Two, 1:01 - 2:19

I have spoken to many groups of singles, and when I say that we must stop doing anything to get other people to like us, a look of horror passes over the faces of many in the crowd, and some even say out loud, "But if I don't do anything to get people to like me, who *will*?" They just can't imagine being loved for who they really are. This speaks volumes to how common our manipulations for attention are.

Imagine that I hire a private detective and do all the other research necessary to learn everything I can about ten people randomly selected from a crowd. With that information I modify what I say and do—I change who I *am*—to win their approval, and in the process I succeed in establishing friendships with eight of the ten.

Now imagine that I do no research at all, and instead I simply share who I am with ten people. Only two people like me, but those two care about me unconditionally, and two sources of Real Love are far more valuable than eight sources of Imitation Love.

We must remember that no matter how much attention we *earn*, it's worthless. Real Love is infinitely valuable, but it can't be bought. It can be *found*, however, after we tell the truth about ourselves.

As you begin the process of telling the truth about yourself, in the space below and on the next page, describe how it feels to be accepted and loved *freely*, without doing anything to earn it.

TWO, 4:43 - 5:52   Quit Trying to Milk the Bull
CD Track Two, 2:19 - 3:28

Describe some relationships where you were irritated at your partner. Can you now see that you were insisting on getting love from someone who either could not or would not love you? At this point many people say, "But I wasn't looking for love. I just wanted a little:

- respect."
- appreciation."
- gratitude."
- cooperation."
- approval."
- honesty."
- attention."
- companionship."
- help."

In the absence of sufficient Real Love, we insist on the items listed above as forms of Imitation Love. In short, we *are* demanding love—we're trying to milk the bull—but what we're seeking is not Real Love.

In the space on the next page describe the consequences that followed your insistence on attention or affection from a partner. Did you notice that:

- you became increasingly demanding?
- your partner became more demanding or defensive?
- your frustration grew?
- your partner became increasingly angry or withdrawn?
- your relationship became more strained?
- you never got the affection you were looking for?

Milking the bull has uniformly unpleasant effects, both for us and for the bull. We need to recognize more quickly when we're doing that.

We feel especially justified in milking the bull when the bull has made a *promise* to give us milk. Many of our parents, for example, told us they loved us on many occasions, which we also interpreted as a promise to continue loving us. And they did their *best* to love us, but because they had never received enough Real Love themselves, they were quite unable to give us the unconditional love we needed and were therefore unable to fulfill their promises to us. In our condition of great emptiness, that failure was and is enormously disappointing.

Our spouses—as another example—stand up in front of our families, friends, the minister, and even God to declare that they will always love us, but again they don't realize that they're making a promise they just can't fulfill. When their performance begins to fall below what we expect, we feel justified in milking the bull.

TWO, 5:52 - 7:46   A Revolutionary Approach to Dating
CD Track Two, 3:28 - 5:20

60% of marriages end in divorce, and roughly 1-2% of marriages end up as happy as both partners had once hoped. In view of these dreadful figures, something is obviously wrong with the process we use to find and build relationships. Something is wrong with the way we date.

No relationship can succeed unless it's built upon a foundation of truth, so why not start off with the truth right from the beginning? Yes, if you tell the truth about yourself, some people you date *won't* like you. So what? You really *don't* want to avoid that. In dating most people are diligently trying to avoid rejection. Wrong approach. You don't want to avoid rejection in dating; rather, you want to get to and through rejection *faster*.

In dating you want to find out *quickly* which partners are not capable of accepting you as you are, so you can move on and find those who *are* capable of accepting you. You want to go through the unworkable relationships faster. It's much more efficient.

To learn a great deal more about how to make dating more productive, and how to tell the truth about yourself in dating,

- read the book, *Real Love in Dating*, available at www.RealLove.com.
- go to www.RealLove.com where you can:
  - watch the Video Coaching sessions with Greg.
  - watch the Live Video Chats with Greg.
  - participate in the Real Love Forums.
  - watch for other materials on dating.

CHAPTER THREE
Defining a Relationship

THREE, 7:46 - 9:33   Definition
CD Track Three, 0:00 - 1:47

A relationship is a natural result of people making independent choices. A relationship is *not*:

- what we *want* it to be.
- what we *hope* it will be.
- what we try to *make* it.
- what we *wish* it were.

The relationships you now have are a natural and unavoidable result of the combination of:

(1) who *you* are, which is a result of a lifetime of experiences and choices *and*
(2) who your *partner* is, also a result of a lifetime of experiences and choices.

It's little wonder, then, that superficial techniques do not produce long-lasting changes in relationships. There are no shortcuts in developing or changing relationships in a meaningful way.

In the space below, discuss a relationship that you want to be different. Do you sense the futility of trying to make that change? Do you feel the impossibility of trying to blend blue and yellow to produce pink or purple?

CHAPTER FOUR
The Law of Choice

FOUR, 9:33 - 11:40   The Law of Choice
CD Track Four, 0:00 - 2:07

Everyone has the right to choose what they say and do. If that were not true, the world would be a dismal place.

Although the truth of this law is obvious, we still resent it when other people's choices inconvenience *us*, and in those moments of irritation we're declaring that we'd like to modify the Law of Choice to read:

- Everyone has a right to make their own choices until they inconvenience *me*.
- Everyone has a right to make their own choices as long as they agree with *me*.
- Everyone has a right to make their own choices—except *my children* or spouse or whoever.

In the space below discuss some occasions when you've been angry at people.

- Have you wanted to stop them from doing something that inconvenienced or hurt you?
- Have you wished you could get them to do something you wanted?
- Have you wanted to change their opinion about something?
- Have you wanted to get them to stop saying something?

If your answer to any of these questions is *yes*, you have at least some desire to violate the Law of Choice, the most important principle governing human behavior.

God and the Law of Choice

It should be obvious that God operates *within* the Law of Choice, that even He is not above it. What evidence do we have for that? The history of this world has been rife with struggle, disease, death, war, and all manner of pain to the children of God. And yet He stands by and allows it to happen.

- Herod killed every child in Bethlehem and in the surrounding area, from age two and younger. (Matthew 2:16)

- And you shall hear of wars and rumors of wars. Nation shall rise against nation. (Matthew 24:6)

- God told Joseph in a dream to leave the place where they lived in Israel and go to Egypt, because otherwise Herod would kill Jesus as a baby. (Matthew 2:13)

For ages men have debated the question of how God could allow such suffering. Does He not care about us? Is He limited in His power? Does He exist at all?

We make a mistake when we try to answer this question without first asking more basic questions that will enable us to establish a firm foundation of understanding upon which we can build the answer to our original question.

Before we ask why God does a specific thing, let's ask what His primary overall purpose is. Jesus established that in a conversation with Simon Peter:

Peter, do you love me more than everyone else? And Peter said, Yes, Lord you know that I love you. Jesus said, Feed my lambs. He said the second time, Peter, do you love me? And he said, Yes, Lord you know that I love you. He said, Feed my sheep. He said the third time, Peter, do you love me? And again he said, Lord, you know all things, so you know I love you. Jesus said, Feed my sheep. (John 21:15-17)

What does God want most? What does he want as evidence of our love for Him? That we feed His sheep, that we devote ourselves to the happiness of His children. God's greatest goal, His highest purpose, is *our happiness*.

It therefore follows that He will do whatever it takes to contribute to our happiness. So now, the next question: What makes *us* happy? When we understand that, we'll comprehend a great deal about why God does anything.

We are here to be happy, but how is that accomplished? What makes us happy? Consider some possibilities:

- Comfort
- Convenience
- Full bellies
- Lack of pain
- Ease
- Wealth
- Entertainment

These couldn't possibly be the answers, and for at least two reasons:

- If these are the things that make us happy, those who have the most of them—the most dollars, the most food, the greatest comfort, and so on—would be the happiest among us, and that has never been the case.
- If these are guarantees of genuine happiness, God would see to it that we always had enough of those things. But He doesn't, so obviously these items are not the keys to happiness.

But you already knew that, because Jesus has told us that *love* is the greatest commandment—and therefore the greatest goal—and we know from experience and from the Spirit that genuine happiness comes from feeling loved and from unconditionally loving others.

It is in love that we find genuine happiness, and *because God's highest purpose is our happiness, He will do whatever is required to help us develop love in our lives*, whereas comfort, convenience, physical safety, and the absence of pain are by far secondary concerns in His eternal perspective. That understanding brings a powerful light to the original question we asked: How could God allow suffering or injustice or sickness or war?

Imagine, for example, that a man is being hateful to me and treating me unfairly. If my goal in life is to learn to be loving, this man's behavior is actually a singular opportunity for me to accomplish my goal. As Jesus said,

Don't resist evil, but whoever hits you on the right cheek, turn your other cheek to him also. And if someone takes away your coat, let him have your cloak also. Whoever forces you to go a mile, go with him two. In the past you have heard that it said, You should love your neighbor and hate your enemy, but I say, Love your enemies, bless those who curse you, do good to those who hate you, and pray for those who cruelly use and persecute you, so you may be the children of your Father in heaven. If you love those who love you, what reward can you expect? Even the worst among you do that. And if you welcome only your brothers, how is that more than anyone does? Don't even the worst of men do that? (Matthew 5:39-47)

There are so many important lessons in this one passage. It's a virtual primer about how to grow in love:

- When someone hits you or forces you to do something, notice that God expresses no interest whatever in stopping them from offending you.
- His emphasis is on how we respond to these inevitable injustices and afflictions.
- But why? Why should we turn our cheek, give our cloak also, and go the second mile? So we can learn to be doormats? So we can learn to suffer? So we won't start a fight with other people? *No*, but so we can learn to be loving under increasingly difficult circumstances.
- If we love only those who are kind to us, we won't grow in our ability to learn. Anyone can love those who are nice to him or her.

A word about this last bulleted point. If you want your muscles to become stronger, you have to actually stress them. You must lift weights at the limit of your capacity, or your muscles will not grow. You must, in fact, experience some discomfort. If you can easily lift ten pounds, for example, it will not matter how many times you lift it, your strength will not change.

It is the same with our spiritual muscles. We can't just meditate in a cloister somewhere and expect to increase in love—although meditation and prayer are certainly beneficial and even necessary. Love is learned by practice, and by increasing the "weight" on the spiritual bar we lift. If we love those who are kind to us, we can't grow. If, on the other hand, we have increasing experiences with people who are difficult to love, we can grow in our ability to be loving.

Imagine that you are an athlete preparing for a weight-lifting competition, and I am your trainer. Because I'm concerned that you might over-exert yourself or become injured in the training process, each time you show up for a practice session I do you a "favor" by giving you only light weights to lift, or I give you heavy weights, but I lift them for you. With that approach I will certainly spare you a lot of sweat and pain, but when the time comes for you to perform in a competition, you will discover that with my favors I have actually crippled you.

It is the same in spiritual matters. If God were to give us only light weights, or if He were to lift all the heavy weights for us, how would we ever grow? How would we become increasingly happy, which is our real reason for being here? If He rescued us from all our trials, He would *hurt* us, and He is wise enough to recognize and remember that.

Jesus recognized the indispensable role of suffering in His own life and actually rebuked Peter for suggesting that it could be avoided:

When Jesus talked about his future suffering, and that He would be killed and raised again the third day, Peter argued, saying, No, Lord, this will not happen to you. And Jesus said, Peter, get out of my sight, Satan. You're not seeing things as God does, but as men do. (Matthew 16:21-27)

So, finally:

1. if God's greatest great purpose is our happiness, and
2. if we learn to be happy as we practice loving, and
3. if we learn the most about loving under difficult circumstances,
4. why in the world would God rescue us from all our difficulties?

He wouldn't. He would allow us to learn from our trials, rejoicing not in our sufferings but in what we're learning from them. He sees the end from the beginning. He's not happy that we experience pain, but He also knows that it's absolutely necessary if we are to become as He is. In suffering we learn best how to love and be happy. Suffering also motivates us to focus on matters of the Spirit and to rely on the hand of God instead of our own strength.

Long ago, the prophet Joshua said, "Choose this day whom you will serve, but as for me and my family, we will serve the Lord." (Joshua 24:15) God Himself—the most powerful Being in the universe—refuses to interfere with our right to make our own choices. He recognizes that without the Law of Choice, we couldn't possibly learn and grow. How could we suppose that by limiting the choices of others we could come up with a better way than God has devised?

More about Affliction

It's very tempting to wish for less trial and affliction in our lives, but when these times come I encourage you to consider the following passages:

- My son, don't despise the correction imposed by the Lord, or lose heart when God reprimands you. Because God corrects those He loves and chastises every son He receives. If you endure correction, God associates with you as a father with his sons, because what son is not corrected by his father? But if you have no correction, which we all have, then you are illegitimate children, not sons. Furthermore, our earthly fathers have corrected us, and we respected them, so is it not even better to obey the Father of spirits and live? Because our earthly fathers corrected us for just a short time in their own way, but God corrects us for our best good, that we might take upon ourselves His holiness. Of course, no correction seems enjoyable at the time, but seems difficult, but afterward it produces the peaceful results of righteousness to those who have been trained by it. (Hebrews 12:5-11)

- My brethren, consider yourselves happy indeed when you fall into various trials, knowing that the trying of your faith develops endurance. Let patience finish its work, that ye may be perfect and whole, lacking nothing. (James 1:2-4)

- The man who endures temptation is blessed, because when he is tested he will receive the crown of life promised by the Lord to those who love Him. Let no man say when he is tempted, it is God who tempts me, because God cannot be tempted with evil, nor does he tempt any man. But every man is tempted instead and seduced by his own lusts. (James 1:12-14)

- Don't think strangely of the fiery trial which will test you, as though it were some odd experience. But rejoice, since you are sharing in the sufferings of Christ, so that when his glory will be revealed, you will be very joyful. If you are criticized for believing in Christ, you are blessed, for the spirit of glory and of God rests upon you. (1 Peter 4:12-14)

- My son, don't despise the correction imposed by the Lord, or get tired of his correction. Because God corrects those He loves, even as a father corrects the son he cherishes. (Proverbs 3:11-12)

FOUR, 11:40 - 12:41   Anger and the Law of Choice
  CD Track 2:07 - 3:09

This conflict between Joan and Tyler is typical of so many: One person in a relationship doesn't like being inconvenienced by the behavior of the other person and feels justified in demanding that the other person change his or her behavior.

But we keep running into the Law of Choice. Other people really do get to make their own choices, *even when we don't like it.* When we really understand the Law of Choice, we realize that it's not a restriction in our lives, but the foundation of personal happiness and great relationships. It actually gives us freedom.

CHAPTER FIVE
The Three Choices

FIVE, 12:41 - 13:23   The Three Choices
  CD Track Five, 0:00 - 0:42

Remember that a relationship is the natural result of people making independent choices. Tyler has the right to be a pig, and Joan doesn't have the right to change that. She does have the right to independently make her own choices, however, and those choices really boil down to just three categories:

- Live with it and like it.
- Live with it and hate it.
- Leave it.

When we can finally give up the fourth choice—which isn't really a choice at all—to change the pig, we can begin to make choices that lead to happiness and to great relationships.

In the space on the next page discuss some of the relationships where you've been angry at people and tried to change them in some way.

- Has trying to change other people ever made you happy?
- Has it ever made you feel genuinely closer to your partner?
- How much work was it? Wasn't it absolutely exhausting?
- Has it ever really worked? With all your efforts did you really change people? Or were the changes you saw just superficial and temporary?

FIVE, 13:23 - 13:58 The Stupid Choice: Live with the Pig and Hate It
CD Track Five, 0:42 - 1:17

In the space on the next page discuss a past relationship that you weren't happy with.

- Did you complain about it to your partner?
- Did you feel frustrated and irritated by it?
- Did you stay in it?
- Did you complain about it to other people?

If so, you were living with the pig and hating it. No one is ever happy while making this choice, and yet we make it frequently. We make it because we don't see the other choices.

FIVE, 13:58 - 16:38   Leave the Pig
CD Track Five, 1:17 - 3:57

In the short term, it's foolish to put yourself in a situation where you *know* beforehand that you're not equipped with enough Real Love to respond well. In those cases, leave the pig. Stay out of that interaction. Stay away from that person, which was the advice I gave in the following situation to a woman named Susan.

"I've really been having a great time with Real Love," she said. I've been practicing with friends, and I've been in a Loving Group for a couple of months. But it all falls apart every time I talk to my mother. She's demanding, critical, and angry, and it just destroys any Real Love I have. I don't know how to handle her."

"*Don't* handle her," I said. "Until you feel more loving, don't talk to her. Not because *she* is a problem, but because *you're* not yet able to love her."

"What a relief that would be," she said, "but how could I do that? I can't just not answer the phone, can I?"

"Actually, you could," I said. But then we discussed some things Susan could say to her mother, including the following:

- "Mom, I'm working on some personal stuff, and I need to do it alone. It's not about you. For a while I need you not to call. I'll call you in _____ weeks and let you know how it's going."
- After just a few minutes, when Susan feels the tension beginning to build in a conversation with her mother, she says, "Mom, I have go to now. I'll call you again in a couple of days."
- "I've been feeling stressed lately, and I need some time alone. This is not your fault. I just need to talk less on the phone for a while."

There are several reasons for leaving a situation or relationship. Let's discuss three of them:

- Temporary separation as an opportunity to grow in Real Love
- Permanent separation, because of inability to grow in Real Love in that situation
- Permanent separation, because of no interest in pursuing a relationship

Temporary Separation as an Opportunity to Grow in Real Love

In the example above with Susan, I was not recommending that she permanently leave her mother. Nor was I suggesting that simply spending time apart would make a difference. Rather, I suggested that Susan use the time away from her mother to continue telling the truth about herself to her friends, so she could heal her existing wounds and build up her storehouse of Real Love. After several months of doing that, Susan had a much larger supply of Real Love, and she was then able to resume interaction with her mother in a more loving way.

In Susan's case, the separation from her mother was one of several months. In many cases, a temporary separation can be for a much shorter period, even as brief as a few minutes, as in the following story of Michael.

Michael could feel himself slipping into one of those familiar old arguments with his wife, Elaine. He had learned enough about Real Love to know that nothing good would come of that, but he also felt trapped. How could he get out of this? The word *trapped* reminded him that he always had three choices. He knew he didn't want to live with it and hate it, and he knew he wasn't loving enough to live with it and like it, so he considered the possibility of "leaving the pig."

He said to Elaine, "Sweetie, I want to hear every word you have to say on this subject—I really do—but I can't do it right now. Can I finish this discussion with you in, say, half an hour?"

Elaine wasn't eager to have another argument either, so she consented to the break. Michael called a friend, Robert, and said, "I was in the middle of another argument with Elaine, but instead of finishing it, I decided to call you."

"Wow," said Robert, "you're getting smarter all the time. So what did Elaine do?"

Michael began to describe some of the unkind things Elaine had said, and after a few sentences, Robert interrupted: "So with her words and behavior, she said she didn't care about you, right?" Notice that this is the first *What* in the *What-What-Why-What-What* sequence we first introduced on page 278.

Robert continued, "So when you heard the deadly 'I don't love you' from Elaine, how did you feel?"

They talked until Michael understood that he had felt empty and afraid (the *Why* of *What-What-Why-What-What*) and that then he had responded with Getting and Protecting Behaviors of his own (the second *What*), which made everything worse. As Michael felt more loved by Robert during his separation from Elaine—which lasted only for a few minutes—his emptiness and fear disappeared. He then went back to his conversation with her and found that talking to her was relatively easy in the absence of emptiness and fear and Getting and Protecting Behaviors. Without emptiness and fear, conflicts just disappear.

Permanent Separation, Because of Inability to Grow in Real Love in That Situation

Let me introduce you to Brenda, who illustrates another reason to "leave the pig." She and her husband, Brian, had been in an unhappy relationship for a dozen years. Like many marriages, theirs was characterized by an increasing exchange of Getting and Protecting Behaviors—natural reactions to the failure of Imitation Love that had once briefly made them "happy." In the two years before I met Brenda, she had learned about Real Love and had begun to experience some genuine happiness as she was loved by a few of her friends.

As Brenda felt more loved, she naturally shared that love with the people around her, including her husband. But Brian was so empty and afraid that he just could not stop protecting himself around Brenda, despite the Real Love she offered. He continued to be critical and angry, and he went out of his way to attack her.

Brenda became quite good at loving many people, but Brian was often so aggressive that she became frightened and protected herself instead of giving him the love he needed. Although she tried to be loving, she came to dread being around him.

As we develop the ability to be unconditionally loving, we don't become perfectly loving all at once. We learn to love gradually, and in the beginning of the process our ability is limited. In the beginning, we can be loving under relatively easy circumstances, but under more difficult conditions—when we're being attacked, for example—we just don't have what it takes.

Our ability to love grows with practice, in much the same way that we increase our ability to do anything else with practice—increasing our physical strength, for example, by lifting weights. Let's imagine that as we first begin lifting weights, we can lift only ten pounds above our heads. Certainly with time our ability to lift will increase, but in the beginning we'd be most unwise to attempt a lift of, say, two hundred pounds. Such an attempt could seriously injure us.

Similarly, as we exercise our ability to love other people in the beginning, we don't want to try to take on too much weight, because such an effort could injure us emotionally and spiritually. Some conditions could be overwhelming. Certain people, could emotionally crush us under the burden of their Getting and Protecting Behaviors. We need to limit our attempts to conditions we can handle. Is it *unloving* for us to avoid these impossible situations or people? Not at all. It's simply good sense. In fact, it's the most loving thing to do.

Such was the case with Brenda. As she received Real Love from her friends, she really did change her life. She gained the ability to be loving in circumstances she couldn't possibly have handled before, but she was still a beginner. Brian was well beyond her ability to love. His needs were just too great and his attacks too much for her.

She, would have liked to avoid interaction with him more completely, but he was her *husband*, so to some extent he was in her face almost every day. With each interaction she couldn't handle well, she suffered yet additional wounds, and it was becoming more than she could bear. She would make two steps forward with her Loving Group, and then with Brian she'd slide three steps back.

Brenda finally made the decision that if she stayed with Brian, she just couldn't keep making progress in her life. She filed for divorce. Whenever she was asked about it, she made it clear that *she* was the problem, not him. Yes, I know that Brian was a major contributor to the conflict in their marriage, but Brenda wisely recognized the axiom that on the whole, the mistakes of other people are pretty much none of our business. As we talked about on page 247, one ounce of effort made to correct our own flaws will be more productive than a ton of effort directed to correct the flaws of others.

Some relationships are so difficult that they bring our own progress in feeling loved and loving others to a complete standstill. This is *not* to blame our partners in those relationships, only to identify that *we* are not loving enough to respond well to some people, for whatever reasons. Life really is like a journey, and as we're growing it can often feel like we're climbing a mountain. Some people and some conditions are just unnecessarily difficult—even crippling—burdens, like carrying an extra hundred pound pack up a mountain. In some cases, it's wiser to set the pack down and move on, rather than continue struggling with a load we can't handle, a load that might even injure us.

In most cases, it's unwise to abandon a relationship—especially a marriage—until *we* have applied ourselves fully to the finding and sharing of Real Love. Until we have brought sufficient Real Love to a relationship, we simply cannot know what that relationship could have been like. Notice that Brenda tried for two years to share Real Love with Brian before she gave up and decided to move on.

More About Divorce

Divorce is one form of "leaving the pig," and I emphasize that the word *pig* is just a reference to the story from the seminar and not intended to be a slur on the person or situation you're leaving. If you are contemplating a divorce, consider the following and discuss the answers in the space on the next page:

- Are you blaming your unhappiness on your partner, when the real cause is the inability you *both* have to feel and share Real Love?
- If you leave your marriage before you've learned how to find and share Real Love, you'll simply move on to another relationship that will be unloving and difficult—because you're the same unloving person as before.
- Are you willing to experience the profound rewards of keeping the commitment you made to stay with your partner and *learn* how to be loving?

Talk to a friend or group about what you realize as you consider the above questions.

If you have a friend who is contemplating a divorce, and who trusts your opinion, share with that person what you know about Real Love and suggest that he or she learn a lot more about how to love unconditionally before ending the relationship with his or her spouse.

If you are already divorced, look back at your marriage and answer the following questions in the space below and on the next page:

- Are you blaming your ex-spouse for your divorce, when the real cause was *your* inability to feel and share Real Love?
- Can you see your ex-spouse's behaviors—no matter how awful they became—as Getting and Protecting Behaviors, proving only that he or she was drowning?
- Understanding that your ex-spouse was drowning—doing the best he or she could do—can you not easily let go of all the hurt and anger?
- Do you really want to spend the rest of your life angry at another person, creating only unhappiness for yourself?

Permanent Separation, Because of
No Interest in Pursuing a Relationship

As Brenda grew in her ability to love, she discovered an ability to love many people, and that greatly enriched the joy in her life. She began to spend more and more time with people who had an interest in Real Love, who wanted to be honest about themselves and practice being loving. Simply put, why participate in a relationship where Real Love isn't being given and/or received?

One of her old friends, Melissa, was deeply mired in acting like a victim. No matter how much Brenda told the truth about herself, Melissa preferred to complain about everything and everybody. Brenda did the simple math regarding this relationship:

- Am I having an opportunity here to be loving? Yes. No matter whom I'm with I can always practice being loving.
- Am I *being* loved? No.
- Is Melissa practicing being loving? No.
- Is Melissa receiving love? No, because of her use of Getting and Protecting Behaviors, she can't *feel* Real Love. She can receive any attention from me only as a form of Imitation Love.

The Real Love Score in this relationship: one: (only the first question scored a *yes*). As hard and cold as it sounds, our time in this life is finite, so we are wise to spend it as efficiently as possible. Brenda recognized that with her other friends, at least they were making efforts to tell the truth and be loving, so the *yes* score in relationships with them was usually 3-4. Her time was more productively spent with such people, so she just made progressively less contact with Melissa. I emphasize that this was not entirely a selfish choice on Brenda's part. Sure, she preferred to be with people who could love her unconditionally, but she also recognized that other people could *receive* her love much more easily than Melissa could. Brenda's choice was actually loving.

Brenda didn't cast Melissa aside like an old rag. Brenda didn't consider herself superior to her friend. She just gradually moved on, and, frankly, Melissa didn't mind. As we change the direction of our lives toward Real Love and genuine happiness, it's a loving act to invite the people around us to enjoy the experience with us. If they choose not to do that, however—which is certainly their right—then our separation is just a natural result of the two different directions we're taking. Remember that a relationship is a natural result of people making independent choices. If you're pursuing Real Love and I am not, we *will* drift apart. I am not *leaving* you, nor are you leaving me; we're just going in different directions.

FIVE, 16:38 - 19:35   Live with the Pig and Like It
CD Track Five, 3:57 - 6:53

Let's examine some of the possible meanings of "Live with the pig and like it":

- Grit your teeth and endure a miserable condition: "This is just the way it is, so learn to like it."
- Live with the pig and enjoy living like a pig.
- Live with the pig, but because you are filled with Real Love, you can love the pig and enjoy living with the pig despite the inconveniences that the pig presents.
- Live with the pig, but because you are filled with Real Love, you can clearly see solutions that will enable you to be far less inconvenienced by the pig.
- Do whatever the pig wants—be a doormat.

Grit your teeth and endure a miserable condition

We could interpret "Live with the pig and like it" to mean that we have to grit our teeth and "tough it out" in a miserable situation. But we really can't do that for long. Nor can we *pretend* that we like it when we don't. Both of these choices would really be "Live with the pig and hate it." Life's too short for this exhausting and dishonest approach.

Live with the pig and enjoy living like a pig

So maybe we could live with the pig and just learn to enjoy living like a pig. Maybe we should tell Joan to just readjust her priorities and decide that living with filth isn't so bad. Ridiculous. If she tries to do this, she'll end up even more resentful and unhappy.

Live with the pig, but because you are filled with Real Love, you can love the pig and enjoy living with the pig despite the inconveniences that the pig presents

We could also call this, Live with the pig, love the pig, and enjoy your life.

Without sufficient Real Love, we're empty and afraid, which is painful. In that condition, very little inconvenience is required to push us over the edge and make our situation intolerable. When we have enough Real Love, however, we have the greatest treasure in the world. We feel complete and happy, and in that condition minor inconveniences become just that—minor. As we discussed on pages 137-8 , when we have twenty million dollars, the loss of two dollars really is a small matter.

In short, the more Real Love Joan has in her life, the less she'll be bothered by socks on the floor. Really.

Why would we choose to live with a pig when we could just leave the pig? In many cases, the pig has numerous other qualities that make a relationship desirable, and with enough Real Love in our lives, we'll finally see the whole person, not just what he or she does that inconveniences us, and then we can learn to live with the negative qualities. Or perhaps there is some degree of obligation to stay with the pig, as with a spouse or family member. This is always a very personal decision, one that none of us can make for someone else.

Live with the pig, but because you are filled with Real Love, you can clearly see solutions that will enable you to be far less inconvenienced by the pig

In the absence of sufficient Real Love, we are consumed by emptiness and fear. We see every situation in terms of how it could serve us or hurt us. Blinded by emptiness and fear, we don't see people or situations clearly. Instead we respond mindlessly with Getting and Protecting Behaviors, which make every interaction far less productive.

When we have enough Real Love, however, our emptiness and fear greatly diminish or even disappear. We can then see people and situations clearly. We can respond to people without Getting and Protecting Behaviors, and then there's a possibility that people won't feel threatened and won't respond in turn with their own Protecting Behaviors.

When we're not selfishly concerned with our own needs and fears, we can pay attention to the needs and fears of others, and then a beautiful cooperation becomes possible. Notice what happened when Joan no longer lashed out at Tyler—when she eliminated the "I don't love you" from the conversation. She was able to implement a solution that both addressed her need for a clean house *and* showed an interest in Tyler's happiness. *That* is what we always want. Any time we attempt to address our needs without paying attention to the needs of our partner, the outcome will not be positive.

In the space on the next page discuss a relationship where you are having frequent conflicts. Explain how you could implement the choice, "Live with it and like it." Following are a few examples to help get you started:

- My wife is late to everything, and we argue about it all the time. Now I see that all this time I've been trying to change her, and she's been hearing me say, "I don't love you." It's not working. I'm going to quit pushing her about being late, and instead I'll try discussing with her calmly what we can do to be on time more often.
- I've been yelling at my son for years to get his room clean. I can get him to do it for a few days, but then we're back to the yelling. This is crazy. Why do I make such a big deal about *his* room when I don't live there and almost never go there anyway?
- My husband and I used to go places together all the time, but now we hardly ever do. I've nagged him about it over and over, but that only makes him mad, and he still doesn't take me anywhere. I'm going to try accepting him—living with it and liking it—and see if loving works better than attacking him.
- I keep picking at my boyfriend for his bad habits, but instead I'm going to learn more about Real Love and see if I can become a better partner. Who knows how he'll react to that.
- I've been talking about my boss behind his back for years, but that's never made the slightest difference. He hasn't changed, and I'm not happier. I'm going to learn more about Real Love and learn how to offer him my unconditional support. We'll see how he responds to that instead of my criticizing him.

Do whatever the pig wants—be a doormat.

I have been asked variations on this question a thousand times: "There's a lot about Real Love that sounds great, but if you really love somebody *unconditionally*, don't you have to do whatever they want you to do? Doesn't that make you kind of like a doormat?"

This misconception is quite understandable, because most people *want* you to believe that *loving* them would mean *giving* them everything they ask for. You'll actually hear people say or imply expressions like, "If you really loved me, you would ____ _____." But it's all another clever lie unconsciously told by people who are empty and afraid in order to get what they want.

So let's review again the definition of Real Love: caring about the happiness of another person without wanting anything for ourselves in return. Now let's suppose that I love a man named Frank, which means that I care about his *happiness*. You and I know that genuine happiness results from:

- telling the truth about ourselves.
- feeling unconditionally loved.
- loving others unconditionally.
- being responsible.

If I care about Frank's genuine happiness, therefore, I would be willing to do what I can to help Frank accomplish the above activities or traits.

Like me, Frank also believes that my loving him means caring about his happiness, but the problem arises with Frank's definition of happiness. Frank believes—as most of the world does—that happiness means having enough:

- excitement.
- comfort.
- ease.
- satisfaction.
- pleasure.
- power.
- approval.
- control.

In *Frank's* world, if I care about his happiness—if I love him—I will always give him any excitement, comfort, and pleasure he demands. I will be his servant, his doormat. But in the world of truth and Real Love, we know that these things—excitement and power, for example—often *detract* from genuine happiness, and if I really care about his happiness, I will specifically *not* grant his requests for those things that could harm him. It can often, therefore, actually be *loving* to refuse the requests or demands of people on many occasions. A drug addict, for example, might request that I give him a dose of mind-altering drugs, but filling his request would not be loving.

In Real Love, we are far from doormats to other people. Rather, with Real Love we see the world and the people in it even more clearly, and we therefore know with greater accuracy when we should and should not fulfill the requests of those around us.

But what if Frank demands something from me that would actually be good for him? For example, what if he requests that I spend time with him? If I am loving, would I not be obligated to fill his request? Again, no. In Real Love, we give freely, not from a sense of obligation. We give what love we are *capable* of giving and what love we *choose* to give. If I'm not in a place to give what he asks, for whatever reason—I'm tired physically, I'm worn out emotionally, or I just plain don't feel like it—what would happen if I gave in and did what Frank wanted anyway? At least two consequences would be fairly uniform:

- Although Frank would enjoy to some extend my fulfilling his request or demand, he would almost certainly sense that I was not giving it freely. In that case, he would not feel loved unconditionally, so what good would I really be doing him? It would not be a genuinely loving act on my part.

- As I give of myself beyond what I freely choose, I deplete even more my store of available Real Love. I become less able to love Frank *and* anyone else. In that case, I harm myself and make myself less capable of helping anyone else.

Loving beyond our capabilities usually harms us and doesn't help others. It's not genuinely loving, and for that reason saying *no* to the requests of others is often a loving response. In Real Love, you are never a doormat.

CHAPTER SIX
The Laws of Responsibility

SIX, 19:35 - 20:05   The Laws of Responsibility
CD Track Six, 0:00 - 0:30

Taken by itself, the Law of Choice could easily be read as follows: "I can do whatever I want, and you can't do anything about it." It could become a formula for chaos and lawlessness. Fortunately, the Law of Choice is accompanied by—and tempered by—the Laws of Responsibility.

SIX, 20:05 - 20:35   The First Law of Responsibility
CD Track Six, 0:30 - 1:01

We can make any choice we want, but we are responsible for the choices we make. The Law of Choice states that we can choose, for example, to be angry, selfish, and unloving, but the Laws of Responsibility state that we are responsible for those choices. The Law of Choice is not meant to be an excuse for behaving badly.

As Paul said to the Galatians, "Brothers, you have been given freedom, but don't use that as an excuse to indulge your earthly desires, but serve one another in love. For all the law is fulfilled in one word, even in this; you shall love your neighbor as yourself." (Galatians 5:13-14)

SIX, 20:35 - 22:12 The Second Law of Responsibility: Consequences of Our Choices
CD Track 1:01 - 2:37

Not only is there a consequence for every choice we make, but the consequence is one that follows because of natural laws, and we can't choose the consequences of our choices. To illustrate:

You can choose	but you *cannot* then choose
to break the speed limit,	not to get a speeding ticket.
take a nap all through planting season,	to harvest a crop.
to plant weeds in your field,	to harvest wheat.
to use Getting and Protecting Behaviors,	to be happy and have loving relationships.
to be selfish,	to be loving and happy.

Remember that on pages 300-2 we looked at some of the consequences described by God for the decisions we make. Notice that He didn't give us a choice about our consequences. Once we make our choices, the consequences just follow.

This could also be called the Law of the Harvest: You really do reap what you sow. The Law of the Harvest isn't a negative concept; it's actually a great promise to us. We talked about how we can't make negative choices and expect positive results, but it's also true that if we make wise, positive choices—if we plant the right seeds—we are *guaranteed* a bounteous, desirable harvest. For example:

If you choose	**you *will***
to tell the truth about yourself,	find people to unconditionally accept and love you.
to devote yourself to finding Real Love,	find Real Love and genuine happiness.
to share Real Love with others,	experience personal happiness and richly rewarding relationships.
to tell the truth about only your own mistakes,	experience a sharp reduction in conflicts.
to follow the way described by Jesus Christ,	inherit all that He has promised us.

The universe is organized and maintained by natural laws, and these apply to our own happiness and to our relationships as well. When we live in accordance with these laws, we can speak and act with great power. When we violate these governing laws, however, we are attempting to succeed despite moving *against* the powers that run the universe. Little wonder that we do poorly on these occasions.

In the space on the next page describe occasions when you have blamed others for your unhappiness, when it was really your choices that caused your misery. Examples:

- I complain that my wife never wants sex, but considering the way I talk to her, why would she ever want to even be around me?
- I yell at my children for quarreling, but I'm the one who taught them their Getting and Protecting Behaviors.
- I complain that I never get promoted at work, but I hardly ever go the extra mile that it would take to be considered for a promotion over others who are working harder than I am.
- I nag my husband to spend more time with me, but my nagging just drives him away. I'm the one who's choosing to be unloving, and then I expect love as a result.

SIX, 22:12 - 23:56   The Laws of Happiness
CD Track Six, 2:37 - 4:21

The houses in which we live were built brick by brick, board by board, nail by nail. Similarly, the lives we now lead are actually the result of countless single choices we have been making over periods of many years, even decades.

Although people like to talk about the "grayness" and fuzziness of the decisions we make, each decision really is either black or white. Each choice is between:

Telling the truth	**and**	Lying
Loving		Being selfish
Feeling loved		Being afraid
Responsibility		Acting like a victim
Freedom		Captivity
Faith		Getting and Protecting Behaviors
Life		Death

If we choose wisely, happiness is a guarantee. If we choose poorly, we should not be surprised when we are miserable.

In the space below, describe some of the decisions you have made over the years that have led to the life you now have.

SIX, 23:56 - 27:36   The Third Law of Responsibility: The Choices of Others
CD Track Six, 4:21 - 8:01

In the seminar you saw the account of the two drunk drivers, as well as the story of my bumping into four people on a path in the woods. We are not responsible for the choices of other people. They really are independent from us and choose how they will react to us.

This is not intended to give us an *excuse* for hurting people. If someone says, "You hurt me," it is not appropriate for us to say, "Well, tough. I'm not responsible for your choices; *you* are. So shut up and quit bothering me."

When people claim that we hurt them, we need to simultaneously:

1. be sensitive to their pain and care about their happiness,
2. not take from them the responsibility that is always theirs to choose Real Love and happiness, and
3. be willing to examine our behavior for selfish motivations.

In the space on the next page discuss some occasions when people have blamed you for hurting them. Most of us can think of many such events. Discover the power and freedom that follow application of the above three steps to each such event. One such example follows:

Two weeks ago my girlfriend told me that she wanted to borrow my car on Friday afternoon to take her mother to do some errands, because my car is bigger. I said sure, no problem, and she asked me to clean it up nice for her mother. Sure, I said, but when Friday came around I had forgotten to clean up the car. It's not like it was a pigsty or anything, but it wasn't very neat, and my girlfriend had a real fit. She said I was being rude to her and to her mother, and she was hurt and offended and angry, and after we argued about it for half an hour, she didn't talk to me for two days.

Our argument went very badly. She was offended and angry. I felt guilty, and then I was mad that she didn't appreciate borrowing my car, even if it wasn't perfectly clean. I mean, good grief, all that fuss over a few things on the floor of the car? Get a life.

A couple of days after our argument, I tried using the three principles above to see how they would have helped me talk to my girlfriend differently. Actually, instead of imagining it, I thought about it, and then I went and did it.

Principle #1. I realized that I do want her to be happy, and my not cleaning the car—and my arguing with her about it—did not help her to be happy.
#3. I was selfish.

#2. Then I realized that although I had been selfish, it was still *her choice* to be offended about it or not. If she had felt enough Real Love—not just from me but in many areas of her life— that one event wouldn't have bothered her at all. So I wasn't responsible for "making" her unhappy. When I eliminated the guilt, I didn't feel as defensive.

#3. Then I told her I'd been selfish and unloving, and immediately she went from being offended to hugging me and thanking me. It was *easier* to just tell the truth about my selfishness and admit being wrong than it was to be defensive.

CHAPTER SEVEN
The Law of Expectations

SEVEN, 27:36 - 30:19   The Law of Expectations
CD Track Seven, 0:00 - 2:43

We must clearly see the nature and effect of expectations. Expectations:

- are selfish.
- are confusing.
- violate the Law of Choice.
- consistently interfere with any possibility of a loving relationship.
- ruin any possibility of feeling loved, which has a terrible effect on our happiness.
- just don't work.

In the space on the next page discuss some occasions where you have been irritated. Now consider and discuss the expectations you had in those moments that your partner would do something or be something for you. For example:

- I was angry at my wife for being ungrateful. She's been that way all her life—trained by her parents to be that way, actually—but when *I'm* involved, I expect her to instantly change a lifelong pattern. Pretty selfish on my part.
- I expect—demand—that my boss appreciate what I do for him. Then if he doesn't, I'm irritated. Ironically, even if he does express any appreciation, I don't feel it. I really set myself up with these expectations.
- I expect my children to respect me, which they feel as a demand for love. Of course, then they feel like withdrawing from me, which I interpret as a lack of respect. My expectations play a big part in the whole problem.
- I expect my husband to do things for me all the time—flowers, gifts, saying "I love you," stuff like that—but I didn't realize until lately what a terrible effect that has had. The expectations

make him feel pushed all the time, and they ruin any chance I had to feel really loved.

- I've always expected my wife to have sex with me. She feels that as a demand, like she's being forced. No wonder she withdraws from me.
- I had an argument with a co-worker the other day over the smallest thing, and then later I realized that I had expected her to be *nice* and *cooperative* with me. When she didn't meet my expectations, I was irritated, and the conversation went quickly downhill from there.

In our defense, why do we have expectations of other people? Why do we keep using this tool that is consistently unproductive?

Imagine that you're out in the middle of the desert, lost and starving. A man who is obviously well-fed walks by with a large sandwich in his hand. What is your reaction? Understandably, you immediately ask him to share his sandwich with you. If he refuses, your request would almost certainly escalate into a plea or demand (remember, you're starving, not just a bit hungry). You would have an *expectation* of this man to share with you what he has.

Now picture a scene where again you're out in the middle of the desert, but this time you've just eaten a large meal, there is a huge table beside you that is groaning under the weight of the food piled on it, and you have a Humvee at your disposal to take you out of the desert whenever you wish. Again a man walks by with a sandwich in his hand. Would you react to him in the same way you did the first time? Of course not. This time you would not have intense expectations that he would share with you. You might not even notice the sandwich.

You have expectations of other people only because you are starving for Real Love. As you fill up with Real Love from those who have it to give, you'll feel complete and satisfied, after which you will naturally and effortlessly begin to lose the expectations that any one person or group of people should give you what you want in any given moment. Without the burden of expectations, you'll find it so much easier to begin and build relationships.

SEVEN, 30:19 - 31:57   Promises
CD Track Seven, 2:43 - 4:21

Some expectations can actually be beneficial when they're associated with promises. In business, for example, we make beneficial promises all the time: I promise to deliver these goods to you, and you promise to pay me.

Regrettably, however, most of us have enormous expectations of other people even when we have no promise from them. We expect people to make our lives convenient all the time, for example, and we prove we have that expectation every time we become disappointed or irritated when they don't do what we want—when our spouses aren't attentive, our children are slow to obey us, or other drivers on the road fail to realize that we're far more important than they are.

Some expectations are wrong even when a promise *is* made. A spouse, for example, may say, "But when we got married, part of the agreement was that my partner would love me. In fact, he/she promised me right there in front of God and everybody." Although in many circumstances expectations are justifiable when promises are made, we still never have the right to expect other people to *love* us or make us happy, *even when they promise to do so*. Unconditional love can only be *freely* given and received. When we *expect* love, we ruin any possibility that we can feel unconditionally accepted or happy.

We can experience Real Love only when we tell the truth about ourselves and wait for *someone*—perhaps many people—to unconditionally accept and love us. That *will* happen, but we don't get to choose *who* that person—or those people—will be. We need to identify our expectations that specific people love us, and we can do that by recognizing our disappointment and anger. Almost without exception, these two feelings are signs that we're expecting but not getting the Real or Imitation Love we want from a particular person. Of course, these expectations are usually unconscious, but they're still quite intense, and the subsequent disappointment and anger are very real.

When we can identify our unreasonable expectations that specific people will love us, we can quit making destructive demands and begin to focus on telling the truth about ourselves. We can allow people to love us unconditionally when they wish, and then whatever acceptance we're offered is real, which feels wonderful.

In the space on the next page discuss the last several times people have broken promises made to you.

- Were you disappointed?
- Were you offended that they could do such a terrible thing as break a promise to *you*?
- Did you get a sense of self-righteousness that the other person was so *wrong*?
- Did you become irritated?
- Did you express your irritation to him or her?

- Did you complain to other people about the person who broke their promise?
- Did your irritation (which followed your expectation) get in the way of a peaceful resolution to the broken promise?

Discuss how you might handle such a situation differently in the future should it arise.

SEVEN, 31:57 - 32:45   Requests
CD Track Seven, 4:21 - 5:09

In the space below discuss some occasions when partners have become irritated at you when you've made requests of them.

- Were you the slightest bit pushy or demanding when you made the "request?"
- Were you the slightest bit irritated?
- Have you been pushy or irritated in the past when making requests with this partner?
- Have you been disappointed or irritated in the past with this partner *after* you didn't get what you wanted from him or her?

If your answer to any of these questions is *yes*, either you did have an expectation on the occasion you're discussing, *or* your partner *believed*—based on past experience—that you were having an expectation. Our partners *feel* our expectations, and they perceive them as attacking and controlling, after which our interactions with them cannot go well.

How can we learn to make loving, effective requests? Read Chapter Three of the book, *Real Love for Wise Men and Women*. To summarize these principles, however:

- Realize that Real Love is always the most important thing. Until you have enough Real Love in your own life, you *will* tend to make demands rather than requests.
- Ask, don't demand. You can't fake this.

- Make requests clear and specific. Don't ask for some general improvement or change in your partner. Such requests are too vague and oppressive. Be specific about what you want, where you want it, and when.
- Listen and accept. Don't immediately argue with the answer to your request. Listen.
- Modify your requests where necessary. Occasionally, you may be able to modify a refused request in such a way that it becomes acceptable to your partner. If you modify the request too many times, however—in an attempt to get a *yes*—you will be perceived as pushing and demanding.

CHAPTER EIGHT
Learning to Love

EIGHT, 32:45 - 33:55 Why We Don't Love
CD Track Eight, 0:00 - 1:11

We all know we *should* be loving. We've heard it enough times from our parents and others: "Be nice to your sister," or "Stop doing that. It's not nice," or "You need to be more kind." In fact, in church we hear that frequent refrain, "Love one another," often voiced in the form of a command. Then we go home and try with all our might to be more loving, but with will power alone how long does that last? Minutes? Hours? Pretty much until somebody does something that inconveniences us, and then our resolution to be more loving goes right out the window.

So why aren't we more loving?

Again imagine that you're starving to death in the middle of the desert. A man walks by—also starving—and asks you for food, but despite his great need you give him nothing. Why? Why would you refuse to satisfy his need? Because you have no food to give.

It's the same with love. You can't give what you don't have, and very few of us were given sufficient Real Love.

In the space below discuss some occasions when you have not been loving in a relationship.

- Looking back, can you now identify the feeling of frustration you felt on those occasions?
- Those feelings indicated that you just *couldn't* have given the love you knew you were supposed to be giving. You didn't have it to give.
- When you understand now that you *couldn't* have been loving on those occasions, what does that do to your feelings of guilt about those unloving events? How can you persist in feeling guilty for something you couldn't possibly have done better?

Loving Ourselves

When we're young children, we *learn* the nature of the world from the people around us. If we are *taught* that love is conditional—as almost all of us are—we naturally tend to believe these lessons, because the adults who teach us—notably our parents—are masters of our universe, all-powerful and all-wise.

But it turns out that our teachers were most often raised without enough Real Love themselves, so their view of the world was *wrong*, and now we carry that mistaken perception of the world and ourselves everywhere we go. We can't suddenly change the view we have of ourselves by willpower alone, because so many important people told us on so many occasions that we were unlovable. We can't now flippantly ignore all that input. We can't suddenly love ourselves, because we *really* don't believe we're lovable, and because we can't give what we don't have.

We need help changing how we feel. We need *new evidence* that we *are* worth loving unconditionally, and we need that evidence from *other people*, from people who can genuinely accept us. We create these opportunities to be unconditionally loved as we tell people the truth about ourselves and allow them to accept and love us as we really are.

Understandably, we've been reluctant to do that because of the many occasions when people have been disappointed in us or angry with us. We remember those painful experiences vividly, and that's why we tend to gravitate toward the advice of people who say, "Love yourself." It seems safer than trying to get love from others, but it also disconnects us from the people whose love we need.

At this point, many people object, "But what you're saying makes us *dependent* on other people. Surely that can't be good." Actually, needing the love of others is delightful. It connects us and gives us a sense of great fulfillment. Needing other people becomes harmful only in the instant we expect love from a given individual or group of people. I need love, and I thoroughly enjoy the love I receive from others. It's the joy of my life, but the instant I require that *you* love me—or anyone else—I ruin everything. When I *expect* it from you, as we've discussed earlier in this module, whatever you give me can't feel unconditionally given anymore, and then it becomes a deadly trading of Imitation Love.

I realize I contradict what many people believe and teach when I say that it's not enough to love ourselves, but I've seen so many people over the years try to do that and fail. For a short time, there are occasional moments where it seems to work, but uniformly it proves to be an illusion. Most people talk about loving themselves because, after consistently disappointing experiences, they've simply given up on looking for love from other people. They advocate loving themselves because they see it as the only choice they have—certainly the safest. A belief in loving ourselves also *justifies* our avoidance of interaction with other people, where we might experience more of the rejection we fear most.

Do this mental exercise:

Imagine that Real Love is a river of infinite proportions, flowing through all the universe. It flows between us and even gets bigger as it flows from one of us to another. In order to drink from the river—in order to find Real Love—you only have to reach out and tap into the river that is all around you. And then you can re-direct the flow to others nearby. At no point, however, do you ever have to dig a well and generate the water for yourself.

And so it is with Real Love. You don't have to create it within you. Take a chance. Reach out and share with people who you really are, and you *will* find people to love you. Then pass it on. Have fun with the flow.

EIGHT, 33:55 - 35:15   Loved → Seeing → Accepting → Loving
CD Track Eight, 1:11 - 2:31

In the space below and on the next page discuss how you felt as you heard the story of the drowning man on page 165. Did you feel a natural inclination to help the man in the pool? As you feel more Real Love in your life, you'll feel a natural urge to share *that* with others too.

Think of someone in your life who is irritating. Now picture that person as drowning. Do you feel less irritation? Do you feel any interest in helping him or her out of the water? We'll talk in the next section about what loving actually looks like.

EIGHT, 35:15 - 36:19   The Miracle of Loving
CD Track Eight, 2:31 - 3:33

Loving other people is a miraculous experience. As we share Real Love with others:

- we *feel* more loved, regardless of whether the people we love return our love.
- we feel consistently happier ourselves.
- our relationships are greatly enriched.

The Gospels speak eloquently of the miracle of loving and how it multiplies, in a parable told multiple times:

Great crowds followed Jesus to hear Him teach. Filled with compassion, He healed their sick and asked His disciples how they might all be fed. The disciples said, We have only five loaves of bread and two fishes. But Jesus told the crowd of five thousand to sit, and after blessing the bread and fish, He gave to the disciples, who in turn gave to the crowd. After everyone had been fed, they gathered up the leftovers, which filled twelve baskets. (Matthew 14:13-21; Matthew 15:30-38; Mark 6:35-44; Luke 9:10-17; John 6:5-13)

This is not a story about bread and fish. It's a story about faith and the power of making a conscious decision to love even when our supply may not be entirely full—when we have only a few loaves and fishes. As we choose to love, what we have multiplies, such that after giving we have more than we started with. The multiplication is miraculous and could be only divine in origin.

What does loving look like? *Accepting* people means that when they behave badly, you don't get afraid or angry or react to control them with other Getting and Protecting Behaviors. *Loving* people is a more active concern for their happiness and is often accompanied by some kind of action. Loving is a result of seeing and accepting and consciously making loving choices. Loving *includes* accepting. There are many ways to love:

- Listen
- Look
- Touch
- Tell the truth about yourself
- Apologize
- Perform random acts of kindness
- Cooperate
- Ask
- Consciously choose to accept and forgive
- Love without expectations

Listen

Many techniques have been described for effective listening and communication, but they often fail to produce significant and lasting positive changes in relationships because they ignore the powerful, primal need we all have for Real Love. One element of communication that is often taught, for example, is our need to acknowledge what we've heard, and even to echo or reflect back to the speaker what he or she has said. Certainly, that *is* a potentially useful approach, but it will rarely lead to the most effective communication if the need for Real Love is disregarded.

To illustrate this concept, imagine that you've spent considerable time and money to purchase a gift for me. You wrap it yourself and bring it to my office, where I'm working at my desk. Taking the gift from your hand, I turn it over a couple of times and write on a piece of paper, "Received: one box, 4x5x8.5 inches, wrapped with blue paper and bow, April 17, 2:00 p.m." Then I photocopy the note, give the original document to you, toss the box onto a pile of objects in the corner of the room, and turn back to my work.

How would you feel? Although I acknowledged receipt of the gift, and even described it accurately, you certainly wouldn't feel appreciated, because you were giving me much more than an object wrapped in a bow. You were giving me a piece of *you*, and I failed miserably to acknowledge and accept that.

Every time someone speaks to you, he or she is offering you a very personal gift—literally a part of who he or she is—and how you listen is naturally perceived as a strong indication of how you receive that precious gift. Genuine listening is much more than simply receiving and acknowledging words with a mechanical communication technique. When we really listen, we communicate to people that we *care about them*. When you listen, you're telling people that they're important to you. Real listening is an expression of love.

In any conversation, people's greatest need is to feel unconditionally accepted and loved. If you fail to communicate that acceptance, people will almost certainly feel more empty and afraid, triggering the Getting and Protecting Behaviors which make genuine communication impossible. The principal goal of listening is to communicate Real Love.

In the space below discuss some occasions when you have employed communications techniques alone, without unconditionally loving other people. How did it turn out?

Although Real Love is the key ingredient to real listening, I will nonetheless describe here some of the mechanical characteristics of listening, and from these we can all learn better to listen to people in ways that are accepting and productive.

Be Quiet

Many people don't really listen—they're only looking for an opportunity to speak themselves, and they frequently jump into the conversation without the slightest regard for their partners. Although we often do need to make responses, one of the most powerful indications we give that we're listening is that our upper and lower lips are sealed together. Let the other person speak until he or she is finished. If you're not sure whether he or she has more to say, simply ask: "There's something I'd like to say, but I don't want to interrupt you. Are you finished with that thought?"

Practice this element of listening. Most of us are so used to interrupting people that we just don't realize it. Practice saying nothing while another person speaks, and in the space below discuss the results:

- Was it difficult initially to say nothing?
- Did you learn more about the other person as you listened?
- As you listened, did you feel closer to the person who was speaking?

Express Your Acceptance Non-Verbally

Some studies suggest that as much as 93% of human communication is non-verbal. At least half of that is transmitted by way of facial expression, while other modes include tone of voice, arm and leg position, foot and hand movement, and overall body posture and motion. As you raise your brows, shift your eyes, furrow your forehead, sigh, shuffle your feet, cross your arms, and change your tone of voice, people can easily recognize your lack of acceptance and/or interest. Then they will usually change what they're saying either to protect themselves or to get something they want— acceptance, cooperation, and so on. When they do that, you're no longer having a conversation with *them*; you're interacting with a defensive posture or manipulation. You're hearing what they think you want them to be, and your conversation becomes an empty lie or contest.

When you're really listening to people, you're leaning slightly forward in your chair, obviously involved physically in the conversation and giving no indication that you're eager to be somewhere else. Expressions of interest dance enthusiastically across your face. I'm not advocating that you attempt to *fabricate* these non-verbal signs of acceptance—you won't be able to fake it for long. If you don't feel accepting toward someone, you *will* communicate that feeling. What I am suggesting is that you be aware of the non-verbal signs that you don't really care, and when you sense them in yourself, recognize that you're not communicating the acceptance other people need.

Observe your non-verbal communication and in the space below discuss what you learn about yourself.

Avoid Verbal Criticism

Every time people speak, they're sharing who they are, creating opportunities for you to see, accept, and love them. If you criticize them on those occasions, they'll stop talking, or they'll defend themselves, and then things will go very badly. We often use people's words as evidence with which to trap them or beat them down. When they speak, for example, often the first word out of our mouths is *but*. To be sure, we may have something brilliant to add to the conversation, but when we say the word *but*, we might as well say, "I'm not really listening to you. My real goal is to be right." When we criticize and contradict people, we feel powerful or think we look good by comparison, and our partners feel it when we use them in that way.

Certainly there are times when you do need to offer suggestions or correct misinformation, but without Real Love you'll almost certainly detract from your partner's ability to feel accepted.

Monitor your tendency to criticize or offer suggestions as other people speak. In the space below, record your observations.

Re-State What You Hear—"Eight"

Although the central need for acceptance must never be forgotten, on many occasions other people also need you to understand and respond to the *content* of what they're saying. If your wife, for example, gives you a description of a task that must be done in a particular way, she needs more from you than a sense of warm, fuzzy acceptance. She needs you to indicate that you understand *what* she's saying, so she'll have a glimmer of hope that the job will be done as she's described.

While it's obvious that understanding the content of a speaker's message is important for the accomplishment of tasks, understanding content is also important as a way of communicating acceptance and concern. One way to demonstrate to someone that you understand what he or she is saying is to re-state what you hear, as demonstrated here by Andrew and his wife, Lynn.

"I feel so mad right now," says Lynn. "I've asked you a million times to put food back in the fridge after you eat, but today I found a jug of milk you left downstairs when you were watching television. It was warm and spoiled, and now I can't use it for the custard I wanted to make."

In the past, whenever Lynn talked about something Andrew had done wrong, he made excuses, frowned, grunted, retaliated with critical comments about *her* behavior, or walked out of the room, none of which had a soothing effect on Lynn. But he's been learning about Real Love and how to listen, so this time he looks directly at her, nods his head as she speaks, and says, "I'm sorry for that."

Of course, Lynn is pleased that he's not lying, attacking, acting like a victim, or running, but still his response is less than completely satisfying, because she's heard him apologize many times before with no subsequent change in his behavior. Wisely, however, she doesn't press her point, having learned a bit about Real Love herself.

A few weeks later, Lynn again makes a comment about something Andrew left out of the fridge, and this time he's armed with even greater understanding and compassion. "I know I should have put that meat back where I got it," he says, "and I can see you're angry at me. I'm sorry." This is an example of what many people call active listening. Andrew has repeated back to Lynn what she said—including the emotion she expressed—and he's done it in his own words. This is certainly better than just an apology—and far superior to responding with Getting and Protecting Behaviors—but so far Andrew has demonstrated only an ability to *repeat* her message, which is not the same as expressing a complete *understanding* of it.

With more time and experience, Andrew begins to understand what acceptance and listening really are. The next time Lynn is irritated about something he left out of the fridge, he goes a significant step farther than before. "Yes, I did that," he says. "I wasn't thinking about you when I left the milk downstairs. I do a lot of things like that, actually, where I don't think about you and inconvenience you—like yesterday when I used your cell phone and didn't put it back in your purse. I know you had to look around for quite a while before you found it. And sometimes I leave my clothes on the floor and hope you'll pick them up. When I do those things, you must feel like I don't care much about you."

Immediately Lynn feels thoroughly seen, because Andrew has heard not only what she was saying about the food but has given *additional examples* of his overall thoughtlessness. More significantly, he has identified and addressed her real concern—that he doesn't care about her. She was really talking about that fear, not a container of milk or piece of food. The effect on Lynn was profound.

Andrew provides an example of a principle I call "Eight." Suppose I say to you, "Two, four, six . . ." and then I wait to see if you understand what I'm saying. You respond, "Two, four, six." Certainly you've demonstrated an ability to *repeat* what I said, but you have not shown that you *understand* what I'm really saying. On the other hand, if you simply respond, "Eight," I know you understand what I said. When other people speak, they are almost always saying, "Two, four, six," and it's quite fulfilling when you say, "Eight."

Practice this higher level of listening. In the space below discuss an occasion when you didn't really listen to someone who was trying to tell you something. These occasions are obvious, because our partners give strong indications with their disappointment and irritation that we're not listening. Discuss how you could show that you understand the real meaning of what he or she is saying. How could you say *eight*? Then actually communicate *eight* to that partner and record what happened. How did your partner respond? Did you feel closer to that person as a result of really listening?

Look

From an early age, we've noticed the intimacy of eye contact. When people look straight into your eyes for more than a few seconds, you can feel them reaching into your soul. If you believe they love you, you'll feel connected and accepted. If, on the other hand, you have any doubt about their acceptance of you, you'll likely feel accused of something—you'll feel criticized, attacked, and even violated. Studies have shown that most of us become uncomfortable if people look directly into our eyes for more than just a few seconds, or even less.

When people are speaking, don't busy yourself with other things. Look directly into their eyes as you listen. Don't do that for too long a period at first, because most people aren't used to this. Discuss your experiences with looking at people. How did you feel? How did they respond?

Touch

Physical touching is another intimate experience. If you know someone loves you, and that person touches you on the hand, shoulder, or face, you'll feel even more accepted and connected in a way that far transcends the physical contact. If you doubt the love of the person touching you, however, you'll probably feel threatened.

Unless you're in an intimate relationship with someone, never touch him or her in a way that could be confused with a sexual overture. To learn more about touching a spouse or boyfriend or girlfriend, see the book, *Real Love in Marriage*.

Tell the Truth About Yourself

When you tell the truth about yourself, you're saying to your partner, I trust you enough—I love you enough—to share with you even the things I'm afraid of or embarrassed about: my selfishness, my laziness, my lack of responsibility, my Getting and Protecting Behaviors. Telling the truth about ourselves is a loving gesture.

Apologize

When you make a mistake, don't minimize it, or hide it, or make excuses. Just tell the truth about it and apologize for the inconvenience and pain you've caused. As you do that, you're communicating your concern for other people's happiness, and that's what Real Love is.

Perform Random Acts of Kindness

Each time you do something to accommodate the needs of other people, you're communicating with your behavior that you care about them. With your time and effort you're saying, "I love you."

- When your wife walks in the room, that should be a cause for celebration. Don't just sit there and let this opportunity pass. Show her how happy you are to see her. Get up from your chair, walk over to her, give her a hug, and tell her you love her.
- Make his or her favorite dessert.
- Say to your boss, "You look like you've been unusually busy lately. Is there something I can do to make your job easier?"
- Ask a child to go on a walk with you.
- Ask your boyfriend if there are any particular drinks or snack foods he'd like to have while he watches the football game this Saturday. And would he like to invite anybody else over?
- Set up a time with your wife every week—a date—when you and she will be completely alone with each other for at least a couple of hours.
- When someone has an errand to run, ask him or her if you could do it instead while he or she stays home and does something else they feel like doing.
- Offer to drive when someone looks tired.
- Ask him if there's anything sexual he or she would like from you.
- Massage your spouse's feet or shoulders.
- When your girlfriend doesn't feel well, ask her if she'd like to lie down and let you take care of her for a while.
- Take her out shopping to get something new to wear. Tell her you don't care how long it takes.
- When he gets angry, tell him how you could have been more sensitive toward him, no matter how wrong he is.
- Bring her some flowers. They don't have to be expensive—it could be a single flower from the roadside, or from a grocery store. Put them in a vase yourself.

- When he fails to take out the garbage, take it out yourself and don't mention that you did it.
- Learn how to cook something you know she likes. If you're absolutely hopeless in the kitchen, bring her something she likes from a restaurant or deli.
- Mow the lawn for him.
- Tell her you'd like to set aside an entire day where you both do whatever she'd like. Then don't object to a single suggestion she makes.
- When you're running an errand, ask her if she'd like to come with you, just so you can be together.
- When you don't like how he's driving, or you're sure he's going the wrong direction, don't say anything.
- Ask her if she'd like you to prepare a bath for her.

In the space below, write down a list of random acts of kindness that you'd like to share with a few of the people in your life.

Then carry out some of these loving acts and record how they contributed to the Real Love felt by both you and the recipient.

Cooperate

One day I offered to help my wife, Donna, sweep and mop the kitchen and dining room floors. As I worked, she kept telling me how to do it. For a moment—maybe two moments—I thought, "You've got to be kidding. I've operated on thousands of patients, climbed mountains, run businesses, and swept hundreds of floors, and you think I need instruction in floor sweeping?" But then I realized that I had an opportunity to simply do it the way she wanted, as a sign of my affection for her—it didn't matter how I usually swept the floor, or what I thought about her method.

When you and a partner are doing something together, it's unavoidable that you'll sometimes want to do it differently. On most occasions, it simply doesn't matter which way it's done. As you cooperate with his or her requests or preferences, you'll introduce yet another level of harmony into your relationship.

Ask

As I said earlier, most communication is non-verbal. If you begin to look for these non-verbal clues, you'll have many opportunities to ask questions that will indicate a sincere interest in your spouse's feelings and activities, as we see with Blaine and Amanda.

As Blaine and Amanda are returning home in the car from a party at Blaine's parents' house, Blaine notices that Amanda is quiet and is leaning slightly away from him. He knows she's mad at him about something, and frankly he'd rather let her sulk about it in silence. He's not in the mood for any kind of confrontation. But he's been learning about the power of expressing love even when he doesn't have much to offer, so he decides to explore how she's feeling. "You don't seem very happy," he says. "Do you want to talk about it?"

"No," she says.

It would be easy for Blaine to leave her alone, but he gently persists. "You don't have to talk about it, but if you want to, I'd be happy to listen."

His making an offer twice to listen to her is enough to convince her of his sincere intention, and she says, "Whenever we go to your parents' house, you don't pay any attention to me at all. You entertain everybody else in the house, but you completely ignore me, like I wasn't even there."

Blaine can think of a dozen brilliant defenses, all quite reasonable, for how he behaved:

- He doesn't get to see his family very often, and when he does, they're quite possessive of his time.
- He *did* come and talk to her several times that night.
- Amanda didn't pay *him* much attention that night, either.
- And so on.

But again he decides to do the loving thing, and he responds to her need for acceptance instead of defending himself. "Whenever we go over there," he says, "I feel this pressure to make everybody happy. If I don't do all the right things, somebody's feelings will be hurt, and then they'll be mad at me. So I spend all my time making my family happy. I don't like it, but I'm afraid not to. And in the process, I ignore you. I'm sorry about that."

Blaine and Amanda then work out something that will satisfy Amanda's need for attention and will allow Blaine to pay attention to his family. When we ask people how they're feeling, we create opportunities for them to share themselves and feel accepted by us.

Consciously Choose to Accept and Forgive

Because people are imperfect, they will often use the Getting and Protecting Behaviors that inconvenience you. In every case, you have a choice to make. You can respond with your own Getting and Protecting Behaviors—which *never* make anyone happy—or you can choose to remember that the other person is simply drowning. When you remember that, your hurt and anger will vanish. You'll find it easy to accept and forgive him or her, just as you would accept and forgive a man for splashing you after you learned he was drowning. We *choose* how we see the behavior of our partners, and with that choice we also determine how we'll respond.

If you choose to hang on to your partner's past offenses, you're choosing to be miserable and injure your relationship. Forgiveness is easy when you see the cause of your partner's behavior and accept that he or she really does get to make mistakes. When you choose to actively care about his happiness, and build a genuinely loving relationship with him, forgiveness becomes the only sensible choice.

Love Without Expectations

One day after Bob had said something especially unkind to Marilyn, she reacted with more than her usual anger, and he realized he'd better do something if he wanted to make any kind of peace. When he came home from work the next day, he brought her some flowers, and she forgave him. They'd repeated many variations of this pattern on other occasions when there was contention between them. When Bob bought her something, or did something she really liked, she saw this as evidence of his love for her, and harmony was restored. The positive effect, however, was always short lived, because Bob was doing these things for her to get something for *himself*—peace, forgiveness, her attention, and so on—which did not fill Marilyn's need for *unconditional* love.

Other people can sense when we give them our time, attention, and affection with an expectation of getting something in return. They feel the disappointment and anger we express—often subtly— when our expectations are not fulfilled, and then they can't feel unconditionally loved by us. We must be honest about identifying our disappointment and anger, because only then can we recognize the expectations that destroy the possibility of Real Love.

Loving God

When Jesus was asked to name the greatest commandment, he specified *two*:

> (1) You shall love the Lord your God with all your heart and with all your soul and with all your mind. This is the first and greatest commandment. And (2) the second is like it, You shall love your neighbor as yourself." (Matthew 22:35-40)

To this point in the *Workbook*, we've talked at great length about the second of the two commandments: loving one another. What about the first? What about loving God? How do we go about doing that? What could we possibly give God that He actually *needs*? Is there any possibility that He doesn't already feel perfectly loved and needs us to care about His happiness? No. So what gives Him pleasure?

Speaking of the time when He would come again in His glory, Jesus said,

> "Then shall the King say unto them on his right hand, Come, you who are blessed of my Father, inherit the kingdom prepared for you from the foundation of the world, because I was hungry, and you gave me food; I was thirsty, and you gave me drink; I was a stranger, and you took me in; I was naked, and you clothed me; I was sick, and you visited me; I was in prison, and you came to me. Then the righteous will say, Lord, when did we see you hungry and feed you? Or thirsty and gave you drink? Or saw you a stranger and took you in? Or naked and clothed you? Or saw you sick or in prison and visited you? And the King will answer and say to them, whatever you have done to the humblest of these my brothers, you have done to me." (Matthew 25:34-40)

In this passage Jesus makes it clear that He personally doesn't need to be clothed, fed, or visited in prison. But when we do the same for His children, He feels the pleasure as though we had done those things directly for Him. So what does God want most? The joy of His children.

How, then, do we love God? By loving His children. If there were any doubt about that, Jesus removed it in a conversation he had with the apostle Peter. He said,

> Peter, do you love me more than everyone else? And Peter said, Yes, Lord you know that I love you. Jesus said, Feed my lambs. He said the second time, Peter, do you love me? And he said, Yes, Lord you know that I love you. He said, Feed my sheep. He

said the third time, Peter, do you love me? And again he said, Lord, you know all things, so you know I love you. Jesus said, Feed my sheep. (John 21:15-17)

CHAPTER NINE
Eliminating Anger from Our Lives

NINE, 36:19 - 36:55 Anger: The Five Steps
CD Track Nine, 0:00 - 0:37

Most of us are literally prisoners to anger, and with it we cause destruction to ourselves and our relationships. What would you give for a solution to that problem?

Write the following five steps on a 3x5 card. Carry it in your pocket, wallet, or purse. Read them every day, not just when you're angry. This will change the rest of your life.

Be quiet
Be wrong
Be loved (remember that you're loved)
Get loved
Be loving

As I've said before, I'm not telling anyone not to be angry. You're welcome to be angry all you want, but do you really want to keep experiencing the negative effects that accompany that expression? Learn a far better way of handling your anger.

NINE, 36:55 - 37:45 Step One: Be Quiet
CD Track Nine, 0:38 - 1:27

The moment you're angry, you begin to communicate "I don't love you" to the people around you, and at that point you couldn't possibly make a positive contribution to any individual interaction or to your relationship. So why keep heading into certain disaster?

Never express disappointment or anger to the person you're angry at. It will be perceived as an attack, and things will go poorly from there. You *can* talk about your anger, but do that only with someone who is capable of loving you. More about that later in this chapter.

Sometimes if you're quiet for just a few moments, your partner's anger will blow off and the situation will defuse. But on other occasions, your partner will demand a response from you, and you do *not* want to respond while you're angry. So now, let's get practical. How in the world can you just "be quiet" in the middle of a difficult conversation? Imagine that someone is attacking you, and you're becoming increasingly angry. How can you just shut your mouth? Won't that actually irritate the other person even more, since it will look as though you are ignoring him or her?

You can be quiet and quite loving at the same time. When you start to feel anxious in a conversation—well before you get to the point of being obviously angry—try saying something like the following:

- What you're saying is important, and I need a little more time to think about it before I respond. Please let me take a break for a while, and I'll come back to finish the conversation in an hour.
- I know you've said this to me before, and it's just now getting through to me that all this time I haven't listened very well. I want to listen better, and right now I need some time to think about it some more. Let's finish this tomorrow, when I've had some time to think about it.
- I really want to hear the rest of what you're saying. It's important to me. Right now I need some time to digest what you're saying, so I can tell you what I really think. I've tried responding off the cuff in the past, and I've done a lousy job. So let me finish this with you at three o'clock.
- Please excuse me. I have to make a phone call. I'll be right back. (You would say this in association with Step Four on pages 381-2.)

- Sweetie, I want to hear every word you have to say on this subject—I really do—but I can't do it right now. Can I finish this discussion with you in, say, half an hour?

In the space below, write down some of your own variations on the above expressions, phrases you believe you could actually say in difficult situations.

How, you might ask, is "being quiet" any different from the Protecting Behavior of running? Running is a mostly involuntary response to fear, designed to protect ourselves. When you're quiet, on the other hand—as the first step to changing your response to anger—you are wisely and consciously withdrawing from a situation where you know you will cause harm to another person. Your motivation is in great part loving, which is quite different from running.

NINE, 37:45 - 38:02 Step Two: Be Wrong
CD Track Nine, 1:28 - 1:43

In the end, the highest purpose of all our activities is to be genuinely happy, and we achieve that condition not from being entertained or excited—as we've discussed elsewhere—but from feeling unconditionally loved and from sharing that love with others. Anything, therefore, that contributes to our feeling loved, loving, and happy would be *right*. Just as obviously, anything that *detracts* from our feeling loved, loving, and happy would be *wrong*.

Because anger always detracts from our feeling loved, loving, and happy, anger is always wrong. It simply doesn't work. It interferes with our accomplishment of the primary goal of our lives. When we're angry—no matter how right we are about everything else—we are wrong.

I talked to a woman one day who presented a brilliant and detailed case proving that all the unhappiness in her life and in her marriage was caused by her selfish, insensitive, and stupid husband. She did everything short of bringing surveillance photographs to confirm the points she was making.

I tried to show her how *she* too had made significant negative contributions to their relationship, making their marriage miserable with her anger, for example. She insisted in a variety of ways that she was right and he was wrong. Finally, when no other reasoning seemed to be capable of reaching her, I said, "Isn't our primary purpose in life to be happy?"

"Yes, it is," she said.

"You're clearly not happy," I said, "so how could you claim to be right?"

For the first time in our conversation, she was silent.

You may be right about all your partner's mistakes. You may be right in your knowledge about a thousand other things too, but if you're angry you're being unloving, and you are therefore wrong. When you can recognize that, it will go far in helping you to stop being angry. It's difficult to remain angry at others when we admit our own faults.

In the space on the next page discuss some moments of contention that you've experienced with others. Now look back and acknowledge that when you were angry, you were unloving and selfish. You were wrong. Write it down. Say it out loud to yourself. Say it to others: "When (name the event), I was *wrong*." Say it and write it repeatedly until you can do it without hesitating or flinching.

NINE, 38:02 - 38:50   Step Three: Feel Loved
CD Track Nine, 1:44 - 2:33

By *feel loved* I mean *remember that you're loved.* As we tell the truth about ourselves, we build up a supply of Real Love. When stressful moments come, however—when people are actively attacking us, for example—it's very easy to forget about all the loving moments. It's easy to be overwhelmed by the fear of the moment, and then we start protecting ourselves again—with anger, for example.

On some frightening occasions, before anger takes over and ruins everything, we can change the course of events by beginning to take the five steps. We need to be quiet and admit we're wrong. Then we need to remember the stores of Real Love we have built up over time. When we can remember that we're loved, it's difficult to remain angry.

Discuss some unconditionally loving experiences that you've had with several people:

- What did you share about yourself?
- What did they say to you?
- What did they do? How did they look?
- How did it feel to be accepted and loved like that?

Now imagine all of those loving people in a room together, in a lovely home in a village in a valley, much like we envisioned in the meditation on page 59. Now whenever you get angry, you can go in your mind to this room, where you are surrounded by these people who love you.

I believe you'll be surprised at the power of this simple exercise. Record how you feel the first time you do it.

The more we become familiar with the feeling of Real Love, the better prepared we are to feel and remember the love of God. When we can tap into that Infinite Source of love, we need never feel empty or afraid. The love of our brothers and sisters is important, but the love of God is so much more powerful. I suggest re-reading John 4:7-14, as found pages 4-5. Additional references about God's love for us are most useful for us to keep in our minds and hearts:

- The author of Psalms spoke of God. "He is my safety and my protection. He is my God, and I will trust Him. He will deliver you from those who would trap you and from the plague. He will cover you with His feathers, and under His wings you will trust in His protection. You shall not fear the terror that comes by night, nor the arrows that come by day. Thousands shall die around you, but not you. Because you have chosen to be with God, He will protect you and keep you safe. Because you have loved Him, he will deliver you and set you up on high." (Psalms 91:2-15)

- And when Jesus saw how many people there were, He was moved with love for them, because they were lost, as sheep not having a shepherd: and He began to teach them many things. (Mark 6:34)

- Five sparrows are sold for two cents, but not one of them is forgotten by God. Even the hairs of your head are all numbered. So fear not, because you are of more value than many sparrows. (Luke 12:6-7)

- Who will separate us from the love of Christ? Will we be separated by affliction, or difficulty, or persecution, or famine, or nakedness, or danger, or sword? No, in all these things we are more than conquerors through Him that loved us. For I am persuaded that neither death, nor life, nor angels, nor kingdoms, nor powers, nor things present, nor things to come, nor height, nor depth, nor any other creature, shall be able to separate us from the love of God, which is in Christ Jesus our Lord. (Romans 8:35-39)

NINE, 38:50 - 41:51   Step Four: Get Loved
CD Track Nine, 2:33 - 5:34

Repeatedly I have said that Getting and Protecting Behaviors are a response to emptiness and fear, so the most powerful tool in eliminating anger (one such behavior) is to get the Real Love we need. With sufficient Real Love, our emptiness and fear go away, after which anger simply has no function.

On pages 273-289, especially page 288, we saw the effect of Real Love on Holly in real life. It can have the same effect on you, but there's only one way to learn this. You can't learn about the power of Real Love only by reading about it. You need to *feel* it.

We all need to have constant access to as many sources of Real Love as possible.

- In the space on the next page, begin a list of people you can call and share the truth about yourself with.
- Keep adding to this list until you have people you can call from early morning until late at night.
- This list is a *lifeline*, so take it seriously. Add to it regularly.

- *Use it.* Call people on this list at least every day, and call each day until you actually speak to someone long enough that you feel loved.

If you create a great call list, and you use it regularly, you'll discover emotional and spiritual benefits that will reward you for the rest of your life:

- You'll stay filled enough with Real Love that your longstanding emptiness and fear will begin to disappear.
- Your Getting and Protecting Behaviors will slowly vanish.
- You'll avoid the crises that characterize the lives of most people.
- You'll become so familiar with the sensation of Real Love that you won't be fooled by Imitation Love anymore.
- You'll replace anger and confusion with peace and confidence in your individual life and in your relationships.
- You'll learn to see other people clearly and will gain the ability to accept and love them.

NINE, 41:51 - 43:51   Step Five: Be Loving
CD Track Nine, 5:35 - 7:33

As we make conscious choices to be loving toward people—as described on pages 358-72—we just can't stay angry.

Name someone you find irritating. In the space below, discuss something loving you could do for or with that person. Plan it, share it with a friend to see if it makes sense, and then actually do it.

CHAPTER TEN
The Power of Real Love

TEN, 43:51 - 45:40 The Healing and Peace of Real Love
CD Track Ten, 0:00 - 1:49

Imagine that you have terminal cancer, and between now and the day of your death you will be in almost constant pain. Your case is hopeless.

But then you learn that there is a cure for your cancer. You visit the doctor, and he says that you must do the following:

- Read a book fifteen minutes a day.
- Watch six hours of video on DVD.
- Watch five minutes of Internet video every weekday.
- Participate in a chat room once a week.
- Call another cancer patient for fifteen minutes every day.

If you'll do that, he says, not only will you be free of your cancer, but you'll be healthier and happier than you've ever been in your life. Would you do as he has suggested?

A similar effort will enable you to save your emotional and spiritual life, and to find a level of happiness that most people can scarcely imagine:

- Watch *The Essentials of Real Love* video on DVD.
- Read the book, *Real Love*, as well as other books in the Real Love series—on dating, marriage, parenting, counseling, and so on.
- Go to www.RealLove.com where you can:
  - watch archived Daily Video Coaching sessions with Greg.
  - watch the archived Video Chats with Greg.
  - participate in the Real Love Forums.
- Tell the truth about yourself to someone on your phone list every day.

It really is possible to live without anger, contention, blaming, confusion, and fear. Are you willing to do what it takes to have that kind of life?

CHAPTER ELEVEN
Module Summary

ELEVEN, 45:40 - 47:45   Module Summary
CD Track Eleven, 0:00 - 2:18

MODULE FIVE

CHAPTER ONE
Libby: Single and Looking for Love

ONE, 0:00 - 0:33   No One Loves Me
CD Track One, 0:00 - 0:33

"I'm afraid that nobody will ever love me." Libby eloquently expresses one of the most predominant and harmful feelings on the planet—which few of us have the insight or courage to say directly. Without our realizing it, most of us are reacting to this fear with our behavior much of the time.

ONE, 00:33 - 1:43 The Seduction of Being Loved
CD Track One, 0:33 - 1:43

"I just want to feel loved," she says—by anybody. This need is so powerful within us that we're willing to do almost anything to fill it. It affects what we wear, how we talk, and what we do. The search for love has become a primal hunt, where we are both hunter and prey, and endless hours of conversation are devoted to how we can more effectively play both roles. From our behavior it's obvious that success in life is virtually defined by our performance in this regard.

When we are successful in the hunt—in either or both roles—a grand celebration is held, where all are invited to gather 'round the campfire, as it were, to hear the exquisite and most particular details. Those of us who are the focus of such social ceremonies are crowned king or queen for the day, and for as long as we are successful hunters or prey we are welcomed as full members of the royal family.

In such a hunting society, the absence of a trophy—worn proudly on the head or around the neck—is glaringly obvious and marks one as seriously defective. Without a boyfriend or girlfriend or spouse we are forced to wear the large red "L"—for Loser—on our foreheads, virtually a mark of social death.

In a culture where there is little Real Love, the game—or the hunt—is unavoidably scored by the piles of Imitation Love we gather. When we can amass great piles, we feel pretty darned good about ourselves—at least temporarily—but when we can't, the social stain is utterly apparent and unbearable. We just gotta have a boyfriend or girlfriend to be seen as worthwhile—to ourselves and to others.

In the space below and on the next page discuss occasions in your life when you have not had such a partner—when you have had no boyfriend, girlfriend, or spouse.

- Did people ask you how the hunt was going? Did they ask:
  - Are you dating?
  - Found someone yet?
  - Did he call again?
  - How's it going with _____?
- Did you feel self-conscious, as though something were wrong with you?
- Did you feel a need to explain yourself to others?
- Did you think about the hunt a great deal—how to find a partner, how to be found by a partner?

ONE, 1:43 - 2:50   Never Settle for Imitation Love
CD Track One, 1:43 - 2:50

We are often so desperate for a partner—and for people to believe that we have one—that we'll settle for partners with qualities far inferior to what we really want. That is a *huge* mistake. Because most of us don't know what Real Love looks like, and because we're desperate for as much Imitation Love as we can find, we tend to settle for partners who give us a relatively good deal in Imitation Love. This, of course, is a set-up for disaster.

If you're dating, *promise yourself* that no matter how long it takes, *you will not settle for a relationship based on anything other than Real Love*. Remind yourself:

- No matter how entertaining Imitation Love is in the beginning, the effects always wear off, and then you're left with disappointment and frustration.
- The promises of praise, power, sex, and so on are an illusion.
- Everybody thinks that the initial excitement of *their* romance is different from everyone else's, but Imitation Love fails predictably.
- Once we're aware of the existence of Real Love, settling for Imitation Love becomes very foolish.
- If we pursue any Imitation Love at all in a relationship, we'll be distracted—perhaps fatally, as far as the relationship goes—from finding the Real Love we need. It's better to have no Imitation Love at all than to be distracted.
- When almost everyone around us seems to be enjoying the temporary excitement of Imitation Love, it's especially tempting to join them. But it's still an illusion. Billions of people have proven that Imitation Love will never make us happy.

ONE, 2:50 - 4:23   The Got-to-Have-a-Boyfriend/Girlfriend Myth
CD Track One, 2:50 - 4:23

Having an exclusive partner is very important in our society:

- It gives us a relationship we can rely on for a steady source of Imitation Love.
- It makes us feel worthwhile. If someone is willing to enter into an exclusive relationship, there must be something desirable about us.

We have come to believe that we must have an exclusive partner in order to be happy, but that is simply not true. What we need in order to be happy is just Real Love, from whatever source, as we discussed on page 274.

CHAPTER TWO
Greg: Teaching Our Children to Pursue Imitation Love

TWO, 4:23 - 5:43   Teaching Our Children to Buy Love
CD Track Two, 0:00 - 1:20

Because we as adults pursue Imitation Love in the hope that it will make us happy, it's only natural that we would teach our children to do the same. Natural and deadly.

If you are a parent, ask yourself the following questions, and record the answers in the space on the next page:

- When your children do what you like—when they're cooperative, clean, convenient, and so on—do you smile at them, speak kind words to them, and obviously accept them? Certainly there's nothing wrong with that, but does your behavior change when they're *not* cooperative, clean, and convenient?

- Is your speech or behavior different in any way when a child *wins* an individual or team athletic event, as compared to when he or she *loses*?
- Do you become irritated when a child disagrees with you and argues with you?

If so, you are teaching your children—without intending to—to buy Imitation Love from you in the forms of praise, power, and safety. Don't feel guilty about it. It's virtually certain that your parents and other adults did the same with you, so you're just passing on what you learned.

In the space on the next page discuss some occasions when you've taught your children to earn Imitation Love. You might find the following examples useful:

- When I go to my son's baseball games, I cheer like crazy when they're winning, but when they're not, I complain about the umpire, the coach, whatever. I make it obvious to my son that *winning*—power—is the reason you play the game. Embarrassing.
- When my daughter does well in school, I say, "I'm so proud of you," but when she slips a bit, I frown, roll my eyes, and tell her that she can do better.
- When my children behave themselves, I tell them I'm so proud of them. When they don't, I behave quite differently. So they work hard to *please me*, not to do the right things for the right reasons.

- When my children receive a gift, I make them say *thank you* to please the person who gave it to them, and sometimes that person is me.

As I've said before, I am *not* suggesting that children don't need to be corrected. They need a great deal of guidance, but we need to offer it without the disappointment and irritation that immediately communicate that we don't love them unconditionally. The moment a child doesn't feel loved unconditionally, he or she will do whatever it takes to earn Imitation Love.

TWO, 5:43 - 7:11   Avoiding the Trap of Praise
CD Track Two, 1:20 - 2:48

Children don't need our praise to be happy. They need our love. That does not mean, however, that praise is always harmful. As I said in Module Two, Chapter One:

> When people have sufficient Real Love, they regard both praise and criticism as merely pieces of *information*. They neither *need* the praise nor *fear* the criticism. With Real Love—the greatest treasure of all—everything else pales by comparison.

We tend to praise our children only because we don't know that there is something available—Real Love—which is much better. If you'd like to learn a great deal more about how to make parenting much easier and more effective, I suggest that you:

- Read the book, *Real Love in Parenting*, available at www.RealLove.com.
- Go to www.RealLove.com where you can:
  - watch Video Coaching sessions with Greg.
  - watch the Live Video Chats with Greg.
  - participate in the Real Love Forums.
  - watch for other materials on parenting.

TWO, 7:11 - 8:59   Teaching Children to Lust after Praise and Power
CD Track Two, 2:48 - 4:36

In the space below and on the next page discuss how you behave in association with competitions (athletic contests, board games, arguments). Some of your answers might include:

- I get annoyed when I'm losing a game or an argument.
- I don't like it when I'm watching one of my teams losing on television. I'm obviously grumpy and say negative things.
- When my favorite team is winning on television, I rub it in with a friend who likes the team that's losing.
- I notice more "unfair" officiating when the calls go against my team.
- Sometimes in competitive situations (athletics, cards, so on), I'm willing to cheat to win.
- I treat members of the opposing team with less respect than I give members of my team.
- When I'm at a game, I sometimes yell unkind comments at the referees.
- When the "other team" makes a great play, I grumble or sulk instead of congratulating them.

If you behave in some of the ways described above, you are teaching your children—mostly unconsciously:

- that winning is more important than having fun.
- to earn Imitation Love in the form of power.
- to be selfish.
- not to care about the happiness of others.
- to find pleasure in beating other people down.

Regrettably, the above views of competition are the norm. Our society is obsessed with winning and the sensation of power that comes from it, and the overall effects of that obsession are not healthy.

I was once the adult leader of a large Boy Scout troop composed of older boys, and one of the first decisions I made was to eliminate score keeping in any athletic activity. We played football, basketball, team handball, volleyball, and more, but we didn't keep score. The effect was miraculous and immediate.

The boys began to cooperate with one another at a level they'd never known before. In the past—when scoring was the goal—the best athletes understandably monopolized the action. With scoring removed, however, the boys began to enjoy *playing*. I'll never forget seeing the expression on the face of the skinny, geeky kid who had never caught a pass in a competitive situation as he caught a touchdown pass from the varsity football quarterback. With power removed as a source of Imitation Love, the boys naturally began to genuinely care about one another. It was amazing.

As parents and as adult leaders, we need at least to be aware of the dangers of an emphasis on winning. It can really distract us and our children from what matters in life.

TWO, 8:59 - 9:59   Peer Pressure
CD Track Two, 4:36 - 5:36

When people are getting all the Imitation Love they want in a given moment, it really does feel good. It feels *real*—although the momentary excitement of praise, sex, and money is superficial and temporary, the excitement itself is still real—and it's natural that we'd therefore want to pursue it. And when our children see their friends "having a good time," it's very tempting indeed for them to want some of that action.

Simply forbidding our children from doing something doesn't usually last long. We need to also show them how the consequences of certain choices just don't produce happiness. They need to understand *why* wise choices are wise.

CHAPTER THREE
Reva: Disobedient and Irresponsible Children

THREE, 9:59 - 11:11   Disobedient Children
CD Track Three, 0:00 - 1:14

In the space below and on the next page discuss how your children behave (or have behaved in the past) in ways similar to those described by Reva:

- Putting my children to bed at night is an endless circus.
- My children will not do their chores around the house.
- I can't get them to do their homework.
- They fight among themselves all the time, no matter what I say.
- I'm sick and tired of telling them to put their stuff away.

THREE, 11:11 - 11:52   The Frustration of Parenting
CD Track Three, 1:14 - 1:54

I can't over-emphasize what was said in this section. When we become disappointed or irritated, our children hear us say only, "I don't love you," and then nothing positive will come of the interaction.

In the space below describe some occasions when you've been angry at your children:

- Did you feel more loving and closer to them?
- Were they happy? Did you even notice?
- Did they suddenly develop a desire to do what you wanted them to do?
- Did they listen to you eagerly?

Anger uniformly hurts our children, and it's exhausting to us.

THREE, 11:52 - 13:04   How Parents Teach Children to Fight
CD Track Three, 1:54 - 3:05

As parents, we're often mystified and frustrated by the behavior of our children. We wonder, Where in the world did they learn to behave like that? The answer—on the whole—is, from us.

In the space below and on the next page discuss some of the Getting and Protecting Behaviors of your children, and describe how they might have learned them from you.

- My children fight all the time, and I used to think I didn't teach them that, but when they fight they're just using anger to protect themselves and to feel stronger. They see me use anger like that all the time.
- I hate it when my children whine and cry, but frankly, I've taught them that *until* they whine, I tend not to listen to them.
- My children lie a lot, and now I'm seeing that I've taught them to do that. When I've learned the truth about their mistakes, I've gotten angry at them and withdrawn my love from them. So they learned to lie to keep me from doing that.
- My oldest daughter runs from me a lot, withdrawing into her room and never coming out. She does that because she doesn't like to be around my disapproval of her all the time.
- They're always telling me how things aren't *fair*, and I'm realizing now that I say the same thing a lot about the situations in my own life. They've learned to act like victims from me.

THREE, 13:04 - 15:22   Telling the Truth About Ourselves as Parents
CD Track Three, 3:05 - 5:23

What keeps us from being better parents? We don't have enough Real Love to give our children. The solution here is therefore obvious. We as parents need to get more Real Love from other adults, and then bring that love back to our children.

We need to tell the truth about ourselves to other adults. We can tell the truth about many aspects of our lives, but following are a few examples of telling the truth about ourselves in our roles as parents:

- When my children have needed me to love them unconditionally, I've often been judgmental and angry instead.
- I just don't know how to love my children.
- When my children fight, I just don't know what to do. I feel helpless.
- I have avoided requiring my children to be responsible, because I don't like it when they're mad at me.
- I've done my best, but overall I've done a lousy job as a parent.

In the space below, take this opportunity to tell the truth about yourself as a parent, perhaps using one of the above examples as guidelines:

If you choose to share these truths with other adults, don't do it for the purpose of:

- condemning yourself.
- feeling guilty.
- confession.

We need to tell the truth about ourselves as parents to other adults for two reasons:

- To create opportunities to feel unconditionally accepted and loved. As we talk about ourselves with other adults, many of them will accept and love us with our flaws, and that's what we need to be better parents.
- So we can learn to make better choices in the future.

As we get more love from other adults, we'll finally have the Real Love to give our children that they've needed all along. There is no *technique* that will successfully raise happy and responsible children. They must *feel loved*, and we can't give them that until we first feel loved ourselves.

Most of us have a very difficult time talking about our flaws as parents. Why?

- In our culture, children occupy a very soft spot in our hearts. To be a "bad" parent—to inadequately care for a child—is to be a bad person.
- We promised ourselves that we wouldn't make the mistakes our own parents made.
- We really do try very hard to be good parents—we have great motives—so it's difficult to admit that we haven't succeeded at something we've put so much effort into.
- When our children were born, we had a dream that we would be great parents. It's hard to let go of that dream.

Until we tell the whole truth about how we're doing as parents, however, we can't grow. The primary job of a parent is teaching and unconditionally loving. No matter what else we do with our children, if we're not doing those two things well, we're lousy parents. There is no accusation or condemnation in that, just a simple description of how we're doing. It's a description—it's just information—from which we can learn and grow.

In the space on the next page discuss some of the mistakes you've made as a parent. You could name some similar to those listed above on page 397. Additional examples follow:

- I was angry at them over and over, and each time they heard that I didn't love them.
- When they've needed my support, I've been critical instead.
- I often pushed them to succeed to make *me* look good, not just for their own benefit.
- When they didn't do what I wanted, I became very disappointed and annoyed at them.

- I didn't spend nearly enough time with them.
- I've allowed my adult son/daughter to live at home far longer than has been productive for either of us.
- I didn't teach them what they needed to know to become loved, loving, and responsible.

Now share some of these insights with your children. Many adult children will experience enormous healing when they finally hear the truth about parental mistakes. Even young children—as young as four years—will understand what you're saying and will feel closer to you because of your sharing the truth. Be prepared for the resistance of some children who will actually cling to the notion that you have been unconditionally loving even when you haven't been. Children often defend your parenting for two reasons: (1) They want to enjoy the ideal in their minds that you've loved them, and (2) they don't want to feel your discomfort as you talk about your faults.

As you tell the truth about yourself, don't forget that the *purpose* of truth telling varies according to the person you're talking to:

- You tell the truth to *adults* for the purpose of finding Real Love for *yourself.*
- You tell the truth about yourself to your *children* so *they* will feel loved. As you tell the truth about your mistakes, they will realize that when you failed to love them in the past, it was a *mistake* on your part—caused by a lack of Real Love—not an intentional wounding of them. The healing from this can be profound. You do not tell the truth about yourself to children so they will love you.

THREE, 15:22 - 17:18   What to Do Differently? Consequences
CD Track Three, 5:23 - 7:20

When we don't understand Real Love, all we can do is trade Imitation Love with our children, and the process becomes an endless game that is exhausting and confusing, for us and for them. It's much easier when we remember that parenting is about loving and teaching. When that approach alone isn't enough, we apply consequences.

As parents we often don't know *how* to use consequences effectively. We discussed this subject somewhat on pages 292-302, and if you'd like to learn a great deal more about consequences and other ways to make parenting much easier and more effective, I suggest that you:

- Read the book, *Real Love in Parenting*, available at www.RealLove.com.
- Go to www.RealLove.com where you can:
  - watch Video Coaching sessions with Greg.
  - watch the Live Video Chats with Greg.
  - participate in the Real Love Forums.
  - watch for other materials on parenting that will be coming out on www.RealLove.com.

THREE, 17:18 - 19:13   Getting Children Ready for School
CD Track Three, 7:20 - 9:15

Reva keeps doing the same unproductive things with her children simply because she *doesn't know another way*. Most of us were given no formal instruction whatever for the most important job on the planet: parenting. More instruction is required to get a driver's license than to become a parent, and that's a huge disservice both to us as parents and to our children.

If you're having a consistent problem with your children in any particular area, you can be certain that you just need some guidance. Parents all over the country are discovering that Real Love provides the direction they need to raise responsible, loving, and happy children.

THREE, 19:13 - 20:17, Teaching Children to Be
Responsible
CD Track Three, 9:15 - 10:19

We don't do this intentionally, but we keep taking responsibility from our children and putting it on our own shoulders. We think we're being helpful, but we're just making them weaker. We're crippling them with our "help."

In the space on the next page describe some responsibilities you carry for your children that they would benefit from taking upon themselves. For example:

- I keep getting my children up in the morning when they're old enough to do that for themselves.
- When they go to school and leave things at home, I take their stuff to school and rescue them, instead of letting them take responsibility for their choices.
- When my son doesn't do his chores, I step in and do them for him.
- When they're late with their homework, I write excuses for them.

- I make small decisions for my children—about what they should wear or eat, for example—that I should leave to them.

CHAPTER FOUR
Amy: My Impatient and Angry Husband

FOUR, 20:17 - 21:09   The Conflict
CD Track Four, 0:00 - 0:54

Notice the words Amy uses to describe the problem she has with her husband:

- *"Whenever* we go *anywhere* . . ."
- ". . . it's a big *huge deal* . . ."
- "There's *always* a big conflict . . ."
- "He *always* gets mad at me and the kids . . ."
- "I *never* want to go."
- ". . . we have a big argument . . ."

Amy and her husband keep having the same terrible conflicts again and again, and until they acquire different tools—until they gain a different understanding and essentially become *different people*—they are guaranteed to repeat this old pattern of behavior.

This tragedy is played out in various ways millions of times every day all over the world. It may be the ultimate frustration in our lives that we keep using old methods and hope for different results.

In the space below describe a conflict that you keep repeating in some aspect of your life:

- My wife and I keep arguing about money.
- Every time we take the kids anywhere, it's the same awful mess: yelling, begging, the usual.
- I keep nagging my husband to take me out more often.
- Every conversation with my mother is awful. She brings up the same old stuff, and then I get defensive. I don't know how to change it.
- My arguments with my wife about sex go the same every time.
- There's a guy at work that I keep having conflicts with. We can't exchange ten words without getting into an argument.
- My spouse keeps telling me that I should help more around the house.

Do you really want to keep having the same conflicts? Or would you prefer to learn a way to break out of these old patterns?

FOUR, 21:09 - 23:05   The Effect of Not Feeling Loved
CD Track Four, 0:54 - 2:48

Amy is having a hard time seeing how there could be any association between feeling loved and being grouchy when the family is leaving on a vacation. What does love have to do with packing a car for a trip, right? She even says, "I just don't understand."

When we don't have enough Real Love in our lives, that is the worst wound in life. Without enough Real Love, we walk around wounded and in pain all the time. In that condition, it takes virtually *nothing* to push us over the edge and make life intolerable. Let's put this and other metaphors we've discussed together, so you can have the tools to see other people more clearly when they behave badly. When people are angry, withdrawn, acting like victims, and so on in response to a single behavior from you, they are:

- badly sunburned, and you probably just bumped them.
- drowning, and you splashed them or failed to help them in some way.
- down to their last two dollars, and you took what little they had.
- starving to death, and you failed to give them whatever morsel of food they were demanding.
- carrying all the burden they can, and you've added one last straw they can't handle.

All day, every day, we are interacting with people who are carrying the burden of a *lifetime* of experiences, and with most people the majority of these experiences have been unloving and painful. When people respond to us, then, they are not reacting to what *we* are doing in that moment. They are usually reacting to what hundreds of people have done to them and with them for a lifetime. When we don't understand that, we're usually quite puzzled at their responses to us.

In the space on the next page discuss some occasions or relationships where people have responded to you in ways that seemed:

- exaggerated, considering what you had done.
- bizarre.
- difficult to understand.
- overly dramatic.
- really out of character for them.
- surprising.

When you remember that people are often reacting to a lifetime of experiences, do these unusual reactions begin to make sense?

FOUR, 23:05 - 24:04 How The Conflict Grows
CD Track Four, 2:48 - 3:47

Observe the use here of the What-What-Why-What-What approach that we first discussed in Module Three.

- What did he do? He lashes out and tries to control everyone in the family (attacking).
- What did she do? She feels wounded (victim) and responds with anger (attacking) and withdrawing (running).
- Why did he behave as he did? He felt empty and afraid already—as a result of a lifetime of unloving experiences. When the family was late and not cooperating with him exactly as he wished, he felt even more helpless—he felt a loss of the

one form of Imitation Love (power) that was keeping him afloat—which proved to be an additional discomfort he just could not bear.

Most conflicts are a result of our responding inappropriately to Getting and Protecting Behaviors. When someone uses these behaviors, they are communicating two messages: "I don't love you" and "Please love me." We hear the first—to which we respond with our own Getting and Protecting Behaviors—but ignore the second, which makes the other person feel even more empty and afraid. He or she increases the uses of Getting and Protecting Behaviors, followed by our own increased response, and now we have a conflict without hope of resolution.

In the space below discuss a conflict where you responded to a partner's Getting and Protecting Behaviors with similar behaviors of your own. Now describe the results:

- Were you happy?
- Did you feel closer to your partner?
- When it was over, were you more likely or less likely to experience another similar conflict?

FOUR, 24:04 - 27:57 It's Always About Real Love
CD Track Four, 3:47 - 7:40

- What
- What
- Why
- What
- *What* will you do now?

Now the last *What* in the above sequence. What could Amy do differently? It's critical to notice that until she understands what is really happening (What-What-Why), it's quite fruitless to talk about a solution.

Also notice that after a lifetime of emptiness and fear and the use of Getting and Protecting Behaviors, we are often absolutely clueless—as Amy is—about how to change that pattern, even when we finally *see* the pattern.

First, I suggest that she say, "I don't think I've really paid attention to your need for us to be on time . . . So let's talk about what would help you feel relaxed."

You do not have to memorize a long list of "right things" to say in conflicts. Keep it very simple. In a conflict, do your *best*—perfection is not required here—to do just two things:

- Tell the truth about yourself ("I don't think I've really paid attention," for example).
- Reach your hand out to the drowning man—the definition of Real Love. ("Let's talk about what would help you feel relaxed.")

After she tells the truth about herself and voices a concern for him, Amy can approach a technical solution to how they can get ready on time.

Amy admits that she's a poor judge of time. No problem. Instead of struggling with that handicap every time, she just needs to admit it and ask for help. Her husband will respond to that a great deal better than to her being consistently late.

Remember the graphic from the video recording of the seminar: "The most important goal in any interaction is not the accomplishment of a task but the communication of Real Love." It's Real Love that brings us happiness in life, not the accomplishment of tasks. If you try to "get things done" without Real Love, you may get away with that for a while, but eventually the tension will build and bring everything to a stop.

Years ago I had a friend who had the worst luck with cars. Now it's true that he always bought old, used cars—it was all he could afford—but still, he was like a death sentence to those cars. He'd buy one, and then one or two years later, it would break down so badly that repairing it was more expensive than replacing it.

So one day I was talking to him about the car he'd just bought, and I asked him, "How often do you change the oil?"

And he said, "Oil?"

In all those years, he had never changed the oil—or done any kind of preventive maintenance, for that matter—on a single one of those cars. Sure, he remembered to fill the tank with gas, because there was a short-term motivation for him to do that—the car stopped immediately if he forgot. But there wasn't any short-term consequence for not changing the oil, so he just put it off. No wonder his cars all died.

Without using Real Love—without changing the oil—you might succeed in accomplishing tasks for a time, but is it worth it? Eventually, your relationships will break down, and, more importantly, you won't be happy throughout the entire process.

Never, never "get things done" at the expense of ignoring Real Love. The cost is much too high.

In every interaction—at home, at work, everywhere—remember the primary goal of communicating Real Love. If you'll do that, you'll be much happier—the most important thing—and you'll discover as a bonus that the tasks you want to accomplish will get done much more smoothly. Everything works better in the presence of Real Love.

In the space below discuss a conflict that you experience fairly regularly, using the following questions and suggestions as guidelines for your discussion.

- How could you do what Amy did?
- How could you tell the truth about yourself?
- How could you extend your hand to the drowning person?
- Plan out what you could say to the person you have the conflict with, and then practice it with another person.

Now go and do it. Tell the truth about *your* mistakes and offer whatever level of love you can to this person you've had a conflict with. Report on the results.

CHAPTER FIVE
Cindy: Teaching and Loving Children

FIVE, 27:57 - 30:37   Children Need to be Independent
CD Track Five, 0:00 - 2:41

Children do need our guidance—lots of it—but we must be careful about violating the Law of Choice with them. They can't learn to be responsible and independent if we control too many of their choices. We must increasingly give them responsibility for their own choices *when they can understand the consequences of their choices*, which is often much sooner than we're ready to let go of controlling them.

When we control our children, we're loudly declaring that we believe that they're too stupid to make the right choices. They will grow much more quickly and become stronger as we demonstrate faith in them, faith that as they learn correct principles, they will learn to make the right decisions.

This does not mean we should just let them make all their own decisions from the beginning. They couldn't handle that. We need to increase their right to make choices as they demonstrate an ability to handle them. Be careful, however, that you don't demand perfection at each level before you give them more responsibility, or they'll never grow.

In the space below, discuss some decisions you now make for your child that he or she might be able to make on his or her own. If your children are grown and out of the house now, discuss some decisions that you made for them too long.

FIVE, 30:37 - 31:20   Putting an End to Whining
CD Track Five, 2:41 - 3:23

We do what works. We do what gets us what we want. We don't stick beans up our nose, for example, because that wouldn't result in anything we want. Similarly, children do what works, and they abandon what doesn't work.

Children whine because it works. When you start making decisions based on loving principles—not your own momentary whims—and you stick with them, they'll stop whining.

In the space below, discuss a child who whines and complains. Now see your part in it. When the child whines long enough, how do you reward the child?

- I give in and let the child have what he or she wants.
- I don't always give in, but I do keep the discussion going for a long time, which gives the child attention and creates the hope that I *might* give in.
- I'm sympathetic, which he or she loves.
- I freak out and become a puppet controlled by my child.

FIVE, 31:20 - 32:18   Wanting Our Children's Love
CD Track Five, 3:23 - 4:21

Parenting is a one way deal. We must love *them* with no expectation of anything in return. The moment we want something from them— love, support, understanding, respect—they feel the burden of our expectations and can't feel unconditionally loved by us.

We want to believe that our children love us unconditionally, but if they haven't received enough Real Love from us—as few of them have—how can they give it to anyone else, including us? In most cases, when we expect love from our children, we're asking them to give us what they've never received sufficiently themselves. Their task is impossible, and the burden is crushing.

Love can be unconditional only when it's freely given. The giver of unconditional love can't be empty or afraid. When people are empty or afraid, they can only manipulate other people to get what they want or protect themselves from being hurt. Almost without exception, our children are both empty and afraid: They badly need us to love them, and they're scared to death of losing our love. These are natural conditions for a child, but they make it very difficult for children to give us Real Love.

We tend to love our children more when they're good—when they do what we want. They can feel that our approval is not unconditional, but it feels better than nothing, so they do their best—in the beginning, at least—to earn more of it by giving us what we want: gratitude, respect, obedience, affection, and so on. We feel good when we get these things, and understandably we then believe that our children are "loving" us. But they need our approval and love far too much to give us anything without expecting something in return. They give us what we want so we'll give them the "love" they desperately need. Or sometimes they're simply satisfied or happy because of love we give them, but their expressions of satisfaction are not unconditional love for us. Although it's unconscious, our children *trade* Imitation Love with us, and we gladly participate in the exchange, all of us just doing our best to survive in the absence of Real Love.

Is it ever possible for a child to unconditionally love his parents? Yes, but only after that child has been consistently and unconditionally loved himself for a long time. Few children have been loved in that way, and no loving parent would expect such love from a child. When a child can love his or her parents, it's just a delightful bonus for those parents, not something they have a right to expect.

In the space below, describe some occasions when you have expected your children to love you. If this doesn't ring a bell, consider this: Any time you become disappointed or irritated at your children, you're expecting some kind of "love" from them, usually Imitation Love.

FIVE, 32:18 - 33:50   Our Responsibility to Love Our Children
CD Track Five, 4:21 - 5:54

Saying *no* to a child is often the most loving response, because Real Love means caring about the child's happiness, which includes teaching him or her to be responsible. We must love and teach simultaneously. You can't productively do one without the other.

CHAPTER SIX
Holly: More about Children and Consequences

SIX, 33:50 - 36:49 Applying Consequences
CD Track Six, 0:00 - 2:59

Remember that the purpose of consequences is to make the wrong choice so inconvenient that children will want to make the right choice. Consequences are not intended to make things inconvenient for *everyone else*.

The general rule is that if you want to do something foolish that affects *you*, fine. Allow the Law of Choice to work. If you want to do something that affects *other people*, however, those people may have a right to give their input.

SIX, 36:49 - 37:32 Judging the Harshness of Consequences
CD Track Six, 2:59 - 3:42

Never impose a consequence while you're irritated, because it will be too harsh. It will be a punishment.

In the space below and on the next page discuss some occasions when you were irritated as you imposed a consequence.

- How did that work out?
- Did you feel loving?
- Did your child feel loved?
- Was the behavior modified in the way you intended?
- Did your child learn genuine responsibility, or did he or she do what was required resentfully?

CHAPTER SEVEN
Cindy: Telling the Truth about Ourselves to Whom?

SEVEN, 37:32 - 38:40   The Fear of Being Wrong
CD Track Seven, 0:00 - 1:08

We are *so* afraid to admit being wrong. Why? Let's look at this from the perspective of Event → Judgment → Feeling → Reaction, a concept we first introduced on pages 192-211.

Event:	Making a mistake
Judgment:	People will laugh at me or be disgusted by me.
Bottom line:	They will love me less. This judgment has come from thousands of experiences that support it.
Feeling:	Fear. Immediately. The thought of losing love is terrifying.
Reaction:	We lie. We hide our mistakes. We defend ourselves and claim to be right.

SEVEN, 38:40 - 41:00   Bringing Real Love into Your Relationship
CD Track Seven, 1:05 - 3:28

So how can we change the deadly reaction of hiding who we are from everyone? Let's look at our options in terms of Event → Judgment → Feeling → Reaction.

We could try to change the *event*. We could try to make no mistakes. Many of us have tried that, and for brief periods of time we can actually succeed. But it's exhausting, and people can't see who we really are, so we also feel alone.

We could change our *feeling*. We could say, "Sure, people will withdraw their love from us, but who cares? We just won't be afraid of that." Ridiculous. Love is too important to just make a decision that we won't care about it.

We could control our *reaction*. We could resolve that while we're deathly afraid of people not loving us, we'll just share the truth about ourselves with them anyway. Fat chance.

The only course left is changing the judgment, and *that* we can do. As we discussed on pages 202-4, we often make two negative judgments simultaneously before we become afraid:

- This person is not loving me (or may not love me).
- No one will *ever* love me unconditionally.

This Person May Not Love Me

Let's look at these two judgments in Cindy's situation. First, "This person may not love me." Is this judgment true? *Yes*. It's obvious from Cindy's reaction that her husband has been less than loving on many past occasions when she has exposed the truth about herself. He may *not* love her if she tells the truth about herself.

If that happens, what should she do? She doesn't need any more wounds in her life, so two courses of action will help minimize her being hurt by this one person:

- She can remember that he is just drowning. When she realizes that, she'll remember that his behavior isn't *about her*. He's just thrashing around in the water. He's emotionally insane, so to speak.
- She can stop telling him the truth about herself—at least temporarily—not because she's afraid, but because there is simply no positive yield anticipated. If he's drowning, he's just not in a *position* to be loving toward her, so why keep telling him the truth about herself?

No One Will Ever Love Me

This is the judgment that frightens us most. Imagine that you take two dollars from me—to use a familiar metaphor. If that's my last two dollars, I will become afraid, but if I have twenty million dollars, I will not. It's not the loss of two dollars I fear but the possibility that I will never have enough.

If Cindy had a life filled with people who unconditionally loved her (twenty million dollars), the possibility of losing two dollars from her husband (his being critical or angry) would mean nothing. But she does *not* have enough Real Love—she really is down to her last two dollars much of the time—so what can we do to help her? Two things:

- We can love her in this moment. We can simply accept her—and possibly teach her some truths about love and relationships.
- We can describe how she can get more Real Love from other people. She needs to tell the truth about herself to others and give them an opportunity to accept her. If necessary, she needs to stop the conversation with her husband on the spot and make a phone call to a loving person.

As we take both of these steps, she'll see that the *No one will ever love me* judgment is wrong. No longer threatened by that dismal prospect, she won't become afraid, and then she won't react to protect herself.

In the space below discuss occasions where people have been critical or angry, or where they have otherwise communicated to you that they didn't have your happiness foremost in their hearts and minds.

- Can you identify now that the terrible feeling you experienced was *not* the I'm-losing-two-dollars feeling?
- Can you see now that you were afraid of not having enough love in your life?
- You have now learned that it *is* possible to tell the truth about yourself and find Real Love from many sources. Can you have faith that that is possible?
- Knowing that you *can* be loved—by many people—are you not less frightened of the possibility that you might not get love from any particular person in a given moment?

Truth Telling Where Expectations are High

Initially, it's often wise to tell the truth about yourself to people for whom you have little or no expectations to love you. Why? Because then if you don't get loved, the disappointment is small, the wound is minor. If you persist in telling the truth about yourself with a spouse or lover or other person close to you—someone you *expect* to love you—the disappointment will be much bigger if they aren't loving.

The idea here is not to replace your spouse or other people close to you. The goal is to get enough Real Love from other people that you can bring that love back to the relationship with your spouse, girlfriend, children, and others close to you. With the introduction of that essential ingredient in these relationships, everything begins to change.

Are you afraid to tell the truth about yourself outside your marriage or family? Does the thought of doing so make you feel:

- disloyal? In many families it is almost a written law that family business is never discussed outside the family. This is a huge Protecting Behavior that keeps everyone trapped in the same old destructive patterns.
- guilty? Would your husband, for example, make you feel bad if you talked about your marriage with others?
- disoriented? Many of us just have no experience with talking about ourselves outside a certain comfortable—though often pathologic—circle of people.

Remember that your goal isn't to talk about other people, or to criticize, or to gossip. You want to practice telling the truth about *yourself,* so that you can begin to feel unconditionally accepted and so you can begin to see choices wiser than the ones you've been making. These benefits will be enormous to you personally and to your marriage and family as you take the healing power of Real Love back to those relationships.

SEVEN, 41:00 - 42:58   The Distraction of Sex
CD Track Seven, 3:28 - 5:38

Avoid the fatal distraction of sex as you tell the truth about yourself. You want to keep the love you get unconditional and pure. Don't make it confusing.

MODULE SIX

CHAPTER ONE
Matt: Fighting with My Sister

ONE, 0:00 - 1:55 What did she do?
CD Track One, 0:00 - 1:55

When I ask Matt to describe his relationship with his sister, notice all the details he provides to make her wrong and himself right:

- I felt rejected by my sister.
- She caused the pain in my mother's life.
- She allowed animals to make a mess of the house.
- Dishes were everywhere.
- Clothes were everywhere.

In any interaction, the other person almost always makes enough mistakes that we can become distracted by listing them. By comparison, then, we look more right. This is a tempting road to travel, but there is no love or happiness at the end of it.

ONE, 1:55 - 2:35 What did you do?
CD Track One, 1:55 - 2:35

When I ask Matt what *he* did in the interaction, at first he responds with, "Well, it was years ago," like he couldn't even remember. We really hate being exposed as wrong. Then he justifies himself:

- I *just* told them to clean their rooms.
- I even *helped* them sometimes.

In the beginning, telling the truth about ourselves can be uncomfortable, like learning a foreign language. It takes faith and courage and practice. I persist in helping Matt tell the truth about himself not to make him feel bad but to help him see what he's been doing—so he can make better decisions—and to create an opportunity for him to feel loved *with* his flaws.

ONE, 2:35 - 3:20   What-what-why-what-what
CD Track One, 2:35 - 3:20

> What
> What
> Why
> What
> What

Don't get distracted by all the details of an event. Boil down the first two *What*s to a single sentence or two. *What* was Matt's sister doing? She was selfish and unloving. That's not an accusation, just an accurate description we can now work with. It's information.

What was Matt doing? Again, no need for a pile of details. He was being unloving, and he hoped that his approach would teach his sister to be loving. Absurd, of course.

You may notice that I often make fun of our behaviors. There's a reason for that, and it's not for the purpose of mocking anyone. I make fun of the way we behave because when we can laugh at our ourselves, we can often finally talk about our behavior and deal with it.

In the space on the next page try the following sequence:

- Describe a recent conflict.
- What did they do? In a single sentence.

- What did you do? Were you unconditionally loving?
- If not, you were acting against your entire reason to be here, which is to be happy. Would that be *smart*? If not smart, what word would describe your destructive behavior? *Stupid* would be pretty accurate, or *foolish*.
- Don't make excuses for your behavior. Just say, "That was really stupid." Practice doing that until you can say these words without accusation or condemnation or guilt. It's just a description, like, "My hair is brown."
- Now you have a reasonable chance of actually changing your behavior.

ONE, 3:20 - 3:35   None of Your Business
CD Track One, 3:20 - 3:35

Matt's not quite finished with making excuses for his behavior. Now he's trying to say that he just doesn't care about his relationship with his sister. His stated goal is to have his sister love his mother.

But that is *none of his business*. We don't have the right to change other people. We can change only ourselves, and that's what we have to focus on. Let me say this for the third time in this workbook: One *ounce* of effort that I put into changing *me* will be more productive than a *ton* of effort that I put into changing *you*.

ONE, 3:35 - 5:12   What Can You Do Differently?
CD Track One, 3:35 - 5:12

Remember, no matter what the circumstances—no matter how distracting the many details appear to be—it's always about Real Love. That's the element that needs to be brought into this situation.

People behave badly because they *don't* feel loved, so we need to love them and supply that missing element first. After that, we can begin to work on the details of the conflict.

ONE, 5:12 - 6:19   It's All Our Parents' Fault
CD Track One, 5:12 - 6:19

Where did we get our judgments that love would be withdrawn from us if we made mistakes? Where did we receive conditional love? Where did we learn our Getting and Protecting Behaviors? From out *parents* and other caregivers.

There is no accusation or blaming here. As we've said before, our parents and others loved us as well as they could. We need to identify our parents' role in our present behavior only so we don't blame people in the *present* for judgments and experiences that were rooted in the *past*. We need to realize, for example, that what someone does in this moment is not causing our anger. We're reacting to a lifetime of emptiness, which began in childhood. This is the *Why* in What-What-Why-What-What.

ONE, 6:19 - 8:31   Again, What Can You Do Differently?
CD Track One, 6:19 - 8:31

Matt understands that he needs to show his sister more unconditional love, but he isn't entirely sure how that would look. It's not enough for us to say, "I just need to be more loving." We must identify exactly what behaviors would be involved in "loving."

We talked about some of these behaviors on pages 359-73. Matt chose one of the simplest and most loving acts possible: He told the truth about his mistakes.

Don't try to tell the truth about yourself to the most difficult people in your life first. In the beginning be truthful with people where you have few expectations and where there is a real likelihood that they'll accept you. As you grow in feeling loved, then you can share who you are with people who are harder to love—eventually with almost anyone.

The audience's reaction to Matt's telling the truth is immediate and unanimous. They're delighted. Every face in the room lights up; they even applaud. And this is a response to Matt's saying "I've been a big jerk." It turns out that it doesn't really matter what mistakes people have made; we feel closer to them just for being truthful, for sharing who they really are. When we tell the truth about ourselves, we offer a precious gift, and most people are grateful for it.

As you tell the truth about your mistakes, don't promise that you won't make them again. Don't wallow in anguish either. Just tell the truth. As you do that, you will become less likely to make the same mistake again. We all really have a desire to do the right thing. We don't need to be beaten in order to do it.

CHAPTER TWO
Adrian: My Wife is a Terrible Driver

TWO, 8:31 - 9:46   Avoiding Conflict
CD Track Two, 0:00 - 1:15

Many of us have a difficult time with conflict. We'll do almost anything to avoid it, as Adrian is doing here. Right from the beginning, he makes excuses for himself and for his wife:

- It's a very small, little situation.
- It's a safety issue.
- She has a lot of things on her mind.
- She has a new job.
- In case you missed it, it's a safety issue.

Again, it's not about safety or a new job or a garage or a truck. It's about Real Love.

TWO, 9:46 - 10:31   Identifying Our Anger
CD Track Two, 1:15 - 2:00

Most of us have been irritated for so long—and been around other people who are irritated so consistently—that we don't even see it. We accept it as normal.

The next time you wonder if you were irritated on a particular occasion, ask the person you were talking to at the time if you were angry. If he or she even pauses before answering you, you were irritated.

TWO, 10:31 - 13:42   Loving People with Their Flaws
CD Track Two, 2:00 - 4:15

All our lives we have heard the use of certain negative words accompanied by numerous signs of disappointment and anger. When people have used words like *stupid*, *mistake*, *wrong*, and so on, we have seen frowns and scowls. We've heard harsh tones of voice. So it's only natural that when we hear these negative words now, we wince. Another reason we avoid these words is that they often describe what is true about us.

Adrian needed to see the truth about his wife, that she was incapable of consistently parking her car without causing damage to it or the garage. Once we accept the truth, we can begin to respond productively to a situation. As long as we deny the truth, however, we'll keep making the same mistakes over and over.

Discuss some situations where not telling the truth about your own flaws, and those of other people, has had a negative effect. For example:

- I've always thought I was good at handling money, but I keep doing a lousy job in that area. I need to admit that I'm just not as good with it as I thought.
- I always thought I was a loving parent, but take a look at my children. They radiate emptiness and fear, and they use Getting and Protecting Behaviors all the time. Considering how they're doing, how could I be a loving parent?
- I keep pushing my son to be an athlete, but darn it, he's not athletic. I need to accept what he is and quit pushing him to be what he's not.
- I always thought of myself as a loving wife, but how could that be true if my husband avoids me all the time. My denial of the truth has kept us right where we are for years.
- For a long time I've been trying to get one of my employees to do a job he simply *can't* do. He's terrible at the job I keep trying to push him to do. I need to recognize that he can't do it and retrain him for another job.

Once we identify someone as *unable* to do something, our irritation vanishes, replaced by a desire to help him or her. This greatly contributes to the love in a relationship.

Once we tell the truth about a situation and set a goal to be more loving, the mechanical solutions to a situation become much clearer.

CHAPTER THREE
Rhett: I Do All the Work Around Here

THREE, 13:42 - 14:50   The Conflict
CD Track Three, 0:00 - 1:08

Rhett is angry because he does all the work, and it's not fair. He asks for help and drops hints (clanging dishes), but he still doesn't get what he's looking for. Hints are rarely effective. Read more about making effective requests on pages 354-5.

THREE, 14:50 - 15:39 It's Always about Real Love
CD Track Three, 1:08- 1:58

In a conflict, we tend to think the problem is the socks on the floor, or another task not accomplished, or the promise broken, or the unkind word. But the real problem is the *message* communicated by these behaviors.

When other people leave their socks on the floor or the milk out of the fridge or whatever, what we hear from their behavior is that they don't care about us. We hear, "I don't love you," and that is the message we respond to.

In the space below and on the next page discuss some occasions when you have been in conflict with other people. Can you see how the conflict began with—or continued because of—the message "I don't love you" that you heard in the behavior and/or words of the other person? We hate hearing that message, however it's delivered, and we react badly to it.

THREE, 15:39 - 16:12   The Expectations of Marriage
CD Track Three, 1:58 - 2:31

The pain of not feeling loved unconditionally is intolerable. Most of us get married precisely because we want to guarantee having someone who will always be there to love us. We marry someone precisely because we believe that that person will stay by our side and supply us with an absolutely reliable flow of love. Our hopes and expectations in this regard are enormous.

If our *spouse* then fails to love us, the disappointment and sense of betrayal are huge, because the expectations are similarly large. That's why we often become more angry at spouses and other family members than we do at others.

THREE, 16:12 - 16:48   The Exchange of I Don't Love You
CD Track Three, 2:31 - 3:07

This is the second *What* of What-What-Why-What-What. Rhett responded to his wife's unloving behavior by being unloving himself. This is the problem in virtually all conflicts. Two people are shooting one another with "I don't love you" bullets, and they each expect the other to somehow respond lovingly to that message. It's quite insane.

Notice that I don't make Rhett feel bad about his unloving response. I just help him *see* it, after which there's a chance he can begin to do something about it. We can't correct a problem until we correctly identify it.

In the space below discuss an occasion when you had a conflict. Can you see how you were hearing your partner say, "I don't love you"? Can you also see how *you* were saying to your partner— either with your words or behavior, or both—"I don't love you"? How could that possibly have turned out well?

THREE, 16:48 - 18:00   What Could You Do Differently? CD Track Three, 3:07 - 4:16

When I ask Rhett what he could do differently, he responds with, "I could be more patient." It's a very common belief that if we simply try harder, that will do the trick. But we've talked about that. Just "being more patient" is an attempt to change the reaction alone in Event → Judgment → Feeling → Reaction, and that approach rarely works well, nor does the effect last long. Using will power alone is a difficult way to change our lives, and in many circumstances it doesn't work at all.

It's the judgment we must change.

How many times have you resolved that you would just change your behavior? Name a few in the space below.

- I will not lose my temper anymore.
- I will lose weight.
- I will be a more loving husband.
- I'll spend more time with my children.
- I'll be nicer to my employees.
- I won't get mad at my mother.
- I'll be less critical of my husband.
- I will not look at women as sexual objects.

THREE, 18:00 - 18:47 Changing the Judgment
CD Track Three, 4:16 - 5:06

When we become afraid, we're usually making two judgments, that we won't be loved in that moment and that we won't be loved ever. We talked about this on pages 202-4 and on pages 417-19.

Rhett sees that the first judgment was probably true in the moments when his wife wasn't helping him, but that's not the most important judgment. He doesn't need to hang on to every two dollars being taken from him. Instead he needs to get twenty million dollars. He needs to feel loved by as many people as possible, and that will happen as he tells the truth about himself.

As he gets twenty million dollars, he'll realize that even if his wife doesn't love him in any given moment, he is still loved, and that's what matters. That's what changes the second judgment, that he'll never feel loved.

He can also change his judgment by seeing his wife clearly, by realizing that she is just drowning. When he recognizes that, he'll understand that she can't take love from him; she can only fail to give it to him. Then his fear will go away, and he'll possibly even be moved to help her.

Three, 18:47 - 20:23   After Changing the Judgment, Solutions Are Possible
CD Track Three, 5:06 - 6:42

Once you see your partner as drowning, it becomes possible to reasonably work out a solution. Two important principles should be remembered here:

1. It's always about Real Love. If you attempt to leave this out of a solution, you will fail.

2. Don't keep going over what is wrong, or who did what to whom. These discussions come across as attacks, and then no one listens well. Focus on what you plan to do *next* to address the problem. Move forward. Be positive. It's much more loving.

Notice how much more relaxed Rhett becomes when he realizes there is a solution. We hate the frustration of repeating the same behaviors over and over. When we can see a way out, what a relief.

CHAPTER FOUR
Matt: Single and Avoiding Commitment

FOUR, 20:23 - 23:25 Men Avoiding Commitment
CD Track Four, 0:00 - 3:01

The idea of commitment is frightening only because we realize that we're committing to a lifetime of what we're known thus far: conditional love, trading Imitation Love, expectations, disappointment, and anger. Why would anybody want to make a commitment to that?

Somehow, deep down, many of us recognize that falling in love is usually an illusion, and we're not willing to make a commitment to an illusion.

FOUR, 23:25 - 24:54 The Field of Death
CD Track Four, 3:01 - 4:30

Everywhere we go, people are trying to find happiness through the use of Imitation Love. They hope they'll succeed if they:

- use it more cleverly.
- use it in greater quantity.
- use it in different forms.
- trade it with others more efficiently.
- tell everyone how happy they are with it.

But no matter how much Imitation Love we get, we're playing on the Field of Death (pages 221-2), and everybody on that field dies. We can find genuine happiness only as we move completely off the Field of Death and play on the Field of Life.

We see the trading of Imitation Love everywhere, but it is especially apparent in dating. If you go to an Internet dating site, you'll see tens of thousands of advertisements by individuals who are selling and buying Imitation Love. The tragedy is that if they get exactly what they're looking for, they still lose, because all those qualities are still traded on the Field of Death, where nobody wins.

FOUR, 24:54 - 26:15   The Truth in Dating
CD Track Four, 4:30 - 5:52

The only foundation that will lead to success in relationships is the truth, which facilitates the creation of Real Love. Don't settle for anything less. If you'd like to learn a great deal more about how to make dating consistently more enjoyable and effective, I suggest that you:

- Read the book, *Real Love in Dating*, available at www.RealLove.com.
- Go to www.RealLove.com where you can:
  - watch Video Coaching sessions with Greg.
  - watch the Live Video Chats with Greg.
  - participate in the Real Love Forums.
  - watch for other materials on dating.

The book *Real Love in Dating* will suggest many practical things you can say about yourself on a date. Read those and then try telling the truth about yourself in some of the ways suggested. Then report here on the results of your experiment.

FOUR, 26:15 - 27:23   What You Want in a Partner
CD Track Four, 5:52 - 6:59

If you had to pick just one criterion for selecting a partner, it could be this: Can he or she easily admit being wrong. When people can do that, they can learn anything. When people have to be right, on the other hand, their minds are closed, and they're capable of learning almost nothing. They cannot have healthy relationships, because their focus is on themselves, not their partners.

CHAPTER FIVE
Virginia: I Keep Rescuing My Adult Son

FIVE, 27:23 - 29:17   The Dangers of Rescuing
CD Track Five, 0:00 - 0:57

In almost all interactions with other people, we have mixed motivations. Virginia really does care about her son. She wants to help him be happy, but she also wants the rewards that come to *her* for rescuing him. When she rescues him, she:

- feels useful.
- feels worthwhile and important.
- receives his gratitude, however brief that might be.
- feels in control. She doesn't like the helpless feeling that accompanies his being in trouble.
- avoids his disapproval, which she gets in abundance when she *doesn't* rescue him.

Regrettably, her rescuing him communicates to him that he *needs* rescuing and that he is incompetent and couldn't possibly get along without her help. She provides a great illustration of the effects of loving without teaching. Parents have a responsibility to do both simultaneously.

FIVE, 29:17 - 31:29   Having Faith in Our Children
CD Track Five, 1:57 - 4:05

Our children are inspired by our faith in them. If we genuinely believe in them, they will begin to believe in themselves. We need to encourage them to try new things, to do things on their own, and eventually to be independent.

Do you have a child you have supported and rescued far too long? Or do you know other parents who have done that? The results of this approach are usually unpleasant:

- The children are not grateful for what they have.
- The children become less and less responsible.
- The children become more demanding about what they believe they deserve.
- The children actually become resentful of the parents who are taking care of them (strange, but true).
- The children become increasingly afraid of being on their own.
- The parents become resentful and angry.
- The relationship becomes strained.

In the space below and on the next page, describe one of your experiences with such children, whether your own or the children of others.

FIVE, 31:29 - 32:56 Loving and Teaching Our Children
CD Track Five, 4:05 - 5:33

Loving our children means to care about their *happiness*, but our children often believe—because most of the world believes the same—that if we really love them, we'll give them all of the following they want:

- Comfort
- Ease
- Satisfaction
- Security
- Pleasure
- Power
- Approval
- Money

But loving people does not mean giving them everything they want. If that were so, we'd give an addict all the drugs he or she wants, and Virginia would keep her 42-year-old son in her house until the end of time.

Loving our children means caring about their happiness, and in order for our children to be happy, they must:

1. feel unconditionally loved.
2. be loving toward others.
3. be responsible.

Children cannot learn to be responsible—and therefore can't learn to be happy—while we are rescuing them from their opportunities to be responsible. It should be obvious, then, that rescuing them actually keeps them from being happy and is not loving.

CHAPTER SIX
Tracy: My Sister is So Demanding and Angry

SIX, 32:56 - 34:28   The Conflict
CD Track Six, 0:00 - 1:31

Tracy relates a lot of details about her sister, but don't get lost in them. Her sister is acting like a victim and attacking.

SIX, 34:28 - 35:16   What Did You Do?
CD Track Six, 1:31 - 2:21

When I ask Tracy what *she* did, she makes her behavior sound as nice as possible:

- "I asked her *politely*."
- "I would *appreciate* it if I wasn't treated that way in my car or my house."

Tracy sounds quite civil, but she is really telling her sister that she has to behave in a certain way before Tracy will find her acceptable. Tracy is saying, "I'll accept you only if you change." That is the definition of conditional love, and it's understandable that her sister doesn't like it.

In the space below and on the next page discuss occasions when you have required people to behave differently during a conversation. You might have said something like the following:

- I have to ask you not to talk to me like that.
- Don't you talk to me in that tone of voice.
- I can't talk to you when you're acting like that.
- We'll talk when you've calmed down.
- I will not tolerate that kind of language.

I'm not saying that you *should* continue every conversation when someone is being abusive. As we discussed on pages 328-9, it's often unwise for you to enter into situations where you know you don't have enough Real Love to handle them.

If you're in a conversation where you feel threatened by someone's attacks, where you are about to defend yourself, follow the five steps described on pages 375-83 for responding to your own anger.

- Be quiet. Do not keep talking when you're upset.
- Be wrong. If you're angry, you're not loving, and that is never the right way to be.
- Feel loved. Try to remember the love of other people, those who *have* loved you unconditionally.
- Get loved. At the first opportunity, leave the difficult conversation and spend time—personally or on the phone—with someone who *can* love you.
- Be loving.

SIX, 35:16 - 36:38   The Trap of Defending Ourselves
CD Track Six, 2:21 - 3:40

When people attack us, we begin to defend ourselves automatically. We've been doing this for so long, we don't even realize it anymore. Consider some of the following ways we defend ourselves:

- *BUT*. This word destroys so many conversations. When we

say it, what our partners hear is, "I'm not listening to you. I'm more interested in being right." People go to great lengths to tell us what they're thinking, for example, and instead of acknowledging a single word they say, the first word out of our mouths is often *but*. That goes over poorly.

- Your partner says, "This is the *fourth* time you've done this," and instead of acknowledging that yes, you certainly have been inconsiderate to have done that (which is the real point), you drag out videotapes to prove that you've done whatever-that-is only *three* times—which is completely irrelevant and serves only to make you right.
- You're accused of doing several things, and you focus on the one thing you *didn't* do instead of admitting your error in the others.
- Excuses. You carefully explain how you just couldn't help it. Your behavior was completely unavoidable.

The irony is that in all these defenses, you might be *entirely right*, and it just *doesn't matter* one bit. None. Because you're missing what's most important. The most important element of every conversation is Real Love, not the accuracy of details, not who is right, not the accomplishment of a task, not anything else. Without sufficient Real Love, nothing else goes well, so we must attend to that critical element first. We must be concerned about the happiness of our partner before we focus on our own interest in being right or even safe.

The problem with defending ourselves is that the instant we do, we're focused on *ourselves*, and at that point we can't be unconditionally concerned about the happiness of anyone. We can't be loving, and the people around us *feel that*. When we defend ourselves, we isolate ourselves from our partners and injure our relationships.

Considering the examples of defending ourselves listed above, in the space on the next page discuss some occasions when you have defended yourself.

- How did that turn out?
- Did you feel more loving as a result?

- Did you feel closer to your partner?
- Did the discussion go more smoothly as you defended yourself?

So if someone is attacking you for something you did, what can you say? Just tell the truth about your mistake.

But what if someone is attacking you for something you *didn't* do? Now what can you say?

First, *listen.* Don't interrupt. Listen to what is being said. That alone is a loving act and will go far to promote a loving conversation.

Second, tell the truth about the mistakes you *did* make. Sure, you may not have done most of what you're being accused of, but it's pretty rare that you were absolutely blameless in a situation. You could have communicated better, for example, or been more sensitive, or done something more efficiently. Talk about your mistakes.

But what if you really didn't make any mistake? None. That is remotely possible, so in that case you should not admit to making a mistake you didn't make. You might, however, offer clarification about what you did—just by way of *information*—without the slightest tinge of defensive attitude. Then if your accuser continues blaming you, you might say something like, "Thanks for telling me all this. It's given me a perspective I didn't have. It's given me something to think about. Thank you." You're listening and loving without either agreeing or disagreeing about *content*. It's loving that's the important action here.

After all that, however, what if someone continues to attack you? You can still be loving as you say, "Again, I'm grateful that you would share all this. It's obvious that we see this differently, but that's all right. I can really see how you've come to your conclusion, and I'll pay closer attention to this in the future." We must accept that even if we are completely loving, some people will still remain angry and accusing. As we adopt a loving attitude, however, *we* can be happy under almost any circumstances.

SIX, 36:38 - 38:05   What Could You Do Differently?
CD Track Six, 3:40 - 5:08

Again, loving people does not mean giving them everything they want. So what *is* involved in loving? When you're loving:

- you give people what will contribute to their genuine happiness, which includes their being loving and responsible—not just what contributes to their feeling entertained and satisfied.
- you give people what you're *able*, not necessarily what they *need*. What they actually need may be far in excess of what you're able to give them.
- you give people what you *choose* to give, not always what they *demand* from you.

On many occasions people will tell you that you don't love them because you're not giving them what they demand from you. When that happens,

- don't argue with them. They'll feel it as an attack.
- don't feel guilty. It's your choice to give what you give.
- don't defend yourself.
- don't apologize. If you do, you'll just be confirming that you're doing something wrong, which may not be the case.

Just emphasize what you *are* willing to give people, and tell them how much you love them. You are not obligated to give anyone anything that he or she demands.

If what you're offering to someone isn't acceptable to him or her, his or her dissatisfaction isn't your responsibility, so don't take it upon yourself. If other people insist on being angry, let them. You are not responsible for making *anyone* happy, only for loving people as well as you can.

SIX, 38:05 - 38:52 How to Be Loving
CD Track Six, 5:08 - 5:55

We have so many opportunities to be loving:

- We can genuinely listen, which most of us rarely do.
- We can admit our mistakes, past and present.
- We can express our understanding for the pain we have caused.
- We can extend ourselves to make phone calls, write e-mails, and visit with people.
- We can simply avoid inconveniencing people.

SIX, 38:52 - 40:52 It's Always About Real Love
CD Track Six, 5:55 - 7:56

If a relationship is important, never give up. Notice that in the example of my family, I could easily have been justified in leaving the pig (page 328). But the relationships mattered to me, so I chose to learn to live with the pig and like it. Love melts monsters—and pigs. Love melts fear and anger and victimhood.

This next exercise/assignment could be a hard one for many of us. In the space below and on the next page describe a relationship that you have relatively abandoned—someone you haven't spoken to in some time, someone you wish you could make things right with, but with whom you've pretty much given up. Listen again to the conversation I had with my brother, and in the space below discuss what you might say with that person in your life. Some suggestions:

- Keep it short. If you haven't talked in a while, a long conversation will be more than either of you can handle in most cases.
- Don't dredge up past wounds. You don't need to do a detailed analysis of the past over the phone. Your intent is just to communicate real caring. Tell him or her briefly what's been going on with you lately. Casually ask how he or she is doing, but do not interrogate or pry.
- Offer this conversation as a *gift*, which means you must have *no expectations* whatever. If the person you call is distant or prickly, so what? You're offering a gift, and he or she can do whatever he wants with it. Remember that you're not calling to get loved. You're calling to love unconditionally.
- Practice what you're going to say with some loving friends first. We often don't realize that we have residual resentments toward people, and then those negative feelings come out in a number of ways in our conversations. Work these feelings out with a loving friend before you try to have this conversation in a more difficult environment.
- The moment you feel the least bit anxious or upset in the conversation, *stop talking*. Nothing you say after that will be productive. Just say, "I've really enjoyed talking to you. I'll call again."

Notice that Tracy admitted being defensive with her sister. That's the beginning of miracles. When we can admit that we're wrong, everything becomes possible.

CHAPTER SEVEN
Mila—My Stepchildren Don't Listen to Me

SEVEN, 40:52 - 42:28   The Horrible Stepmother
CD Track Seven, 0:00 - 1:36

Mila is trying to help her step children learn to read, and they are not grateful for her help. They resist her, their birth mother resists her, and it's all quite frustrating.

SEVEN, 42:28 - 43:12   What Did You Do?
CD Track Seven, 1:36 - 2:24

When I ask Mila about her response to the children's resistance, she says that at first she *calmly* tells them they just have to learn to read.

Of course, we know the *calm* didn't last long, because earlier she said she found the whole experience *frustrating*.

Mila admits to becoming impatient with the children, and *that* is the beginning of seeing the real problem. It's always about Real Love—really. The instant a child doesn't feel loved by us, the teaching is *over*. Regrettably, we don't notice that, so we persist in teaching—usually harder and harsher, which only makes things much worse. We can never ignore the role of Real Love in teaching children or in any relationship.

SEVEN, 43:12 - 44:12   It's Always About Real Love
CD Track Seven, 2:24 - 3:24

Because most of us have rarely seen Real Love in any consistent way, we're just not aware of its importance in every conversation. So we mis-prioritize things all the time. Mila thought her primary goal was to teach her step children to read. Wrong. Until they feel loved, she can't teach them anything for long. Oh sure, she might actually be able to teach them to read somewhat, but at what price? As she describes, she actually got one of the boys to read fairly well, but at the price of hating reading and hating her. Hardly worth it.

In the space on the next page discuss some occasions when you have tried to get children—or anyone else—to accomplish something at the expense of Real Love. For example:

- I pushed my daughter to practice the piano, even though she obviously didn't want to do it. She ended up hating the piano, and it strained our relationship.
- I practiced baseball with my son for many hours, so he would play well in his games, but I wasn't kind or loving about pointing out his mistakes. I look back now and cringe at the expression of pain on his face as I spoke harshly to him.
- I yell at my employees to improve their performance, but I don't think about them as individuals at all. No wonder they avoid me, and no wonder the morale in the office isn't good.
- I made my children do their homework diligently, but oh,

the scenes we had. There was yelling and crying and the whole bit. They got their homework done, but the cost was astronomical.

Notice that Mila says that the boys were "pushing all her buttons" to see if she would run away. No, actually, human behavior isn't that complicated. We don't push people's buttons to see what they'll do. We're not that conniving. Drowning people don't splash you to see what you'll do. They're just drowning, and in the process of drowning, they splash water on the people around them. The boys were just empty and afraid, and in the process of filling their emptiness and protecting themselves, they used Getting and Protecting Behaviors to keep *their own heads* above water. These behaviors just happened to splash water on Mila. The boys primary goal was not to affect her.

SEVEN, 44:12 - 46:27   Getting Children to Do Homework
CD Track Seven, 3:24 - 5:31

No success in life is worth sacrificing Real Love. Don't intimidate and push children to do anything. Let consequences teach, as we've discussed before.

Children need to see that they always have a choice, and it's *their* choice. They don't learn anything when they're always doing what you *make* them do. They learn the most as they see that there are positive consequences for wise choices and negative consequences for foolish choices. Read much more about consequences and choices in the book, *Real Love in Parenting*.

I emphasize that I am not advocating permissive parenting here. Sometimes—as in the case of young children doing their homework—their only choice may be whether they do their home *now* or *later*, but they still must do it. Children can't be allowed to make *some* choices—whether or not to do their homework, for example, or to play in the street, or to drink cleaning solvent—until they understand the consequences.

Again, as you did above, discuss in the space below and on the next page some occasions when you have tried to get children— or anyone else—to accomplish something at the expense of Real Love. Now tell your children—whether they're still at home or long gone—the mistakes you've made as a parent. Tell the truth about the times when you put their success—or your convenience—ahead of their need to feel loved. Discuss what happened when you were truthful. This will go far to bring you much closer to them.

SEVEN, 46:27 - 47:37   Positive Direction
CD Track Seven, 5:37 - 6:43

The birth mother of the stepchildren is an obstacle. So what? We can't change other people. We can only focus on what *we* do.

Consequences must be imposed in a way that they are reasonable, in a way that they teach rather than punish. Consequences are positive teaching tools, not punishments or obstacles. Again, there is much more about this in *Real Love in Parenting*.

SEVEN, 47:37 - 48:29   The Promise of Happiness
CD Track Seven, 6:43 - 7:48

The entire goal of learning about Real Love is not to become more lovable, because then we'd be back in the trap of earning love. The goal of learning about Real Love is to become genuinely happy. That's the ultimate reward.

MODULE SEVEN

48:55 - 49:47 The Power of Real Love
CD, 0:15 - 1:08

In the space below discuss how much of your time, energy, and attention are occupied with:

- disappointment.
- irritation.
- frustration.
- being offended.
- defending yourself.
- being angry.
- fear.
- contention.

Can you even imagine a life where these behaviors or qualities were virtually gone? It's not a dream. People all over the world are discovering that as they find Real Love, the traits listed above are being replaced with:

- love.
- peace.
- confidence.
- peacemaking.
- laughter.
- unbelievably fulfilling relationships.

Delightfully, these latter traits do not require more work to acquire. They just require faith and a different approach from what we've used thus far.

49:47 - 50:33   Real Love in Dating
CD, 1:08 - 1:53

The principles of Real Love are revolutionizing dating. If you'd like to learn a great deal more about how to make dating consistently more fun and effective, I suggest you:

- Read the book, *Real Love in Dating*, available at www.RealLove.com.
- Go to www.RealLove.com where you can:
  - watch archived Daily Video Coaching sessions with Greg.
  - watch the archived Video Chats with Greg.
  - participate in the Real Love Forums.
  - watch for other materials on dating.

50:33 - 52:32   Real Love in Marriage
CD, 1:53 - 3:50

Notice that Holly—from Module Three—was absolutely certain that she was angry because of her husband. And because of that she had been his prisoner for years, reacting automatically to his behavior. This is characteristic of most marriages.

As people learn about Real Love and about Getting and Protecting Behaviors, they come to understand the real cause of all conflicts, and then they can begin to change their behavior. There is amazing power and freedom in that. Remember the relief on Holly's face as she realizes that there is a better way of being a partner in a marriage.

If you'd like to learn a great deal more about how to make marriage consistently more fulfilling, fun, and effective, I suggest that you:

- Read the book, *Real Love in Marriage*, available at www.RealLove.com.
- Go to www.RealLove.com where you can:
  - watch archived Daily Video Coaching sessions with Greg.
  - watch the archived Video Chats with Greg.
  - participate in the Real Love Forums.
  - watch for other materials on marriage.

52:32 - 54:52 Real Love in Parenting
CD, 3:50 - 6:11

Parenting is probably the most important job on the planet, and yet most of us receive little or no training for this responsibility. So on the whole we fail miserably to give our children what they need most.

As we find Real Love ourselves, and as we share this with our children, everything about parenting changes. What a relief. If you'd like to learn a great deal more about how to make parenting consistently more enjoyable and effective, I suggest that you:

- Read the book, *Real Love in Parenting*, available at www.RealLove.com.
- Go to www.RealLove.com where you can:
  - watch archived Daily Video Coaching sessions with Greg.
  - watch the archived Video Chats with Greg.
  - participate in the Real Love Forums.
  - watch for other materials on parenting.

54:51 - 55:47   The Real Love Institute
CD, 6:11 - 7:08

Finding Real Love and becoming more loving isn't a matter of learning a technique. It's a result of a lifetime of consistent effort, and it's the mission of The Real Love Institute to help you every step of the way.

Review *The Essentials of Real Love*, either online or on DVD or on the audio CDs. The more times you watch it, the more you'll find to learn. Moreover, as you complete *The Essentials of Real Love Workbook*, or *The Essentials of Real Love Bible Workbook*, your learning will be accelerated. After completing the *Workbook*, come back in a few months and review what you've written. You'll be surprised at how much you've learned.

55:47 - 56:37   Books, Video Coaching, Radio Talk Show
CD, 7:08 - 7:59

In addition to the book, *Real Love*, there are other books available that apply the principles of Real Love to dating, marriage, parenting, and counseling. We can't have too much interaction with Real Love principles, and to give us more such opportunities the Real Love Institute is providing:

- Daily coaching segments with Greg. In these online archived videos, Greg explains the principles of Real Love in greater detail, answers questions from callers, and tell stories of people who have successfully applied the principles in their lives.
- The Real Love Radio Network. Greg hosted a radio talk show, where he answered the live questions of callers from around the world. These archived conversations are endlessly educational and usually quite entertaining.
- Additional video seminars online and on DVD, on a wide variety of subjects.
- Live seminars will be held regionally all around the country on a regular basis and on a variety of subjects.

- Real Love Chat Rooms. Now you have an opportunity to ask questions of certified Real Love Institute Professionals, people who have been trained by Greg to help you apply Real Love principles to the daily situations in your lives. You can also talk to other people who are beginning the process of learning about Real Love.

56:37 - 57:47 Practice Truth Telling
CD, 7:59 - 9:53

In the end, Real Love is a power that must be *felt*. Take every opportunity to practice telling the truth about yourself, as described in:

- *The Essentials of Real Love*—on DVD and CD.
- *The Essentials of Real Love Workbook* and *The Essentials of Real Love Bible Workbook.*
- the book, *Real Love.*
- *The Real Love Companion.*
- *Real Love for Wise Men and Women.*
- other Real Love books, CDs, and DVDs.

As you do this, you *will* find Real Love, you will learn to share this love with others, and you'll experience a happiness beyond expression.

Index

Index

Selected Exercises in the *Workbook*
(29 of 186 in the Workbook)

Following is a list of abbreviated descriptions of some of the exercises found in the *Workbook*. For a complete description—and in many cases, for extensive examples of how to complete the exercises—see the page(s) indicated.

After studying the Real Love seminar and workbook, describe how your understanding of anger has changed: 54.

Describe the effects of your disappointment and anger in a specific situation: 56.

Describe the approval you saw as a chid when you were "good": 65.

Describe how you were treated as a child when you were "bad": 66.

Discuss how that conditional love felt for you as a child: 67.

Discuss examples of how you are conditionally loved now as an adult: 67.

Discuss how you've used praise as form of Imitation Love: 85.

Discuss how you use power as a form of Imitation Love: 87-8.

Discuss how you use pleasure as form of Imitation Love: 90-1.

Discuss how you use safety as a form of Imitation Love: 93-4.

Discuss the patterns of Imitation Love you use: 111-12.

Discuss how you lie as a Getting and Protecting Behavior: 122-3.

Describe how you attack as a Getting and Protecting Behavior: 126-7.

Describe when you have acted like a victim: 141-2.

Describe how you use clinging: 143-4.

Describe how you use running: 144-5.

Understanding Getting and Protecting Behaviors, describe behaviors in yourself and others that have previously puzzled you: 147-9.

Use the drowning metaphor to help you see someone differently: 173-4.

Make a list of loving acts you could share: 217-18.

Describe how you were wrong in a conflict: 240-1.

Describe your relationship with God: 269.

Discuss a conflict in terms of What-What-Why-What-What: 280-8

Make list of people you will tell the truth about yourself to: 304-5.

Discuss the role of expectations in times you have been irritated: 349-51.

Describe some moments of contention and admit how your anger was wrong: 378-9.

Describe an occasion where you exchanged Getting and Protecting Behaviors with a partner: 406.

Describe how you can handle conflicts differently now, in light of what you know: 409.

Describe occasions when you've defended yourself in a conflict: 442-3.

Describe occasions when you have tried to get people to accomplish something at the expense of Real Love: 448-9.